THE BODLEY HEAD

SCOTT FITZGERALD
VOLUME III

THE
BODLEY HEAD
SCOTT
FITZGERALD

VOL. III

THIS SIDE OF PARADISE

THE CRACK-UP

AND OTHER AUTOBIOGRAPHICAL PIECES

THE BODLEY HEAD
LONDON SYDNEY
TORONTO

All rights reserved
ISBN 0 370 00539 2
Printed in Great Britain for
The Bodley Head Ltd
9 Bow Street, London, WC2
by William Clowes and Sons Ltd, Beccles
Set in Monotype Plantin
First published in this edition 1960
Revised edition 1965
Reprinted 1971

CONTENTS

PUBLISHER'S NOTE

Scott Fitzgerald's first novel *This Side of Paradise*, originally published in 1920, is printed here in full. This was the novel which rocketed him to celebrity overnight, made him a wealthy and solicited writer while still in his early twenties, and endeared him to his own generation, the bright young things of the Jazz Age.

Its hero, who closely resembles Fitzgerald himself, is seen growing up in a Middle Western town, at length to become a 'college man' in the gay and hectic world of Princeton, the university which never quite forgave him for the picture he drew of it.

The volume also contains all Fitzgerald's published autobiographical writing with the following exceptions: the notebooks, which, while they are valuable as source material, do not belong in a collected edition; pieces written in collaboration with his wife, Zelda; and a few pieces which, while they have some autobiographical content, fall uneasily between fact and fiction. The pieces are printed in chronological order.

The dates given in the text are those of first publication.

THIS
SIDE OF PARADISE
[1920]

. . . Well this side of Paradise! . . .
There's little comfort in the wise.
RUPERT BROOKE

Experience is the name so many
people give to their mistakes.
OSCAR WILDE

To
Sigourney Fay

THIS SIDE OF PARADISE

BOOK ONE
THE ROMANTIC EGOTIST

I. AMORY, SON OF BEATRICE

AMORY BLAINE inherited from his mother every trait, except
the stray inexpressible few, that made him worth while. His
father, an ineffectual, inarticulate man with a taste for
Byron and a habit of drowsing over the *Encyclopædia
Britannica*, grew wealthy at thirty through the death of two
elder brothers, successful Chicago brokers, and in the first
flush of feeling that the world was his, went to Bar Harbor
and met Beatrice O'Hara. In consequence, Stephen Blaine
handed down to posterity his height of just under six feet
and his tendency to waver at crucial moments, these two
abstractions appearing in his son Amory. For many years he
hovered in the background of his family's life, an unasser-
tive figure with a face half-obliterated by lifeless, silky hair,
continually occupied in 'taking care' of his wife, continually
harassed by the idea that he didn't and couldn't understand
her.

But Beatrice Blaine! There was a woman! Early pictures
taken on her father's estate at Lake Geneva, Wisconsin, or
in Rome at the Sacred Heart Convent – an educational
extravagance that in her youth was only for the daughters
of the exceptionally wealthy – showed the exquisite delicacy
of her features, the consummate art and simplicity of her
clothes. A brilliant education she had – her youth passed in
renaissance glory, she was versed in the latest gossip of the

13

Older Roman Families; known by name as a fabulously wealthy American girl to Cardinal Vitori and Queen Margherita and more subtle celebrities that one must have had some culture even to have heard of. She learned in England to prefer whisky and soda to wine, and her small talk was broadened in two senses during a winter in Vienna. All in all Beatrice O'Hara absorbed the sort of education that will be quite impossible ever again; a tutelage measured by the number of things and people one could be contemptuous of and charming about; a culture rich in all arts and traditions, barren of all ideas, in the last of those days when the great gardener clipped the inferior roses to produce one perfect bud.

In her less important moments she returned to America, met Stephen Blaine and married him – this almost entirely because she was a little bit weary, a little bit sad. Her only child was carried through a tiresome season and brought into the world on a spring day in ninety-six.

When Amory was five he was already a delightful companion for her. He was an auburn-haired boy, with great, handsome eyes which he would grow up to in time, a facile imaginative mind and a taste for fancy dress. From his fourth to his tenth year he *did* the country with his mother in her father's private car, from Coronado, where his mother became so bored that she had a nervous breakdown in a fashionable hotel, down to Mexico City, where she took a mild, almost epidemic consumption. This trouble pleased her, and later she made use of it as an intrinsic part of her atmosphere – especially after several astounding bracers.

So, while more or less fortunate little rich boys were defying governesses on the beach at Newport, or being spanked or tutored or read to from 'Do and Dare', or 'Frank on the Mississippi', Amory was biting acquiescent bell-boys in the Waldorf, outgrowing a natural repugnance to chamber music and symphonies, and deriving a highly specialized education from his mother.

'Amory.'

'Yes, Beatrice.' (Such a quaint name for his mother; she encouraged it.)

'Dear, don't *think* of getting out of bed yet. I've always suspected that early rising in early life makes one nervous. Clothilde is having your breakfast brought up.'

'All right.'

'I am feeling very old to-day, Amory,' she would sigh, her face a rare cameo of pathos, her voice exquisitely modulated, her hands as facile as Bernhardt's. 'My nerves are on edge – on edge. We must leave this terrifying place to-morrow and go searching for sunshine.'

Amory's penetrating green eyes would look out through tangled hair at his mother. Even at this age he had no illusions about her.

'Amory.'

'Oh, *yes*.'

'I want you to take a red-hot bath – as hot as you can bear it, and just relax your nerves. You can read in the tub if you wish.'

She fed him sections of the 'Fêtes Galantes' before he was ten; at eleven he could talk glibly, if rather reminiscently, of Brahms and Mozart and Beethoven. One afternoon, when left alone in the hotel at Hot Springs, he sampled his mother's apricot cordial, and as the taste pleased him, he became quite tipsy. This was fun for a while, but he essayed a cigarette in his exaltation, and succumbed to a vulgar, plebeian reaction. Though this incident horrified Beatrice, it also secretly amused her and became part of what in a later generation would have been termed her 'line.'

'This son of mine,' he heard her tell a room full of awe-struck, admiring women one day, 'is entirely sophisticated and quite charming – but delicate – we're all delicate; *here*, you know.' Her hand was radiantly outlined against her beautiful bosom; then sinking her voice to a whisper, she told them of the apricot cordial. They rejoiced, for she was a brave raconteuse, but many were the keys turned in side-board locks that night against the possible defection of little Bobby or Barbara . . .

These domestic pilgrimages were invariably in state; two maids, the private car, or Mr. Blaine when available, and very often a physician. When Amory had the whooping-cough four disgusted specialists glared at each other hunched around his bed; when he took scarlet fever the number of attendants, including physicians and nurses, totalled fourteen. However, blood being thicker than broth, he was pulled through.

The Blaines were attached to no city. They were the Blaines of Lake Geneva; they had quite enough relatives to serve in place of friends, and an enviable standing from Pasadena to Cape Cod. But Beatrice grew more and more prone to like only new acquaintances, as there were certain stories, such as the history of her constitution and its many amendments, memories of her years abroad, that it was necessary for her to repeat at regular intervals. Like Freudian dreams, they must be thrown off, else they would sweep in and lay siege to her nerves. But Beatrice was critical about American women, especially the floating population of ex-Westerners.

'They have accents, my dear,' she told Amory, 'not Southern accents or Boston accents, not an accent attached to any locality, just an accent' – she became dreamy. 'They pick up old, moth-eaten London accents that are down on their luck and have to be used by some one. They talk as an English butler might after several years in a Chicago grand-opera company.' She became almost incoherent – 'Suppose – time in every Western woman's life – she feels her husband is prosperous enough for her to have – accent – they try to impress *me*, my dear——'

Though she thought of her body as a mass of frailties, she considered her soul quite as ill, and therefore important in her life. She had once been a Catholic, but discovering that priests were infinitely more attentive when she was in process of losing or regaining faith in Mother Church, she maintained an enchantingly wavering attitude. Often she deplored the bourgeois quality of the American Catholic clergy, and was quite sure that had she lived in the shadow

of the great Continental cathedrals her soul would still be a
thin flame on the mighty altar of Rome. Still, next to doctors,
priests were her favorite sport.

'Ah, Bishop Wiston,' she would declare, 'I do not *want*
to talk of myself. I can imagine the stream of hysterical
women fluttering at your doors, beseeching you to be sim-
*pat*ico' – then after an interlude filled by the clergyman –
'but my mood – is – oddly dissimilar.'

Only to bishops and above did she divulge her clerical
romance. When she had first returned to her country there
had been a pagan, Swinburnian young man in Ashville, for
whose passionate kisses and unsentimental conversations
she had taken a decided penchant – they had discussed the
matter pro and con with an intellectual romancing quite
devoid of soppiness. Eventually she had decided to marry
for background, and the young pagan from Asheville had
gone through a spiritual crisis, joined the Catholic Church,
and was now – Monsignor Darcy.

'Indeed, Mrs. Blaine, he is still delightful company –
quite the cardinal's right-hand man.'

'Amory will go to him one day, I know,' breathed the
beautiful lady, 'and Monsignor Darcy will understand him
as he understood me.'

Amory became thirteen, rather tall and slender, and more
than ever on to his Celtic mother. He had tutored occasionally – the idea being that he was to 'keep up,' at each place
'taking up the work where he left off,' yet as no tutor ever
found the place he left off, his mind was still in very good
shape. What a few more years of this life would have made
of him is problematical. However, four hours out from land,
Italy bound, with Beatrice, his appendix burst, probably
from too many meals in bed, and after a series of frantic
telegrams to Europe and America, to the amazement of the
passengers the great ship slowly wheeled around and returned to New York to deposit Amory at the pier. You will
admit that if it was not life it was magnificent.

After the operation Beatrice had a nervous breakdown
that bore a suspicious resemblance to delirium tremens, and

Amory was left in Minneapolis, destined to spend the ensuing two years with his aunt and uncle. There the crude,
vulgar air of Western civilization first catches him – in his
underwear, so to speak.

A Kiss For Amory

His lip curled when he read it.

'*I am going to have a bobbing party,*' it said, '*on Thursday,
December the seventeenth, at five o'clock, and I would like it
very much if you could come.*

Yours truly,

R.S.V.P.   *Myra St. Claire.*'

He had been two months in Minneapolis, and his chief
struggle had been the concealing from 'the other guys at
school' how particularly superior he felt himself to be, yet
this conviction was built upon shifting sands. He had shown
off one day in French class (he was in senior French class)
to the utter confusion of Mr. Reardon, whose accent Amory
damned contemptuously, and to the delight of the class.
Mr. Reardon, who had spent several weeks in Paris ten
years before, took his revenge on the verbs, whenever he had
his book open. But another time Amory showed off in
history class, with quite disastrous results, for the boys
there were his own age, and they shrilled innuendoes at
each other all the following week:

'Aw – I b'lieve, doncherknow, the Umuricun revolution
was *lawgely* an affair of the middul *clawses,*' or

'Washington came of very good blood – aw, quite good –
I b'lieve.'

Amory ingeniously tried to retrieve himself by blundering
on purpose. Two years before he had commenced a history
of the United States which, though it only got as far as the
Colonial Wars, had been pronounced by his mother completely enchanting.

His chief disadvantage lay in athletics, but as soon as he
discovered that it was the touchstone of power and popular-

ity at school, he began to make furious, persistent efforts to excel in the winter sports, and with his ankles aching and bending in spite of his efforts, he skated valiantly around the Lorelie rink every afternoon, wondering how soon he would be able to carry a hockey-stick without getting it inexplicably tangled in his skates.

The invitation to Miss Myra St. Claire's bobbing party spent the morning in his coat pocket, where it had an intense physical affair with a dusty piece of peanut brittle. During the afternoon he brought it to light with a sigh, and after some consideration and a preliminary draft in the back of Collar and Daniel's 'First-Year Latin,' composed an answer:

My dear Miss St. Claire:
Your truly charming envitation for the evening of next Thursday evening was truly delightful to receive this morning. I will be charm and inchanted indeed to present my compliments on next Thursday evening.
Faithfully,
Amory Blaine.

On Thursday, therefore, he walked pensively along the slippery, shovel-scraped sidewalks, and came in sight of Myra's house, on the half-hour after five, a lateness which he fancied his mother would have favoured. He waited on the door-step with his eyes nonchalantly half-closed, and planned his entrance with precision. He would cross the floor, not too hastily, to Mrs. St. Claire, and say with exactly the correct modulation:

'My *dear* Mrs. St. Claire, I'm *frightfully* sorry to be late, but my maid' – he paused there and realized he would be quoting – 'but my uncle and I had to see a fella – Yes, I've met your enchanting daughter at dancing-school.'

Then he would shake hands, using that slight, half-foreign bow, with all the starchy little females, and nod to the fellas who would be standing 'round, paralyzed into rigid groups for mutual protection.

A butler (one of the three in Minneapolis) swung open the door. Amory stepped inside and divested himself of cap and coat. He was mildly surprised not to hear the shrill squawk of conversation from the next room, and he decided it must be quite formal. He approved of that – as he approved of the butler.

'Miss Myra,' he said.

To his surprise the butler grinned horribly.

'Oh, yeah,' he declared, 'she's here.' He was unaware that his failure to be cockney was ruining his standing. Amory considered him coldly.

'But,' continued the butler, his voice rising unnecessarily, 'she's the only one what *is* here. The party's gone.'

Amory gasped in sudden horror.

'What?'

'She's been waitin' for Amory Blaine. That's you, ain't it? Her mother says that if you showed up by five-thirty you two was to go after 'em in the Packard.'

Amory's despair was crystallized by the appearance of Myra herself, bundled to the ears in a polo coat, her face plainly sulky, her voice pleasant only with difficulty.

''Lo, Amory.'

''Lo, Myra.' He had described the state of his vitality.

'Well – you *got* here, *any*ways.'

'Well – I'll tell you. I guess you don't know about the auto accident,' he romanced.

Myra's eyes opened wide.

'Who was it to?'

'Well,' he continued desperately, 'uncle'n aunt'n I.'

'Was any one *killed*?'

Amory paused and then nodded.

'Your uncle?' – alarm.

'Oh, no – just a horse – a sorta grey horse.'

At this point the Erse butler snickered.

'Probably killed the engine,' he suggested. Amory would have put him on the rack without a scruple.

'We'll go now,' said Myra coolly. 'You see, Amory, the bobs were ordered for five and everybody was here, so we couldn't wait——'

'Well, I couldn't help it, could I?'

'So mama said for me to wait till ha'past five. We'll catch the bob before it gets to the Minnehaha Club, Amory.'

Amory's shredded poise dropped from him. He pictured the happy party jingling along snowy streets, the appearance of the limousine, the horrible public descent of him and Myra before sixty reproachful eyes, his apology – a real one this time. He sighed aloud.

'What ?' inquired Myra.

'Nothing. I was just yawning. Are we going to *surely* catch up with 'em before they get there ?' He was encouraging a faint hope that they might slip into the Minnehaha Club and meet the others there, be found in blasé seclusion before the fire and quite regain his lost attitude.

'Oh, sure Mike, we'll catch 'em all right – let's hurry.'

He became conscious of his stomach. As they stepped into the machine he hurriedly slapped the paint of diplomacy over a rather box-like plan he had conceived. It was based upon some 'trade-lasts' gleaned at dancing-school, to the effect that he was 'awful good-looking and *English*, sort of.'

'Myra,' he said, lowering his voice and choosing his words carefully, 'I beg a thousand pardons. Can you ever forgive me ?'

She regarded him gravely, his intent green eyes, his mouth, that to her thirteen-year-old, arrow-collar taste was the quintessence of romance. Yes, Myra could forgive him very easily.

'Why – yes – sure.'

He looked at her again, and then dropped his eyes. He had lashes.

'I'm awful,' he said sadly. 'I'm diff'runt. I don't know why I make faux pas. 'Cause I don't care, I s'pose.' Then, recklessly: 'I been smoking too much. I've got t'bacca heart.'

Myra pictured an all-night tobacco debauch, with Amory pale and reeling from the effect of nicotined lungs. She gave a little gasp.

'Oh, *Amory*, don't smoke. You'll stunt your *growth* !'

'I don't care,' he persisted gloomily. 'I gotta. I got the habit. I've done a lot of things that if my fambly knew' – he hesitated, giving her imagination time to picture dark horrors– 'I went to the burlesque show last week.'

Myra was quite overcome. He turned the green eyes on her again.

'You're the only girl in town I like much,' he exclaimed in a rush of sentiment. 'You're simpatico.'

Myra was not sure that she was, but it sounded stylish though vaguely improper.

Thick dusk had descended outside, and as the limousine made a sudden turn she was jolted against him; their hands touched.

'You shouldn't smoke, Amory,' she whispered. 'Don't you know that?'

He shook his head.

'Nobody cares.'

Myra hesitated.

'*I* care.'

Something stirred within Amory.

'Oh, yes, you do! You got a crush on Froggy Parker. I guess everybody knows that.'

'No, I haven't,' very slowly.

A silence, while Amory thrilled. There was something fascinating about Myra, shut away here cosily from the dim, chill air. Myra, a little bundle of clothes, with strands of yellow hair curling out from under her skating cap.

'Because I've got a crush, too –' He paused, for he heard in the distance the sound of young laughter, and, peering through the frosted glass along the lamp-lit street, he made out the dark outline of the bobbing party. He must act quickly. He reached over with a violent, jerky effort, and clutched Myra's hand – her thumb, to be exact.

'Tell him to go to the Minnehaha straight,' he whispered. 'I wanta talk to you – I *got* to talk to you.'

Myra made out the party ahead, had an instant vision of her mother, and then – alas for convention – glanced into the eyes beside.

'Turn down this side street, Richard, and drive straight to the Minnehaha Club!' she cried through the speaking tube. Amory sank back against the cushions with a sigh of relief.

'I can kiss her,' he thought. 'I'll bet I can. I'll *bet* I can!'

Overhead the sky was half crystalline, half misty, and the night around was chill and vibrant with rich tension. From the Country Club steps the roads stretched away, dark creases on the white blanket; huge heaps of snow lining the sides like the tracks of giant moles. They lingered for a moment on the steps, and watched the white holiday moon.

'Pale moons like that one' – Amory made a vague gesture – 'make people mysterieuse. You look like a young witch with her cap off and her hair sorta mussed' – her hands clutched at her hair – 'Oh, leave it, it looks *good*.'

They drifted up the stairs and Myra led the way into the little den of his dreams, where a cosy fire was burning before a big sink-down couch. A few years later this was to be a great stage for Amory, a cradle for many an emotional crisis. Now they talked for a moment about bobbing parties.

'There's always a bunch of shy fellas,' he commented, 'sitting at the tail of the bob, sorta lurkin' an' whisperin' an' pushin' each other off. Then there's always some crazy cross-eyed girl' – he gave a terrifying imitation – 'she's always talkin' *hard*, sorta, to the chaperon.'

'You're such a funny boy,' puzzled Myra.

'How d'y' mean?' Amory gave immediate attention, on his own ground at last.

'Oh – always talking about crazy things. Why don't you come ski-ing with Marylyn and I to-morrow?'

'I don't like girls in the daytime,' he said shortly, and then, thinking this a bit abrupt, he added: 'But I like you.' He cleared his throat. 'I like you first and second and third.'

Myra's eyes became dreamy. What a story this would make to tell Marylyn! Here on the couch with this *wonderful*-looking boy – the little fire – the sense that they were alone in the great building——

Myra capitulated. The atmosphere was too appropriate.

'I like you the first twenty-five,' she confessed, her voice trembling, 'and Froggy Parker twenty-sixth.'

Froggy had fallen twenty-five places in one hour. As yet he had not even noticed it.

But Amory, being on the spot, leaned over quickly and kissed Myra's cheek. He had never kissed a girl before, and he tasted his lips curiously, as if he had munched some new fruit. Then their lips brushed like young wild flowers in the wind.

'We're awful,' rejoiced Myra gently. She slipped her hand into his, her head drooped against his shoulder. Sudden revulsion seized Amory, disgust, loathing for the whole incident. He desired frantically to be away, never to see Myra again, never to kiss any one; he became conscious of his face and hers, of their clinging hands, and he wanted to creep out of his body and hide somewhere safe out of sight, up in the corner of his mind.

'Kiss me again.' Her voice came out of a great void.

'I don't want to,' he heard himself saying. There was another pause.

'I don't want to!' he repeated passionately.

Myra sprang up, her cheeks pink with bruised vanity, the great bow on the back of her head trembling sympathetically.

'I hate you!' she cried. 'Don't you ever dare to speak to me again!'

'What?' stammered Amory.

'I'll tell mama you kissed me! I will too! I will too! I'll tell mama, and she won't let me play with you!'

Amory rose and stared at her helplessly, as though she were a new animal of whose presence on the earth he had not heretofore been aware.

The door opened suddenly, and Myra's mother appeared on the threshold, fumbling with her lorgnette.

'Well,' she began, adjusting it benignantly, 'the man at the desk told me you two children were up here – How do you do, Amory.'

Amory watched Myra and waited for the crash – but none came. The pout faded, the high pink subsided, and Myra's voice was placid as a summer lake when she answered her mother.

'Oh, we started so late, mama, that I thought we might as *well*——'

He heard from below the shrieks of laughter, and smelled the vapid odour of hot chocolate and tea-cakes as he silently followed mother and daughter downstairs. The sound of the graphophone mingled with the voices of many girls humming the air, and a faint glow was born and spread over him:

> *'Casey-Jones – mounted to the cab-un*
> *Casey-Jones – 'th his orders in his hand.*
> *Casey-Jones – mounted to the cab-un*
> *Took his farewell journey to the prom-ised land.'*

Snapshots of the Young Egotist

Amory spent nearly two years in Minneapolis. The first winter he wore moccasins that were born yellow, but after many applications of oil and dirt assumed their mature colour, a dirty, greenish brown; he wore a grey plaid mackinaw coat, and a red toboggan cap. His dog, Count Del Monte, ate the red cap, so his uncle gave him a grey one that pulled down over his face. The trouble with this one was that you breathed into it and your breath froze; one day the darn thing froze his cheek. He rubbed snow on his cheek, but it turned bluish-black just the same.

The Count Del Monte ate a box of bluing once, but it didn't hurt him. Later, however, he lost his mind and ran madly up the street, bumping into fences, rolling in gutters, and pursuing his eccentric course out of Amory's life. Amory cried on his bed.

'Poor little Count,' he cried. 'Oh, *poor* little *Count!*'

After several months he suspected Count of a fine piece of emotional acting.

Amory and Frog Parker considered that the greatest line in literature occurred in Act III of 'Arsene Lupin.'

They sat in the first row at the Wednesday and Saturday matinées. The line was:

'If one can't be a great artist or a great soldier, the next best thing is to be a great criminal.'

Amory fell in love again, and wrote a poem. This was it:

'Marylyn and Sall*ee*,
    Those are the girls for me.
Marylyn stands above
    Sall*ee* in that sweet, deep love.'

He was interested in whether McGovern of Minnesota would make the first or second All-American, how to do the card-pass, how to do the coin-pass, chameleon ties, how babies were born, and whether Three-fingered Brown was really a better pitcher than Christie Mathewson.

Among other things he read: 'For the Honour of the School,' 'Little Women' (twice), 'The Common Law,' 'Sapho,' 'Dangerous Dan McGrew,' 'The Broad Highway' (three times), 'The Fall of the House of Usher,' 'Three Weeks,' 'Mary Ware, the Little Colonel's Chum,' 'Gunga Dhin,' *The Police Gazette*, and *Jim-Jam Jems*.

He had all the Henty biasses in history, and was particularly fond of the cheerful murder stories of Mary Roberts Rineheart.

School ruined his French and gave him a distaste for standard authors. His masters considered him idle, unreliable and superficially clever.

He collected locks of hair from many girls. He wore the rings of several. Finally he could borrow no more rings, owing to his nervous habit of chewing them out of shape. This, it seemed, usually aroused the jealous suspicions of the next borrower.

All through the summer months Amory and Frog Parker

went each week to the Stock Company. Afterwards they would stroll home in the balmy air of August night, dreaming along Hennepin and Nicollet Avenues, through the gay crowd. Amory wondered how people could fail to notice that he was a boy marked for glory, and when faces of the throng turned toward him and ambiguous eyes stared into his, he assumed the most romantic of expressions and walked on the air cushions that lie on the asphalts of fourteen.

Always, after he was in bed, there were voices – indefinite, fading, enchanting – just outside his window, and before he fell asleep he would dream one of his favourite waking dreams, the one about becoming a great half-back, or the one about the Japanese invasion, when he was rewarded by being made the youngest general in the world. It was always the becoming he dreamed of, never the being. This, too, was quite characteristic of Amory.

Code of the Young Egotist

Before he was summoned back to Lake Geneva, he had appeared, shy but inwardly glowing, in his first long trousers, set off by a purple accordion tie and a 'Belmont' collar with the edges unassailably meeting, purple socks, and handkerchief with a purple border peeping from his breast pocket. But more than that, he had formulated his first philosophy, a code to live by, which, as near as it can be named, was a sort of aristocratic egotism.

He had realized that his best interests were bound up with those of a certain variant, changing person, whose label, in order that his past might always be identified with him, was Amory Blaine. Amory marked himself a fortunate youth, capable of infinite expansion for good or evil. He did not consider himself a 'strong char'c'ter,' but relied on his facility (learn things sorta quick) and his superior mentality (read a lotta deep books). He was proud of the fact that he could never become a mechanical or scientific genius. From no other heights was he debarred.

Physically. – Amory thought that he was exceedingly

handsome. He was. He fancied himself an athlete of possibilities and a supple dancer.

Socia ly. – Here his condition was, perhaps, most dangerous. He granted himself personality, charm, magnetism,
poise, the power of dominating all contemporary males, the
gift of fascinating all women.

Mentally. – Complete, unquestioned superiority.

Now a confession will have to be made. Amory had rather
a Puritan conscience. Not that he yielded to it – later in life
he almost completely slew it – but at fifteen it made him
consider himself a great deal worse than other boys . . . un-
scrupulousness . . . the desire to influence people in almost
every way, even for evil . . . a certain coldness and lack of
affection, amounting sometimes to cruelty . . . a shifting
sense of honour . . . an unholy selfishness . . . a puzzled,
furtive interest in everything concerning sex.

There was, also, a curious strain of weakness running
crosswise through his make-up . . . a harsh phrase from the
lips of an older boy (older boys usually detested him) was
liable to sweep him off his poise into surly sensitiveness, or
timid stupidity . . . he was a slave to his own moods and he
felt that though he was capable of recklessness and audacity,
he possessed neither courage, perseverance, nor self-respect.

Vanity, tempered with self-suspicion if not self-know-
ledge, a sense of people as automatons to his will, a desire to
'pass' as many boys as possible and get to a vague top of the
world . . . with this background did Amory drift into
adolescence.

Preparatory to the Great Adventure

The train slowed up with midsummer languor at Lake
Geneva, and Amory caught sight of his mother waiting in
her electric on the gravelled station drive. It was an ancient
electric, one of the early types, and painted grey. The sight
of her sitting there, slenderly erect, and of her face, where
beauty and dignity combined, melting to a dreamy recollected smile, filled him with a sudden great pride of her. As

they kissed coolly and he stepped into the electric, he felt a quick fear lest he had lost the requisite charm to measure up to her.

'Dear boy – you're *so* tall . . . look behind and see if there's anything coming . . .'

She looked left and right, she slipped cautiously into a speed of two miles an hour, beseeching Amory to act as sentinel; and at one busy crossing she made him get out and run ahead to signal her forward like a traffic policeman. Beatrice was what might be termed a careful driver.

'You *are* tall – but you're still very handsome – you've skipped the awkward age, or is that sixteen; perhaps it's fourteen or fifteen; I can never remember; but you've skipped it.'

'Don't embarrass me,' murmured Amory.

'But, my dear boy, what odd clothes! They look as if they were a *set* – don't they ? Is your underwear purple, too ?'

Amory grunted impolitely.

'You must go to Brooks' and get some really nice suits. Oh, we'll have a talk to-night or perhaps to-morrow night. I want to tell you about your heart – you've probably been neglecting your heart – and you don't *know*.'

Amory thought how superficial was the recent overlay of his own generation. Aside from a minute shyness, he felt that the old cynical kinship with his mother had not been one bit broken. Yet for the first few days he wandered about the gardens and along the shore in a state of superloneliness, finding a lethargic content in smoking 'Bull' at the garage with one of the chauffeurs.

The sixty acres of the estate were dotted with old and new summer houses and many fountains and white benches that came suddenly into sight from foliage-hung hiding-places; there was a great and constantly increasing family of white cats that prowled the many flower-beds and were silhouetted suddenly at night against the darkening trees. It was on one of the shadowy paths that Beatrice at last captured Amory, after Mr. Blaine had, as usual, retired for the evening to his private library. After reproving him for avoiding her, she took him for a long tête-à-tête in the moonlight. He could not reconcile himself to her beauty, that was mother to his own, the exquisite neck and shoulders, the grace of a fortunate woman of thirty.

'Amory, dear,' she crooned softly, 'I had such a strange, weird time after I left you.'

'Did you, Beatrice?'

'When I had my last breakdown' – she spoke of it as a sturdy, gallant feat.

'The doctors told me' – her voice sang on a confidential note – 'that if any man alive had done the consistent drinking that I have, he would have been physically *shattered*, my dear, and in his *grave* – long in his grave.'

Amory winced, and wondered how this would have sounded to Froggy Parker.

'Yes,' continued Beatrice tragically, 'I had dreams – wonderful visions.' She pressed the palms of her hands into her eyes. 'I saw bronze rivers lapping marble shores, and great birds that soared through the air, parti-coloured birds with iridescent plumage. I heard strange music and the flare of barbaric trumpets – what?'

Amory had snickered.

'What, Amory?'

'I said go on, Beatrice.'

'That was all – it merely recurred and recurred – gardens that flaunted colouring against which this would be quite dull, moons that whirled and swayed, paler than winter moons, more golden than harvest moons –'

'Are you quite well now, Beatrice?'

'Quite well – as well as I will ever be. I am not understood, Amory. I know that can't express it to you, Amory, but – I am not understood.'

Amory was quite moved. He put his arm around his mother, rubbing his head gently against her shoulder.

'Poor Beatrice – poor Beatrice.'

'Tell me about *you*, Amory. Did you have two *horrible* years?'

Amory considered lying, and then decided against it.

'No, Beatrice. I enjoyed them. I adapted myself to the bourgeoisie. I became conventional.' He surprised himself by saying that, and he pictured how Froggy would have gaped.

'Beatrice,' he said suddenly, 'I want to go away to school. Everybody in Minneapolis is going to go away to school.'

Beatrice showed some alarm.

'But you're only fifteen.'

'Yes, but everybody goes away to school at fifteen, and I *want* to, Beatrice.'

On Beatrice's suggestion the subject was dropped for the rest of the walk, but a week later she delighted him by saying:

'Amory, I have decided to let you have your way. If you still want to, you can go to school.'

'Yes ?'

'To St. Regis's in Connecticut.'

Amory felt a quick excitement.

'It's being arranged,' continued Beatrice. 'It's better that you should go away. I'd have preferred you to have gone to Eton, and then to Christ Church, Oxford, but it seems impracticable now – and for the present we'll let the university question take care of itself.'

'What are you going to do, Beatrice ?'

'Heaven knows. It seems my fate to fret away my years in this country. Not for a second do I regret being American – indeed, I think that a regret typical of very vulgar people, and I feel sure we are the great coming nation – yet' – and she sighed – 'I feel my life should have drowsed away close to an older, mellower civilization, a land of greens and autumnal browns——'

Amory did not answer, so his mother continued:

'My regret is that you haven't been abroad, but still, as you are a man, it's better that you should grow up here under the snarling eagle – is that the right term ?'

Amory agreed that it was. She would not have appreciated the Japanese invasion.

'When do I go to school ?'

'Next month. You'll have to start East a little early to take

your examinations. After that you'll have a free week, so I
want you to go up the Hudson and pay a visit.'

'To who?'

'To Monsignor Darcy, Amory. He wants to see you. He
went to Harrow and then to Yale – became a Catholic. I
want him to talk to you – I feel he can be such a help –' She
stroked his auburn hair gently. 'Dear Amory, dear Amory –'

'Dear Beatrice——'

So early in September Amory, provided with 'six suits
summer underwear, six suits winter underwear, one sweater
or T shirt, one jersey, one overcoat, winter, etc.,' set out for
New England, the land of schools.

There were Andover and Exeter with their memories of
New England dead – large, college-like democracies; St.
Mark's, Groton, St. Regis' – recruited from Boston and the
Knickerbocker families of New York; St. Paul's, with its
great rinks; Pomfret and St. George's, prosperous and well-
dressed; Taft and Hotchkiss, which prepared the wealth of
the Middle West for social success at Yale; Pawling, West-
minster, Choate, Kent, and a hundred others; all milling
out their well-set-up, conventional, impressive type, year
after year; their mental stimulus the college entrance exams;
their vague purpose set forth in a hundred circulars as 'To
impart a Thorough Mental, Moral, and Physical Training
as a Christian Gentleman, to fit the boy *for meeting the problems of his day and generation*, and to give a solid foundation
in the Arts and Sciences.'

At St. Regis' Amory stayed three days and took his exams
with a scoffing confidence, then doubling back to New York
to pay his tutelary visit. The metropolis, barely glimpsed,
made little impression on him, except for the sense of
cleanliness he drew from the tall white buildings seen from
a Hudson River steamboat in the early morning. Indeed, his
mind was so crowded with dreams of athletic prowess at
school that he considered this visit only as a rather tiresome
prelude to the great adventure. This, however, it did not
prove to be.

Monsignor Darcy's house was an ancient, rambling structure set on a hill overlooking the river, and there lived its owner, between his trips to all parts of the Roman-Catholic world, rather like an exiled Stuart king waiting to be called to the rule of his land. Monsignor was forty-four then, and bustling – a trifle too stout for symmetry, with hair the colour of spun gold, and a brilliant, enveloping personality. When he came into a room clad in his full purple regalia from thatch to toe, he resembled a Turner sunset, and attracted both admiration and attention. He had written two novels: one of them violently anti-Catholic, just before his conversion, and five years later another, in which he had attempted to turn all his clever jibes against Catholics into even cleverer innuendoes against Episcopalians. He was intensely ritualistic, startlingly dramatic, loved the idea of God enough to be a celibate, and rather liked his neighbour.

Children adored him because he was like a child; youth revelled in his company becau e he was still a youth, and couldn't be shocked. In the proper land and century he might have been a Richelieu – at present he was a very moral, very religious (if not particularly pious) clergyman, making a great mystery about pulling rusty wires, and appreciating life to the fullest, if not entirely enjoying it.

He and Amory took to each other at first sight – the jovial, impressive prelate who could dazzle an embassy ball, and the green-eyed, intent youth, in his first long trousers, accepted in their own minds a relation of father and son within a half-hour's conversation.

'My dear boy, I've been waiting to see you for years. Take a big chair and we'll have a chat.'

'I've just come from school – St. Regis's, you know.'

'So your mother says – a remarkable woman; have a cigarette – I'm sure you smoke. Well, if you're like me, you loathe all science and mathematics——'

Amory nodded vehemently.

'Hate 'em all. Like English and history.'

'Of course. You'll hate school for a while, too, but I'm glad you're going to St. Regis's.'

'Why ?'

'Because it's a gentleman's school, and democracy won't hit you so early. You'll find plenty of that in college.'

'I want to go to Princeton,' said Amory. 'I don't know why, but I think of all Harvard men as sissies, like I used to be, and all Yale men as wearing big blue sweaters and smoking pipes.'

Monsignor chuckled.

'I'm one, you know.'

'Oh, you're different – I think of Princeton as being lazy and good-looking and aristocratic – you know, like a spring day. Harvard seems sort of indoors——'

'And Yale is November, crisp and energetic,' finished Monsignor.

'That's it.'

They slipped briskly into an intimacy from which they never recovered.

'I was for Bonnie Prince Charlie,' announced Amory.

'Of course you were – and for Hannibal——'

'Yes, and for the Southern Confederacy.' He was rather sceptical about being an Irish patriot – he suspected that being Irish was being somewhat common – but Monsignor assured him that Ireland was a romantic lost cause and Irish people quite charming, and that it should, by all means, be one of his principal biasses.

After a crowded hour which included several more cigarettes, and during which Monsignor learned, to his surprise but not to his horror, that Amory had not been brought up a Catholic, he announced that he had another guest. This turned out to be the Honorable Thornton Hancock, of Boston, ex-minister to The Hague, author of an erudite history of the Middle Ages and the last of a distinguished, patriotic, and brilliant family.

'He comes here for a rest,' said Monsignor confidentially, treating Amory as a contemporary. 'I act as an escape from the weariness of agnosticism, and I think I'm the only man who knows how his staid old mind is really at sea and longs for a sturdy spar like the Church to cling to.

Their first luncheon was one of the memorable events of Amory's early life. He was quite radiant and gave off a peculiar brightness and charm. Monsignor called out the best that he had thought by question and suggestion, and Amory talked with an ingenious brilliance of a thousand impulses and desires and repulsions and faiths and fears. He and Monsignor held the floor, and the older man, with his less receptive, less accepting, yet certainly not colder mentality, seemed content to listen and bask in the mellow sunshine that played between these two. Monsignor gave the effect of sunlight to many people; Amory gave it in his youth and, to some extent, when he was very much older, but never again was it quite so mutually spontaneous.

'He's a radiant boy,' thought Thornton Hancock, who had seen the splendour of two continents and talked with Parnell and Gladstone and Bismarck – and afterward he added to Monsignor: 'But his education ought not to be entrusted to a school or college.'

But for the next four years the best of Amory's intellect was concentrated on matters of popularity, the intricacies of a university social system and American Society as represented by Biltmore Teas and Hot Springs golf-links.

... In all, a wonderful week, that saw Amory's mind turned inside out, a hundred of his theories confirmed, and his joy of life crystallized to a thousand ambitions. Not that the conversation was scholastic – heaven forbid! Amory had only the vaguest idea as to what Bernard Shaw was – but Monsignor made quite as much out of 'The Beloved Vagabond' and 'Sir Nigel,' taking good care that Amory never once felt out of his depth.

But the trumpets were sounding for Amory's preliminary skirmish with his own generation.

'You're not sorry to go, of course. With people like us our home is where we are not,' said Monsignor.

'I *am* sorry——'

'No, you're not. No one person in the world is necessary to you or to me.'

'Well——'
'Good-bye.'

The Egotist Down

Amory's two years at St. Regis', though in turn painful and triumphant, had as little real significance in his own life as the American 'prep' school, crushed as it is under the heel of the universities, has to American life in general. We have no Eton to create the self-consciousness of a governing class; we have, instead, clean, flaccid and innocuous prep-aratory schools.

He went all wrong at the start, was generally considered both conceited and arrogant, and universally detested. He played football intensely, alternating a reckless brilliancy with a tendency to keep himself as safe from hazard as decency would permit. In a wild panic he backed out of a fight with a boy his own size, to a chorus of scorn, and a week later, in desperation, picked a battle with another boy very much bigger, from which he emerged badly beaten, but rather proud of himself.

He was resentful against all those in authority over him, and this, combined with a lazy indifference toward his work, exasperated every master in school. He grew discouraged and imagined himself a pariah; took to sulking in corners and reading after lights. With a dread of being alone he attached a few friends, but since they were not among the élite of the school, he used them simply as mirrors of himself, audiences before which he might do that posing absolutely essential to him. He was unbearably lonely, desperately unhappy.

There were some few grains of comfort. Whenever Amory was submerged, his vanity was the last part to go below the surface, so he could still enjoy a comfortable glow when 'Wookey-wookey,' the deaf old housekeeper, told him that he was the best-looking boy she had ever seen. It had pleased him to be the lightest and youngest man on the first football squad; it pleased him when Doctor Dougall told him at the end of a heated conference that he could, if he wished, get the best marks in school. But Doctor Dougall was wrong. It was temperamentally impossible for Amory to get the best marks in school.

Miserable, confined to bounds, unpopular with both faculty and students – that was Amory's first term. But at Christmas he had returned to Minneapolis, tight-lipped and strangely jubilant.

'Oh, I was sort of fresh at first,' he told Frog Parker patronizingly, 'but I got along fine – lightest man on the squad. You ought to go away to school, Froggy. It's great stuff.'

Incident of the Well-Meaning Professor

On the last night of his first term, Mr. Margotson, the senior master, sent word to study hall that Amory was to come to his room at nine. Amory suspected that advice was forthcoming, but he determined to be courteous, because this Mr. Margotson had been kindly disposed toward him.

His summoner received him gravely, and motioned him to a chair. He hemmed several times and looked consciously kind, as a man will when he knows he's on delicate ground.

'Amory,' he began. 'I've sent for you on a personal matter.'

'Yes, sir.'

'I've noticed you this year and I – I like you. I think you have in you the makings of a – a very good man.'

'Yes, sir,' Amory managed to articulate. He hated having people talk as if he were an admitted failure.

'But I've noticed,' continued the older man blindly, 'that you're not very popular with the boys.'

'No, sir.' Amory licked his lips.

'Ah – I thought you might not understand exactly what it was they – ah – objected to. I'm going to tell you, because I believe – ah – that when a boy knows his difficulties he's better able to cope with them – to conform to what others expect of him.' He a-hemmed again with delicate reticence, and continued: 'They seem to think that you're – ah – rather too fresh——'

Amory could stand no more. He rose from his chair, scarcely controlling his voice when he spoke.

'I know – oh, *don't* you s'pose I know.' His voice rose. 'I know what they think; do you s'pose you have to *tell* me!' He paused. 'I'm – I've got to go back now – hope I'm not rude——'

He left the room hurriedly. In the cool air outside, as he walked to his house, he exulted in his refusal to be helped.

'That *damn* old fool!' he cried wildly. 'As if I didn't *know !*'

He decided, however, that this was a good excuse not to go back to study hall that night, so, comfortably couched up in his room, he munched nabiscos and finished 'The White Company.'

Incident of the Wonderful Girl

There was a bright star in February. New York burst upon him on Washington's Birthday with the brilliance of a long-anticipated event. His glimpse of it as a vivid white-ness against a deep-blue sky had left a picture of splendour that rivalled the dream cities in the Arabian Nights; but this time he saw it by electric light, and romance gleamed from the chariot-race sign on Broadway and from the women's eyes at the Astor, where he and young Paskert from St. Regis' had dinner. When they walked down the aisle of the theatre, greeted by the nervous twanging and discord of untuned violins, and the sensuous, heavy frag-rance of paint and powder, he moved in a sphere of epi-curean delight. Everything enchanted him. The play was 'The Little Millionaire,' with George M. Cohan, and there was one stunning young brunette who made him sit with brimming eyes in the ecstasy of watching her dance.

> '*Oh – you – wonderful girl,*
> *What a wonderful girl you are—*'

sang the tenor, and Amory agreed silently, but passionately.

> '*All – your – wonderful words*
> *Thrill me through——*'

The violins swelled and quavered on the last notes, the girl
sank to a crumpled butterfly on the stage, a great burst of
clapping filled the house. Oh, to fall in love like that, to the
languorous magic melody of such a tune!

The last scene was laid on a roof-garden, and the 'cellos
sighed to the musical moon, while light adventure and
facile froth-like comedy flitted back and forth in the calcium.
Amory was on fire to be an habitué of roof-gardens, to meet
a girl who should look like that – better, that very girl;
whose hair would be drenched with golden moonlight, while
at his elbow sparkling wine was poured by an unintelligible
waiter. When the curtain fell for the last time he gave such a
long sigh that the people in front of him twisted around and
stared and said loud enough for him to hear:

'What a *remarkable*-looking boy!'

This took his mind off the play, and he wondered if he
really did seem handsome to the population of New York.

Paskert and he walked in silence toward their hotel. The
former was the first to speak. His uncertain fifteen-year-old
voice broke in in a melancholy strain on Amory's musings:

'I'd marry that girl to-night.'

There was no need to ask what girl he referred to.

'I'd be proud to take her home and introduce her to my
people,' continued Paskert.

Amory was distinctly impressed. He wished he had said
it instead of Paskert. It sounded so mature.

'I wonder about actresses; are they all pretty bad?'

'No, *sir*, not by a darn sight,' said the worldly youth with
emphasis, 'and I know that girl's as good as gold. I can tell.'

They wandered on, mixing in the Broadway crowd,
dreaming on the music that eddied out of the cafés. New
faces flashed on and off like myriad lights, pale or rouged
faces, tired, yet sustained by a weary excitement. Amory
watched them in fascination. He was planning his life. He
was going to live in New York, and be known at every restaurant and café, wearing a dress-suit from early evening to
early morning, sleeping away the dull hours of the forenoon.

'Yes, *sir*, I'd marry that girl to-night!'

Heroic in General Tone

October of his second and last year at St. Regis' was a high point in Amory's memory. The game with Groton was played from three of a snappy, exhilarating afternoon far into the crisp autumnal twilight, and Amory at quarter-back, exhorting in wild despair, making impossible tackles, calling signals in a voice that had diminished to a hoarse, furious whisper, yet found time to revel in the blood-stained bandage around his head, and the straining glorious heroism of plunging, crashing bodies and aching limbs. For those minutes courage flowed like wine out of the November dusk, and he was the eternal hero, one with the sea-rover on the prow of a Norse galley, one with Roland and Horatius, Sir Nigel and Ted Coy, scraped and stripped into trim and then flung by his own will into the breach, beating back the tide, hearing from afar the thunder of cheers . . . finally bruised and weary, but still elusive, circling an end, twisting, changing pace, straight-arming . . . falling behind the Groton goal with two men on his legs, in the only touch-down of the game.

The Philosophy of the Slicker

From the scoffing superiority of sixth-form year and success Amory looked back with cynical wonder on his status of the year before. He was changed as completely as Amory Blaine could ever be changed. Amory plus Beatrice plus two years in Minneapolis – these had been his in-gredients when he entered St. Regis'. But the Minneapolis years were not a thick enough overlay to conceal the 'Amory plus Beatrice' from the ferreting eyes of a boarding-school, so St. Regis' had very painfully drilled Beatrice out of him, and begun to lay down new and more conventional planking on the fundamental Amory. But both St. Regis' and Amory were unconscious of the fact that this funda-mental Amory had not in himself changed. Those qualities for which he had suffered, his moodiness, his tendency to pose, his laziness, and his love of playing the fool, were now taken as a matter of course, recognized eccentricities in a star quarter-back, a clever actor, and the editor of the *St. Regis Tatler:* it puzzled him to see impressionable small boys imitating the very vanities that had not long ago been contemptible weaknesses.

After the football season he slumped into dreamy content. The night of the pre-holiday dance he slipped away and went early to bed for the pleasure of hearing the violin music cross the grass and come surging in at his window. Many nights he lay there dreaming awake of secret cafés in Mont Martre, where ivory women delved in romantic mysteries with diplomats and soldiers of fortune, while orchestras played Hungarian waltzes and the air was thick and exotic with intrigue and moonlight and adventure. In the spring he read 'L'Allegro,' by request, and was inspired to lyrical outpourings on the subject of Arcady and the pipes of Pan. He moved his bed so that the sun would wake him at dawn that he might dress and go out to the archaic swing that hung from an apple-tree near the sixth-form house. Seating himself in this he would pump higher and higher until he got the effect of swinging into the wide air, into a fairy-land of piping satyrs and nymphs with the faces of fair-haired girls he passed in the streets of Eastchester. As the swing reached its highest point, Arcady really lay just over the brow of a certain hill, where the brown road dwindled out of sight in a golden dot.

He read voluminously all spring, the beginning of his eighteenth year: 'The Gentleman from Indiana,' 'The New Arabian Nights,' 'The Morals of Marcus Ordeyne,' 'The Man Who Was Thursday,' which he liked without understanding; 'Stover at Yale,' that became somewhat of a textbook; 'Dombey and Son,' because he thought he really should read better stuff; Robert Chambers, David Graham Phillips, and E. Phillips Oppenheim complete, and a scattering of Tennyson and Kipling. Of all his classwork only 'L'Allegro' and some quality of rigid clarity in solid geometry stirred his languid interest.

As June drew near, he felt the need of conversation to

formulate his own ideas, and, to his surprise, found a co-philosopher in Rahill, the president of the sixth form. In many a talk, on the highroad or lying belly-down along the edge of the baseball diamond, or late at night with their cigarettes glowing in the dark, they threshed out the questions of school, and there was developed the term 'slicker.'

'Got tobacco?' whispered Rahill one night, putting his head inside the door five minutes after lights.

'Sure.'

'I'm coming in.'

'Take a couple of pillows and lie in the window-seat, why don't you.'

Amory sat up in bed and lit a cigarette while Rahill settled for a conversation. Rahill's favourite subject was the respective futures of the sixth form, and Amory never tired of outlining them for his benefit.

'Ted Converse? 'At's easy. He'll fail his exams, tutor all summer at Harstrum's, get into Sheff with about four conditions, and flunk out in the middle of the freshman year. Then he'll go back West and raise hell for a year or so; finally his father will make him go into the paint business. He'll marry and have four sons, all bone heads. He'll always think St. Regis's spoiled him, so he'll send his sons to day school in Portland. He'll die of locomotor ataxia when he's forty-one, and his wife will give a baptizing stand or whatever you call it to the Presbyterian Church, with his name on it——'

'Hold up, Amory. That's too darned gloomy. How about yourself?'

'I'm in a superior class. You are, too. We're philosophers.'

'I'm not.'

'Sure you are. You've got a darn good head on you.' But Amory knew that nothing in the abstract, no theory or generality, ever moved Rahill until he stubbed his toe upon the concrete minutiæ of it.

'Haven't,' insisted Rahill. 'I let people impose on me here and don't get anything out of it. I'm the prey of my friends, damn it – do their lessons, get 'em out of trouble, pay 'em stupid summer visits, and always entertain their kid sisters; keep my temper when they get selfish and *then* they think they pay me back by voting for me and telling me I'm the 'big man' of St. Regis's. I want to get where everybody does their own work and I can tell people where to go. I'm tired of being nice to every poor fish in school.'

'You're not a slicker,' said Amory suddenly.

'A what?'

'A slicker.'

'What the devil's that?'

'Well, it's something that – that – there's a lot of them. You're not one, and neither am I, though I am more than you are.'

'Who is one? What makes you one?'

Amory considered.

'Why – why, I suppose that the *sign* of it is when a fellow slicks his hair back with water.'

'Like Carstairs?'

'Yes – sure. He's a slicker.'

They spent two evenings getting an exact definition. The slicker was good-looking or *clean*-looking; he had brains, social brains, that is, and he used all means on the broad path of honesty to get ahead, be popular, admired, and never in trouble. He dressed well, was particularly neat in appearance, and derived his name from the fact that his hair was inevitably worn short, soaked in water or tonic, parted in the middle, and slicked back as the current of fashion dictated. The slickers of that year had adopted tortoise-shell spectacles as badges of their slickerhood, and this made them so easy to recognize that Amory and Rahill never missed one. The slicker seemed distributed through school, always a little wiser and shrewder than his contemporaries, managing some team or other, and keeping his cleverness carefully concealed.

Amory found the slicker a most valuable classification until his junior year in college, when the outline became so blurred and indeterminate that it had to be subdivided many times, and became only a quality. Amory's secret ideal had all the slicker qualifications, but, in addition, courage and tremendous brains and talents – also Amory conceded him a bizarre streak that was quite irreconcilable to the slicker proper.

This was a first real break from the hypocrisy of school tradition. The slicker was a definite element of success, differing intrinsically from the prep school 'big man.'

'The Slicker'	'The Big Man'
1. Clever sense of social values.	1. Inclined to stupidity and unconscious of social values.
2. Dresses well. Pretends that dress is superficial – but knows that it isn't.	2. Thinks dress is superficial, and is inclined to be careless about it.
3. Goes into such activities as he can shine in.	3. Goes out for everything from a sense of duty.
4. Gets to college and is, in a worldly way, successful.	4. Gets to college and has a problematical future. Feels lost without his circle, and always says that school days were happiest, after all. Goes back to school and makes speeches about what St. Regis's boys are doing.
5. Hair slicked.	5. Hair not slicked.

Amory had decided definitely on Princeton, even though he would be the only boy entering that year from St. Regis'. Yale had a romance and glamour from the tales of Minneapolis, and St. Regis' men who had been 'tapped for Skull and Bones,' but Princeton drew him most, with its atmosphere of bright colours and its alluring reputation as the pleasantest country club in America. Dwarfed by the menacing college exams, Amory's school days drifted into the past. Years afterward, when he went back to St. Regis', he seemed to have forgotten the successes of sixth-form year, and to be able to picture himself only as the unadjustable boy who had hurried down corridors, jeered at by his rabid contemporaries mad with common sense.

II. SPIRES AND GARGOYLES

At first Amory noticed only the wealth of sunshine creeping across the long, green swards, dancing on the leaded window-panes, and swimming around the tops of spires and towers and battlemented walls. Gradually he realized that he was really walking up University Place, self-conscious about his suitcase, developing a new tendency to glare straight ahead when he passed any one. Several times he could have sworn that men turned to look at him critically. He wondered vaguely if there was something the matter with his clothes, and wished he had shaved that morning on the train. He felt unnecessarily stiff and awkward among these white-flannelled, bareheaded youths, who must be juniors and seniors, judging from the savoir faire with which they strolled.

He found that 12 University Place was a large, dilapidated mansion, at present apparently uninhabited, though he knew it housed usually a dozen freshmen. After a hurried skirmish with his landlady he sallied out on a tour of exploration, but he had gone scarcely a block when he became horribly conscious that he must be the only man in town who was wearing a hat. He returned hurriedly to 12 University, left his derby, and, emerging bareheaded, loitered down Nassau Street, stopping to investigate a display of athletic photographs in a store window, including a large one of Allenby, the football captain, and next attracted by the sign 'Jigger Shop' over a confectionary window. This sounded familiar, so he sauntered in and took a seat on a high stool.

'Chocolate sundae,' he told a coloured person.

'Double chocolate jiggah? Anything else?'

'Why – yes.'

'Bacon bun ?'

'Why – yes.'

He munched four of these, finding them of pleasing savour, and then consumed another double-chocolate jigger before ease descended upon him. After a cursory inspection of the pillow-cases, leather pennants, and Gibson Girls that lined the walls, he left, and continued along Nassau Street with his hands in his pockets. Gradually he was learning to distinguish between upper classmen and entering men, even though the freshman cap would not appear until the following Monday. Those who were too obviously, too nervously at home were freshmen, for as each train brought a new contingent it was immediately absorbed into the hatless, white-shod, book-laden throng, whose function seemed to be to drift endlessly up and down the street, emitting great clouds of smoke from brand-new pipes. By afternoon Amory realized that now the newest arrivals were taking him for an upper classman, and he tried conscientiously to look both pleasantly blasé and casually critical, which was as near as he could analyze the prevalent facial expression.

At five o'clock he felt the need of hearing his own voice, so he retreated to his house to see if any one else had arrived. Having climbed the rickety stairs he scrutinized his room resignedly, concluding that it was hopeless to attempt any more inspired decoration than class banners and tiger pictures. There was a tap at the door.

'Come in!'

A slim face with grey eyes and a humorous smile appeared in the doorway.

'Got a hammer ?'

'No – sorry. Maybe Mrs. Twelve, or whatever she goes by, has one.'

The stranger advanced into the room.

'You an inmate of this asylum ?'

Amory nodded.

'Awful barn for the rent we pay.'

Amory had to agree that it was.

'I thought of the campus,' he said, 'but they say there's so

few freshmen that they're lost. Have to sit around and study
for something to do.'

The grey-eyed man decided to introduce himself.

'My name's Holiday.'

'Blaine's my name.'

They shook hands with the fashionable low swoop.
Amory grinned.

'Where'd you prep?'

'Andover – where did you?'

'St. Regis's.'

'Oh, did you? I had a cousin there.'

They discussed the cousin thoroughly, and then Holiday
announced that he was to meet his brother for dinner at six.

'Come along and have a bite with us.'

'All right.'

At the Kenilworth Amory met Burne Holiday – he of the
grey eyes was Kerry – and during a limpid meal of thin
soup and anæmic vegetables they stared at the other freshmen, who sat either in small groups looking very ill at ease,
or in large groups seeming very much at home.

'I hear Commons is pretty bad,' said Amory.

'That's the rumour. But you've got to eat there – or pay
anyways.'

'Crime!'

'Imposition!'

'Oh, at Princeton you've got to swallow everything the
first year. It's like a damned prep school.'

Amory agreed.

'Lot of pep, though,' he insisted. 'I wouldn't have gone to
Yale for a million.'

'Me either.'

'You going out for anything?' inquired Amory of the
elder brother.

'Not me – Burne here is going out for the Prince – the
Daily Princetonian, you know.'

'Yes, I know.'

'You going out for anything?'

'Why – yes. I'm going to take a whack at freshman foot-ball.'

'Play at St. Regis's?'

'Some,' admitted Amory depreciatingly, 'but I'm getting so damned thin.'

'You're not thin.'

'Well, I used to be stocky last fall.'

'Oh!'

After supper they attended the movies, where Amory was fascinated by the glib comments of a man in front of him, as well as by the wild yelling and shouting.

'*Yoho!*'

'Oh, honey-*baby* – you're so big and strong, but oh, so *gentle!*'

'Clinch!'

'Oh, *Clinch!*'

'Kiss her, kiss 'at lady, *quick!*'

'Oh-h-h——!'

A group began whistling 'By the Sea,' and the audience took it up noisily. This was followed by an indistinguishable song that included much stamping and then by an endless, incoherent dirge.

> 'Oh-h-h-h-h
> She works in a Jam Factoree
> And – that-may-be-all-right
> But you can't-fool-me
> For I know – DAMN – WELL
> That she DON'T-make-jam-all-night!
> Oh-h-h-h!'

As they pushed out, giving and receiving curious imper-sonal glances, Amory decided that he liked the movies, wanted to enjoy them as the row of upper classmen in front had enjoyed them, with their arms along the backs of the seats, their comments Gaelic and caustic, their attitude a mixture of critical wit and tolerant amusement.

'Want a sundae – I mean a jigger?' asked Kerry.

'Sure.'

They suppered heavily and then, still sauntering, eased back to 12.

'Wonderful night.'

'It's a whiz.'

'You men going to unpack?'

'Guess so. Come on, Burne.'

Amory decided to sit for a while on the front steps, so he bade them good night.

The great tapestries of trees had darkened to ghosts back at the last edge of twilight. T he early moon had drenched the arches with pale blue, and, weaving over the night, in and out of the gossamer rifts of moon, swept a song, a song with more than a hint of sadness, infinitely transient, infinitely regretful.

He remembered that an alumnus of the nineties had told him of one of Booth Tarkington's amusements: standing in mid-campus in the small hours and singing tenor songs to the stars, arousing mingled emotions in the couched undergraduates according to the sentiment of their moods.

Now, far down the shadowy line of University Place a white-clad phalanx broke the gloom, and marching figures, white-shirted, white-trousered, swung rhythmically up the street, with linked arms and heads thrown back:

> *'Going back – going back,*
> *Going – back – to – Nas-sau – Hall,*
> *Going back – going back –*
> *To the – Best – Old – Place – of – All.*
> *Going back – going back,*
> *From all – this – earth-ly – ball,*
> *We'll – clear – the – track – as – we – go – back–*
> *Going – back – to – Nas-sau – Hall!'*

Amory closed his eyes as the ghostly procession drew near. The song soared so high that all dropped out except the tenors, who bore the melody triumphantly past the danger-point and relinquished it to the fantastic chorus. Then Amory opened his eyes, half afraid that sight would spoil the rich illusion of harmony.

He sighed eagerly. There at the head of the white platoon marched Allenby, the football captain, slim and defiant, as if aware that this year the hopes of the college rested on him, that his hundred-and-sixty pounds were expected to dodge to victory through the heavy blue and crimson lines.

Fascinated, Amory watched each rank of linked arms as it came abreast, the faces indistinct above the polo shirts, the voices blent in a pæan of triumph – and then the procession passed through shadowy Campbell Arch, and the voices grew fainter as it wound eastward over the campus.

The minutes passed and Amory sat there very quietly. He regretted the rule that would forbid freshmen to be out-doors after curfew, for he wanted to ramble through the shadowy scented lanes, where Witherspoon brooded like a dark mother over Whig and Clio, her Attic children, where the black Gothic snake of Little curled down to Cuyler and Patton, these in turn flinging the mystery out over the placid slope rolling to the lake.

Princeton of the daytime filtered slowly into his con-sciousness – West and Reunion, redolent of the sixties, Seventy-nine Hall, brick-red and arrogant, Upper and Lower Pyne, aristocratic Elizabethan ladies not quite con-tent to live among shopkeepers, and, topping all, climbing with clear blue aspiration, the great dreaming spires of Holder and Cleveland towers.

From the first he loved Princeton – its lazy beauty, its half-grasped significance, the wild moonlight revel of the rushes, the handsome, prosperous big-game crowds, and under it all the air of struggle that pervaded his class. From the day when, wild-eyed and exhausted, the jerseyed fresh-men sat in the gymnasium and elected some one from Hill School class president, a Lawrenceville celebrity vice-president, a hockey star from St. Paul's secretary, up until the end of sophomore year it never ceased, that breathless social system, that worship, seldom named, never really admitted, of the bogey 'Big Man.'

First it was schools, and Amory, alone from St. Regis',

watched the crowds form and widen and form again; St. Paul's, Hill, Pomfret, eating at certain tacitly reserved tables in Commons, dressing in their own corners of the gymnasium, and drawing unconsciously about them a barrier of the slightly less important but socially ambitious to protect them from the friendly, rather puzzled high-school element. From the moment he realized this Amory resented social barriers as artificial distinctions made by the strong to bolster up their weak retainers and keep out the almost strong.

Having decided to be one of the gods of the class, he reported for freshman football practice, but in the second week, playing quarter-back, already paragraphed in corners of the *Princetonian*, he wrenched his knee seriously enough to put him out for the rest of the season. This forced him to retire and consider the situation.

'12 Univee' housed a dozen miscellaneous questionmarks. There were three or four inconspicuous and quite startled boys from Lawrenceville, two amateur wild men from a New York private school (Kerry Holiday christened them the 'plebeian drunks'), a Jewish youth, also from New York, and, as compensation for Amory, the two Holidays, to whom he took an instant fancy.

The Holidays were rumoured twins, but really the darkhaired one, Kerry, was a year older than his blond brother, Burne. Kerry was tall, with humorous grey eyes, and a sudden, attractive smile; he became at once the mentor of the house, reaper of ears that grew too high, censor of conceit, vendor of rare, satirical humour. Amory spread the table of their future friendship with all his ideas of what college should and did mean. Kerry, not inclined as yet to take things seriously, chided him gently for being curious at this inopportune time about the intricacies of the social system, but liked him and was both interested and amused.

Burne, fair-haired, silent, and intent, appeared in the house only as a busy apparition, gliding in quietly at night and off again in the early morning to get up his work in the library – he was out for the *Princetonian*, competing furiously against forty others for the coveted first place. In December he came down with diphtheria, and some one else won the competition, but, returning to college in February, he dauntlessly went after the prize again. Necessarily, Amory's acquaintance with him was in the way of three-minute chats, walking to and from lectures, so he failed to penetrate Burne's one absorbing interest and find what lay beneath it.

Amory was far from contented. He missed the place he had won at St. Regis', the being known and admired, yet Princeton stimulated him, and there were many things ahead calculated to arouse the Machiavelli latent in him, could he but insert a wedge. The upper-class clubs, concerning which he had pumped a reluctant graduate during the previous summer, excited his curiosity: Ivy, detached and breathlessly aristocratic; Cottage, an impressive mélange of brilliant adventurers and well-dressed philan-derers; Tiger Inn, broad-shouldered and athletic, vitalized by an honest elaboration of prep-school standards; Cap and Gown, anti-alcoholic, faintly religious and politically powerful; flamboyant Colonial; literary Quadrangle; and the dozen others, varying in age and position.

Anything which brought an under classman into too glaring a light was labelled with the damning brand of 'running it out.' The movies thrived on caustic comments, but the men who made them were generally running it out; talking of clubs was running it out; standing for anything very strongly, as, for instance, drinking parties or teetotalling, was running it out; in short, being personally conspicuous was not tolerated, and the influential man was the non-committal man, until at club elections in sophomore year every one should be sewed up in some bag for the rest of his college career.

Amory found that writing for the *Nassau Literary Maga-zine* would get him nothing, but that being on the board of the *Daily Princetonian* would get any one a good deal. His vague desire to do immortal acting with the English Dramatic Association faded out when he found that the most ingenious brains and talents were concentrated upon the Triangle Club, a musical comedy organization that every year took a great Christmas trip. In the meanwhile, felling strangely alone and restless in Commons, with new desires and ambitions stirring in his mind, he let the first term go by between an envy of the embryo successes and a puzzled fretting with Kerry as to why they were not accepted immediately among the élite of the class.

Many afternoons they lounged in the windows of 12 Univee and watched the class pass to and from Commons, noting satellites already attaching themselves to the more prominent, watching the lonely grind with his hurried step and downcast eye, envying the happy security of the big school groups.

'We're the damned middle class, that's what!' he complained to Kerry one day as he lay stretched out on the sofa, consuming a family of Fatimas with contemplative precision.

'Well, why not? We came to Princeton so we could feel that way toward the small colleges – have it on 'em, more self-confidence, dress better, cut a swathe——'

'Oh, it isn't that I mind the glittering caste system,' admitted Amory. 'I like having a bunch of hot cats on top, but gosh, Kerry, I've got to be one of them.'

'But just now, Amory, you're only a sweaty bourgeois.'

Amory lay for a moment without speaking.

'I won't be – long,' he said finally. 'But I hate to get anywhere by working for it. I'll show the marks, don't you know.'

'Honorable scars.' Kerry craned his neck suddenly at the street. 'There's Langueduc, if you want to see what he looks like – and Humbird just behind.'

Amory rose dynamically and sought the windows.

'Oh,' he said, scrutinizing these worthies, 'Humbird looks like a knockout, but this Langueduc – he's the rugged type, isn't he? I distrust that sort. All diamonds look big in the rough.'

'Well,' said Kerry, as the excitement subsided, 'you're a
literary genius. It's up to you.'

'I wonder' – Amory paused – 'if I could be. I honestly
think so sometimes. That sounds like the devil, and I
wouldn't say it to anybody except you.'

'Well – go ahead. Let your hair grow and write poems
like this guy D'Invilliers in the Lit.'

Amory reached lazily at a pile of magazines on the table.
'Read his latest effort?'

'Never miss 'em. They're rare.'

Amory glanced through the issue.

'Hello!' he said in surprise, 'he's a freshman, isn't he?'

'Yeah.'

'Listen to this! My God!

> *"A serving lady speaks:*
> > *Black velvet trails its folds over the day,*
> > *White tapers, prisoned in their silver frames,*
> > *Wave their thin flames like shadows in the wind,*
> > *Pia, Pompia, come – come away——'*

'Now, what the devil does that mean?'

'It's a pantry scene.'

> *"Her toes are stiffened like a stork's in flight;*
> > *She's laid upon her bed, on the white sheets,*
> > *Her hands pressed on her smooth bust like a saint,*
> > *Bella Cunizza, come into the light!'*

'My gosh, Kerry, what in hell is it all about? I swear I
don't get him at all, and I'm a literary bird myself.'

'It's pretty tricky,' said Kerry, 'only you've got to think
of hearses and stale milk when you read it. That isn't as
pash as some of them.'

Amory tossed the magazine on the table.

'Well,' he sighed, 'I sure am up in the air. I know I'm
not a regular fellow, yet I loathe anybody else that isn't. I
can't decide whether to cultivate my mind and be a great

THIS SIDE OF PARADISE

dramatist, or to thumb my nose at the Golden Treasury and be a Princeton slicker.'

'Why decide?' suggested Kerry. 'Better drift, like me. I'm going to sail into prominence on Burne's coat-tails.'

'I can't drift – I want to be interested. I want to pull strings, even for somebody else, or be Princetonian chairman or Triangle president. I want to be admired, Kerry.'

'You're thinking too much about yourself.'

Amory sat up at this.

'No. I'm thinking about you, too. We've got to get out and mix around the class right now, when it's fun to be a snob. I'd like to bring a sardine to the prom in June, for instance, but I wouldn't do it unless I could be damn debonair about it – introduce her to all the prize parlour-snakes, and the football captain, and all that simple stuff.'

'Amory,' said Kerry impatiently, 'you're just going around in a circle. If you want to be prominent, get out and try for something; if you don't, just take it easy.' He yawned. 'Come on, let's let the smoke drift off. We'll go down and watch football practice.'

Amory gradually accepted this point of view, decided that next fall would inaugurate his career, and relinquished himself to watching Kerry extract joy from 12 Univee.

They filled the Jewish youth's bed with lemon pie; they put out the gas all over the house every night by blowing into the jet in Amory's room, to the bewilderment of Mrs. Twelve and the local plumber; they set up the effects of the plebeian drunks – pictures, books, and furniture – in the bathroom, to the confusion of the pair, who hazily discovered the transposition on their return from a Trenton spree; they were disappointed beyond measure when the plebeian drunks decided to take it as a joke; they played red-dog and twenty-one and jack-pot from dinner to dawn, and on the occasion of one man's birthday persuaded him to buy sufficient champagne for a hilarious celebration. The donor of the party having remained sober, Kerry and Amory accidently dropped him down two flights of stairs and called, shame-faced and penitent, at the infirmary all the following week.

'Say, who are all these women?' demanded Kerry one day, protesting at the size of Amory's mail. 'I've been looking at the postmarks lately – Farmington and Dobbs and Westover and Dana Hall – what's the idea?'

Amory grinned.

'All from the Twin Cities.' He named them off. 'There's Marylyn De Witt – she's pretty, got a car of her own and that's damn convenient; there's Sally Weatherby – she's getting too fat; there's Myra St. Claire, she's an old flame, easy to kiss if you like it——'

'What line do you throw 'em?' demanded Kerry. 'I've tried everything, and the mad wags aren't even afraid of me.'

'You're the "nice boy" type,' suggested Amory.

'That's just it. Mother always feels the girl is safe if she's with me. Honestly, it's annoying. If I start to hold somebody's hand, they laugh at me, and *let* me, just as if it wasn't part of them. As soon as I get hold of a hand they sort of disconnect it from the rest of them.'

'Sulk,' suggested Amory. 'Tell 'em you're wild and have 'em reform you – go home furious – come back in half an hour – startle 'em.'

Kerry shook his head.

'No chance. I wrote a St. Timothy girl a really loving letter last year. In one place I got rattled and said: 'My God, how I love you!' She took a nail scissors, clipped out the "My God" and showed the rest of the letter all over school. Doesn't work at all. I'm just "good old Kerry" and all that rot.'

Amory smiled and tried to picture himself as 'good old Amory.' He failed completely.

February dripped snow and rain, the cyclonic freshman mid-years passed, and life in 12 Univee continued interesting if not purposeful. Once a day Amory indulged in a club sandwich, cornflakes, and Julienne potatoes at 'Joe's,' accompanied usually by Kerry or Alec Connage. The latter was a quiet, rather aloof slicker from Hotchkiss, who lived next door and shared the same enforced singleness as Amory, due to the fact that his entire class had gone to Yale. 'Joe's' was unæsthetic and faintly unsanitary, but a limitless charge account could be opened there, a convenience that Amory appreciated. His father had been experimenting with mining stocks and, in consequence, his allowance, while liberal, was not at all what he had expected.

'Joe's' had the additional advantage of seclusion from curious upper-class eyes, so at four each afternoon Amory, accompanied by friend or book, went up to experiment with his digestion. One day in March, finding that all the tables were occupied, he slipped into a chair opposite a freshman who bent intently over a book at the last table. They nodded briefly. For twenty minutes Amory sat consuming bacon buns and reading 'Mrs. Warren's Profession' (he had discovered Shaw quite by accident while browsing in the library during mid-years); the other freshman, also intent on his volume, meanwhile did away with a trio of chocolate malted milks.

By and by Amory's eyes wandered curiously to his fellow-luncher's book. He spelled out the name and title upside down – 'Marpessa,' by Stephen Phillips. This meant nothing to him, his metrical education having been confined to such Sunday classics as 'Come into the Garden, Maude,' and what morsels of Shakespeare and Milton had been recently forced upon him.

Moved to address his vis-à-vis, he simulated interest in his book for a moment, and then exclaimed aloud as if involuntarily:

'Ha! Great stuff!'

The other freshman looked up and Amory registered artificial embarrassment.

'Are you referring to your bacon buns?' His cracked, kindly voice went well with the large spectacles and the impression of a voluminous keenness that he gave.

'No,' Amory answered. 'I was referring to Bernard Shaw.' He turned the book around in explanation.

'I've never read any Shaw. I've always meant to.' The boy paused and then continued: 'Did you ever read Stephen Phillips, or do you like poetry?'

'Yes, indeed,' Amory affirmed eagerly. 'I've never read much of Phillips, though.' (He had never heard of any Phillips except the late David Graham.)

'It's pretty fair, I think. Of course he's a Victorian.' They sallied into a discussion of poetry, in the course of which they introduced themselves, and Amory's companion proved to be none other than 'that awful highbrow, Thomas Parke D'Invilliers,' who signed the passionate love-poems in the *Lit*. He was, perhaps, nineteen, with stooped shoulders, pale blue eyes, and, as Amory could tell from his general appearance, without much conception of social competition and such phenomena of absorbing interest. Still, he liked books, and it seemed forever since Amory had met any one who did; if only that St. Paul's crowd at the next table would not mistake *him* for a bird, too, he would enjoy the encounter tremendously. They didn't seem to be noticing, so he let himself go, discussed books by the dozens – books he had read, read about, books he had never heard of, rattling off lists of titles with the facility of a Brentano's clerk. D'Invilliers was partially taken in and wholly delighted. In a good-natured way he had almost decided that Princeton was one part deadly Philistines and one part deadly grinds, and to find a person who could mention Keats without stammering, yet evidently washed his hands, was rather a treat.

'Ever read any Oscar Wilde?' he asked.

'No. Who wrote it?'

'It's a man – don't you know?'

'Oh, surely.' A faint chord was struck in Amory's memory. 'Wasn't the comic opera, "Patience," written about him?'

'Yes, that's the fella. I've just finished a book of his, "The Picture of Dorian Gray," and I certainly wish you'd read it. You'd like it. You can borrow it if you want to.'

'Why, I'd like it a lot – thanks.'

'Don't you want to come up to the room? I've got a few other books.'

Amory hesitated, glanced at the St. Paul's group – one of them was the magnificent, exquisite Humbird – and he considered how determinate the addition of this friend would be. He never got to the stage of making them and getting rid of them – he was not hard enough for that – so he measured Thomas Parke D'Invilliers' undoubted attractions and value against the menace of cold eyes behind tortoise-rimmed spectacles that he fancied glared from the next table.

'Yes, I'll go.'

So he found 'Dorian Gray' and the 'Mystic and Sombre Dolores' and the 'Belle Dame sans Merci'; for a month was keen on naught else. The world became pale and interesting, and he tried hard to look at Princeton through the satiated eyes of Oscar Wilde and Swinburne – or 'Fingal O'Flaherty' and 'Algernon Charles,' as he called them in précieuse jest. He read enormously every night – Shaw, Chesterton, Barrie, Pinero, Yeats, Synge, Ernest Dowson, Arthur Symons, Keats, Sudermann, Robert Hugh Benson, the Savoy Operas – just a heterogeneous mixture, for he suddenly discovered that he had read nothing for years.

Tom D'Invilliers became at first an occasion rather than a friend. Amory saw him about once a week, and together they gilded the ceiling of Tom's room and decorated the walls with imitation tapestry, bought at an auction, tall candlesticks and figured curtains. Amory liked him for being clever and literary without effeminacy or affectation. In fact, Amory did most of the strutting and tried painfully to make every remark an epigram, than which, if one is content with ostensible epigrams, there are many feats harder. 12 Univee was amused. Kerry read 'Dorian Gray' and simulated Lord Henry, following Amory about, addressing him as 'Dorian' and pretending to encourage in him wicked fancies and attenuated tendencies to ennui. When he carried it into commons, to the amazement of the others at table, Amory became furiously embarrassed, and after that made epigrams only before D'Invilliers or a convenient mirror.

One day Tom and Amory tried reciting their own and

Lord Dunsany's poems to the music of Kerry's graphophone.

'Chant!' cried Tom. 'Don't recite! *Chant!*'

Amory, who was performing, looked annoyed, and claimed that he needed a record with less piano in it. Kerry thereupon rolled on the floor in stifled laughter.

'Put on "Hearts and Flowers"!' he howled. 'Oh, my Lord, I'm going to cast a kitten.'

'Shut off the damn graphophone,' Amory cried, rather red in the face. 'I'm not giving an exhibition.'

In the meanwhile Amory delicately kept trying to awaken a sense of the social system in D'Invilliers, for he knew that this poet was really more conventional than he, and needed merely watered hair, a smaller range of conversation, and a darker brown hat to become quite regular. But the liturgy of Livingstone collars and dark ties fell on heedless ears; in fact D'Invilliers faintly resented his efforts; so Amory confined himself to calls once a week, and brought him occasionally to 12 Univee. This caused mild titters among the other freshmen, who called them 'Doctor Johnson and Boswell.'

Alec Connage, another frequent visitor, liked him in a vague way, but was afraid of him as a highbrow. Kerry, who saw through his poetic patter to the solid, almost respectable depths within, was immensely amused and would have him recite poetry by the hour, while he lay with closed eyes on Amory's sofa and listened:

> *'Asleep or waking is it? for her neck*
> *Kissed over close, wears yet a purple speck*
> *Wherein the pained blood falters and goes out;*
> *Soft and stung softly – fairer for a fleck . . .'*

'That's good,' Kerry would say softly. 'It pleases the elder Holiday. That's a great poet, I guess.' Tom, delighted at an audience, would ramble through the 'Poems and Ballades' until Kerry and Amory knew them almost as well as he.

Amory took to writing poetry on spring afternoons, in the gardens of the big estates near Princeton, while swans made effective atmosphere in the artificial pools, and slow clouds sailed harmoniously above the willows. May came too soon, and suddenly unable to bear walls, he wandered the campus at all hours through starlight and rain.

A Damp Symbolic Interlude

The night mist fell. From the moon it rolled, clustered about the spires and towers, and then settled below them, so that the dreaming peaks were still in lofty aspiration toward the sky. Figures that dotted the day like ants now brushed along as shadowy ghosts, in and out of the foreground. The Gothic halls and cloisters were infinitely more mysterious as they loomed suddenly out of the darkness, outlined each by myriad faint squares of yellow light. Indefinitely from somewhere a bell boomed the quarter-hour, and Amory, pausing by the sun-dial, stretched himself out full length on the damp grass. The cool bathed his eyes and slowed the flight of time – time that had crept so insidiously through the lazy April afternoons, seemed so intangible in the long spring twilights. Evening after evening the senior singing had drifted over the campus in melancholy beauty, and through the shell of his undergraduate consciousness had broken a deep and reverent devotion to the grey walls and Gothic peaks and all they symbolized as warehouses of dead ages.

The tower that in view of his window sprang upward, grew into a spire, yearning higher until its uppermost tip was half invisible against the morning skies, gave him the first sense of the transiency and unimportance of the campus figures except as holders of the apostolic succession. He liked knowing that Gothic architecture, with its upward trend, was peculiarly appropriate to universities, and the idea became personal to him. The silent stretches of green, the quiet halls with an occasional late-burning scholastic light held his imagination in a strong grasp, and the chastity of the spire became a symbol of this perception.

'Damn it all,' he whispered aloud, wetting his hands in the damp and running them through his hair. 'Next year I work!' Yet he knew that where now the spirit of spires and towers made him dreamily acquiescent, it would then over-awe him. Where now he realized only his own inconse-quence, effort would make him aware of his own impotency and insufficiency.

The college dreamed on – awake. He felt a nervous excite-ment that might have been the very throb of its slow heart. It was a stream where he was to throw a stone whose faint ripple would be vanishing almost as it left his hand. As yet he had given nothing, he had taken nothing.

A belated freshman, his oilskin slicker rasping loudly, slushed along the soft path. A voice from somewhere called the inevitable formula, 'Stick out your head!' below an un-seen window. A hundred little sounds of the current drifting on under the fog pressed in finally on his consciousness.

'Oh, *God!*' he cried suddenly, and started at the sound of his voice in the stillness. The rain dripped on. A minute longer he lay without moving, his hands clenched. Then he sprang to his feet and gave his clothes a tentative pat.

'I'm very damn wet!' he said aloud to the sun-dial.

Historical

The war began in the summer following his freshman year. Beyond a sporting interest in the German dash for Paris the whole affair failed either to thrill or interest him. With the attitude he might have held toward an amusing melodrama he hoped it would be long and bloody. If it had not continued he would have felt like an irate ticket-holder at a prize-fight where the principals refused to mix it up.

That was his total reaction.

'Ha-Ha Hortense!'

'All right, *ponies!*'

'Shake it up!'

'Hey, ponies – how about easing up on the crap game and shaking a mean hip?'

'Hey, *ponies!*'

The coach fumed helplessly, the Triangle Club president, glowering with anxiety, varied between furious bursts of authority and fits of temperamental lassitude, when he sat spiritless and wondered how the devil the show was ever going on tour by Christmas.

'All right. We'll take the pirate song.'

The ponies took last drags at their cigarettes and slumped into place; the leading lady rushed into the foreground, setting his hands and feet in an atmospheric mince; and as the coach clapped and stamped and tumped and da-da'd, they hashed out a dance.

A great, seething ant-hill was the Triangle Club. It gave a musical comedy every year, travelling with cast, chorus, orchestra, and scenery all through Christmas vacation. The play and music were the work of undergraduates, and the club itself was the most influential of institutions, over three hundred men competing for it every year.

Amory, after an easy victory in the first sophomore *Princetonian* competition, stepped into a vacancy of the cast as *Boiling Oil, a Pirate Lieutenant*. Every night for the last week they had rehearsed 'Ha-Ha Hortense!' in the Casino, from two in the afternoon until eight in the morning, sustained by dark and powerful coffee, and sleeping in lectures through the interim. A rare scene, the Casino. A big, barn-like auditorium, dotted with boys as girls, boys as pirates, boys as babies; the scenery in course of being violently set up; the spotlight man rehearsing by throwing weird shafts into angry eyes; over all the constant tuning of the orchestra or the cheerful tumpty-tump of a Triangle tune. The boy who writes the lyrics stands in the corner, biting a pencil, with twenty minutes to think of an encore; the business manager argues with the secretary as to how much money can be spent on 'those damn milkmaid costumes'; the old graduate, president in ninety-eight, perches on a box and thinks how much simpler it was in his day.

How a Triangle show ever got off was a mystery, but it was a riotous mystery, anyway, whether or not one did enough service to wear a little gold Triangle on his watch-

chain. 'Ha-Ha Hortense!' was written over six times and had
the names of nine collaborators on the programme. All
Triangle shows started by being 'something different – not
just a regular musical comedy,' but when the several authors,
the president, the coach and the faculty committee finished
with it, there remained just the old reliable Triangle show
with the old reliable jokes and the star comedian who got
expelled or sick or something just before the trip, and the
dark-whiskered man in the pony-ballet, who 'absolutely
won't shave twice a day, dog-gone it!'

There was one brilliant place in 'Ha-Ha Hortense!' It is
a Princeton tradition that whenever a Yale man who is a
member of the widely advertised 'Skull and Bones' hears
the sacred name mentioned, he must leave the room. It is
also a tradition that the members are invariably successful
in later life, amassing fortunes or votes or coupons or whatever they choose to amass. Therefore, at each performance
of 'Ha-Ha Hortense!' half-a-dozen seats were kept from sale
and occupied by six of the worst-looking vagabonds that
could be hired from the streets, further touched up by the
Triangle make-up man. At the moment in the show where
Firebrand, the Pirate Chief, pointed at his black flag and said,
'I am a Yale graduate – note my Skull and Bones!' – at this
very moment the six vagabonds were instructed to rise
conspicuously and leave the theatre with looks of deep melancholy and an injured dignity. It was claimed though never
proved that on one occasion the hired Elis were swelled by
one of the real thing.

They played through vacation to the fashionable of eight
cities. Amory liked Louisville and Memphis best: these
knew how to meet strangers, furnished extraordinary punch,
and flaunted an astonishing array of feminine beauty.
Chicago he approved for a certain verve that transcended its
loud accent – however, it was a Yale town, and as the Yale
Glee Club was expected in a week the Triangle received
only divided homage. In Baltimore, Princeton was at home,
and every one fell in love. There was a proper consumption
of strong waters all along the line; one man invariably went

on the stage highly stimulated, claiming that his particular interpretation of the part required it. There were three private cars; however, no one slept except in the third car, which was called the 'animal car,' and where were herded the spectacled wind-jammers of the orchestra. Everything was so hurried that there was no time to be bored, but when they arrived in Philadelphia, with vacation nearly over, there was rest in getting out of the heavy atmosphere of flowers and grease-paint, and the ponies took off their corsets with abdominal pains and sighs of relief.

When the disbanding came, Amory set out post-haste for Minneapolis, for Sally Weatherby's cousin, Isabelle Borgé, was coming to spend the winter in Minneapolis while her parents went abroad. He remembered Isabelle only as a little girl with whom he had played sometimes when he first went to Minneapolis. She had gone to Baltimore to live – but since then she had developed a past.

Amory was in full stride, confident, nervous, and jubilant. Scurrying back to Minneapolis to see a girl he had known as a child seemed the interesting and romantic thing to do, so without compunction he wired his mother not to expect him . . . sat in the train, and thought about himself for thirty-six hours.

'Petting'

On the Triangle trip Amory had come into constant contact with that great current American phenomenon, the 'petting party.'

None of the Victorian mothers – and most of the mothers were Victorian – had any idea how casually their daughters were accustomed to be kissed. '*Servant*-girls are that way,' says Mrs. Huston-Carmelite to her popular daughter. 'They are kissed first and proposed to afterward.'

But the Popular Daughter becomes engaged every six months between sixteen and twenty-two, when she arranges a match with young Hambell, of Cambell & Hambell, who fatuously considers himself her first love, and between engagements the P. D. (she is selected by the cut-in system at

dances, which favours the survival of the fittest) has other
sentimental last kisses in the moonlight, or the firelight, or
the outer darkness.

Amory saw girls doing things that even in his memory
would have been impossible: eating three-o'clock, after-
dance suppers in impossible cafés, talking of every side of
life with an air half of earnestness, half of mockery, yet with
a furtive excitement that Amory considered stood for a real
moral let-down. But he never realized how widespread it
was until he saw the cities between New York and Chicago
as one vast juvenile intrigue.

Afternoon at the Plaza, with winter twilight hovering outside and faint drums downstairs . . . they strut and fret in
the lobby, taking another cocktail, scrupulously attired and
waiting. Then the swinging doors revolve and three bundles
of fur mince in. The theatre comes afterward; then a table
at the Midnight Frolic – of course, mother will be along
there, but she will serve only to make things more secretive
and brilliant as she sits in solitary state at the deserted table
and thinks such entertainments as this are not half so bad as
they are painted, only rather wearying. But the P. D. is in
love again . . . it was odd, wasn't it ? – that though there was
so much room left in the taxi the P. D. and the boy from
Williams were somehow crowded out and had to go in a
separate car. Odd! Didn't you notice how flushed the P. D.
was when she arrived just seven minutes late ? But the P. D.
'gets away with it.'

The 'belle' had become the 'flirt,' the 'flirt' had become
the 'baby vamp.' The 'belle' had five or six callers every
afternoon. If the P. D., by some strange accident, has two,
it is made pretty uncomfortable for the one who hasn't a
date with her. The 'belle' was surrounded by a dozen men
in the intermissions between dances. Try to find the P. D.
between dances, just *try* to find her.

The same girl . . . deep in an atmosphere of jungle music
and the questioning of moral codes. Amory found it rather
fascinating to feel that any popular girl he met before eight
he might quite possibly kiss before twelve.

'Why on earth are we here?' he asked the girl with the green combs one night as they sat in some one's limousine, outside the Country Club in Louisville.

'I don't know. I'm just full of the devil.'

'Let's be frank – we'll never see each other again. I wanted to come out here with you because I thought you were the best-looking girl in sight. You really don't care whether you ever see me again, do you?'

'No – but is this your line for every girl? What have I done to deserve it?'

'And you didn't feel tired dancing or want a cigarette or any of the things you said? You just wanted to be——'

'Oh, let's go in,' she interrupted, 'if you want to *analyze.* Let's not *talk* about it.'

When the hand-knit, sleeveless jerseys were stylish, Amory, in a burst of inspiration, named them 'petting shirts.' The name travelled from coast to coast on the lips of parlour-snakes and P. D.'s.

Descriptive

Amory was now eighteen years old, just under six feet tall and exceptionally, but not conventionally, handsome. He had rather a young face, the ingenuousness of which was marred by the penetrating green eyes, fringed with long dark eyelashes. He lacked somehow that intense animal magnetism that so often accompanies beauty in men or women; his personality seemed rather a mental thing, and it was not in his power to turn it on and off like a water-faucet. But people never forgot his face.

Isabelle

She paused at the top of the staircase. The sensations attributed to divers on spring-boards, leading ladies on opening nights, and lumpy, husky young men on the day of the Big Game, crowded through her. She should have descended to a burst of drums or a discordant blend of themes from 'Thais' and 'Carmen.' She had never been so curious about her appearance, she had never been so satisfied with it. She had been sixteen years old for six months.

'Isabelle!' called her cousin Sally from the doorway of the dressing-room.

'I'm ready.' She caught a slight lump of nervousness in her throat.

'I had to send back to the house for another pair of slippers. It'll be just a minute.'

Isabelle started toward the dressing-room for a last peek in the mirror, but something decided her to stand there and gaze down the broad stairs of the Minnehaha Club. They curved tantalizingly, and she could catch just a glimpse of two pairs of masculine feet in the hall below. Pump-shod in uniform black, they gave no hint of identity, but she wondered eagerly if one pair were attached to Amory Blaine. This young man, not as yet encountered, had nevertheless taken up a considerable part of her day – the first day of her arrival. Coming up in the machine from the station, Sally had volunteered, amid a rain of question, comment, revelation, and exaggeration:

'You remember Amory Blaine, of *course*. Well, he's simply mad to see you again. He's stayed over a day from college, and he's coming to-night. He's heard so much about you – says he remembers your eyes.'

This had pleased Isabelle. It put them on equal terms, although she was quite capable of staging her own romances, with or without advance advertising. But following her happy tremble of anticipation, came a sinking sensation that made her ask:

'How do you mean he's heard about me? What sort of things?'

Sally smiled. She felt rather in the capacity of a showman with her more exotic cousin.

'He knows you're – you're considered beautiful and all that' – she paused – 'and I guess he knows you've been kissed.'

At this Isabelle's little fist had clenched suddenly under the fur robe. She was accustomed to be thus followed by her desperate past, and it never failed to rouse in her the same feeling of resentment; yet – in a strange town it was an advantageous reputation. She was a 'Speed,' was she? Well – let them find out.

Out of the window Isabelle watched the snow glide by in the frosty morning. It was ever so much colder here than in Baltimore; she had not remembered; the glass of the side door was iced, the windows were shirred with snow in the corners. Her mind played still with one subject. Did *he* dress like that boy there, who walked calmly down a bustling business street, in moccasins and winter-carnival costume? How very *Western!* Of course he wasn't that way: he went to Princeton, was a sophomore or something. Really she had no distinct idea of him. An ancient snap-shot she had preserved in an old kodak book had impressed her by the big eyes (which he had probably grown up to by now). However, in the last month, when her winter visit to Sally had been decided on, he had assumed the proportions of a worthy adversary. Children, most astute of match-makers, plot their campaigns quickly, and Sally had played a clever correspondence sonata to Isabelle's excitable temperament. Isabelle had been for some time capable of very strong, if very transient emotions . . .

They drew up at a spreading, white-stone building, set back from the snowy street. Mrs. Weatherby greeted her warmly and her various younger cousins were produced from the corners where they skulked politely. Isabelle met them tactfully. At her best she allied all with whom she came in contact – except older girls and some women. All the impressions she made were conscious. The half-dozen girls she renewed acquaintance with that morning were all rather impressed and as much by her direct personality as by her reputation. Amory Blaine was an open subject. Evidently a bit light of love, neither popular nor unpopular – every girl there seemed to have had an affair with him at some time or other, but no one volunteered any really useful information. He was going to fall for her . . . Sally had published that information to her young set and they were retailing it back to Sally as fast as they set eyes on Isabelle. Isabelle resolved secretly that she would, if necessary, *force* herself to like him – she owed it to Sally. Suppose she were terribly disappointed. Sally had painted him in such glowing colours – he was good-looking, 'sort of distinguished, when he wants to be,' had a line, and was properly inconstant. In fact, he summed up all the romance that her age and environment led her to desire. She wondered if those were his dancing-shoes that fox-trotted tentatively around the soft rug below.

All impressions and, in fact, all ideas were extremely kaleidoscopic to Isabelle. She had that curious mixture of the social and the artistic temperaments found often in two classes, society women and actresses. Her education or, rather, her sophistication, had been absorbed from the boys who had dangled on her favour; her tact was instinctive, and her capacity for love-affairs was limited only by the number of the susceptible within telephone distance. Flirt smiled from her large black-brown eyes and shone through her intense physical magnetism.

So she waited at the head of the stairs that evening while slippers were fetched. Just as she was growing impatient, Sally came out of the dressing-room, beaming with her accustomed good nature and high spirits, and together they descended to the floor below, while the shifting searchlight of Isabelle's mind flashed on two ideas: she was glad she had high colour to-night, and she wondered if he danced well.

Downstairs, in the club's great room, she was surrounded for a moment by the girls she had met in the afternoon, then she heard Sally's voice repeating a cycle of names, and found herself bowing to a sextet of black and white, terribly stiff, vaguely familiar figures. The name Blaine figured somewhere, but at first she could not place him. A very confused, very juvenile moment of awkward backings and bumpings followed, and every one found himself talking to the person he least desired to. Isabelle manœuvred herself and Froggy Parker, freshman at Harvard, with whom she had once played hop-scotch, to a seat on the stairs. A humorous reference to the past was all she needed. The things Isabelle could do socially with one idea were remarkable. First, she repeated it rapturously in an enthusiastic contralto with a soupçon of Southern accent; then she held it off at a distance and smiled at it – her wonderful smile; then she delivered it in variations and played a sort of mental catch with it, all this in the nominal form of dialogue. Froggy was fascinated and quite unconscious that this was being done, not for him, but for the green eyes that glistened under the shining carefully watered hair, a little to her left, for Isabelle had discovered Amory. As an actress even in the fullest flush of her own conscious magnetism gets a deep impression of most of the people in the front row, so Isabelle sized up her antagonist. First, he had auburn hair, and from her feeling of disappointment she knew that she had expected him to be dark and of garter-advertisement slenderness . . . For the rest, a faint flush and a straight, romantic profile; the effect set off by a close-fitting dress suit and a silk ruffled shirt of the kind that women still delight to see men wear, but men were just beginning to get tired of.

During this inspection Amory was quietly watching.

'Don't *you* think so?' she said suddenly, turning to him, innocent-eyed.

There was a stir, and Sally led the way over to their table. Amory struggled to Isabelle's side, and whispered:

'You're my dinner partner, you know. We're all coached for each other.'

Isabelle gasped – this was rather right in line. But really she felt as if a good speech had been taken from the star and given to a minor character . . . She mustn't lose the leadership a bit. The dinner-table glittered with laughter at the confusion of getting places, and then curious eyes were turned on her, sitting near the head. She was enjoying this immensely, and Froggy Parker was so engrossed with the added sparkle of her rising colour that he forgot to pull out Sally's chair, and fell into a dim confusion. Amory was on the other side, full of confidence and vanity, gazing at her in open admiration. He began directly, and so did Froggy:

'I've heard a lot about you since you wore braids——'

'Wasn't it funny this afternoon——'

Both stopped. Isabelle turned to Amory shyly. Her face was always enough answer for any one, but she decided to speak.

'How – from whom?'

'From everybody – for all the years since you've been away.' She blushed appropriately. On her right Froggy was *hors de combat* already, although he hadn't quite realized it.

'I'll tell you what I remembered about you all these years,' Amory continued. She leaned slightly toward him and looked modestly at the celery before her. Froggy sighed – he knew Amory, and the situations that Amory seemed born to handle. He turned to Sally and asked her if she was going away to school next year. Amory opened with grape-shot.

'I've got an adjective that just fits you.' This was one of his favourite starts – he seldom had a word in mind, but it was a curiosity provoker, and he could always produce something complimentary if he got in a tight corner.

'Oh – what?' Isabelle's face was a study in enraptured curiosity.

Amory shook his head.

'I don't know you very well yet.'

'Will you tell me – afterward?' she half whispered.

He nodded.

'We'll sit out.'

Isabelle nodded.

'Did any one ever tell you, you have keen eyes?' she said.

Amory attempted to make them look even keener. He fancied, but he was not sure, that her foot had just touched his under the table. But it might possibly have been only the table leg. It was so hard to tell. Still it thrilled him. He wondered quickly if there would be any difficulty in securing the little den upstairs.

Babes in the Woods

Isabelle and Amory were distinctly not innocent, nor were they particularly brazen. Moreover, amateur standing had very little value in the game they were playing, a game that would presumably be her principal study for years to come. She had begun as he had, with good looks and an excitable temperament, and the rest was the result of accessible popular novels and dressing-room conversation culled from a slightly older set. Isabelle had walked with an artificial gait at nine and a half, and when her eyes, wide and starry, proclaimed the ingenue most. Amory was proportionately less deceived. He waited for the mask to drop off, but at the same time he did not question her right to wear it. She, on her part, was not impressed by his studied air of blasé sophistication. She had lived in a larger city and had slightly an advantage in range. But she accepted his pose – it was one of the dozen little conventions of this kind of affair. He was aware that he was getting this particular favour now because she had been coached; he knew that he stood for merely the best game in sight, and that he would have to improve his opportunity before he lost his advantage. So they proceeded with an infinite guile that would have horrified her parents.

After the dinner the dance began ... smoothly. Smoothly? – boys cut in on Isabelle every few feet and then squabbled in the corners with: 'You might let me get more than an inch!' and 'She didn't like it either – she told me so next time I cut in.' It was true – she told every one so, and gave every hand a parting pressure that said: 'You know that your dances are *making* my evening.'

But time passed, two hours of it, and the less subtle beaux had better learned to focus their pseudo-passionate glances elsewhere, for eleven o'clock found Isabelle and Amory sitting on the couch in the little den off the reading-room upstairs. She was conscious that they were a handsome pair, and seemed to belong distinctively in this seclusion, while lesser lights fluttered and chattered downstairs.

Boys who passed the door looked in enviously – girls who passed only laughed and frowned and grew wise within themselves.

They had now reached a very definite stage. They had

traded accounts of their progress since they had met last, and she had listened to much she had heard before. He was a sophomore, was on the *Princetonian* board, hoped to be chairman in senior year. He learned that some of the boys she went with in Baltimore were 'terrible speeds' and came to dances in states of artificial stimulation; most of them were twenty or so, and drove alluring red Stutzes. A good half seemed to have already flunked out of various schools and colleges, but some of them bore athletic names that made him look at her admiringly. As a matter of fact, Isabelle's closer acquaintance with the universities was just commencing. She had bowing acquaintance with a lot of young men who thought she was a 'pretty kid – worth keeping an eye on.' But Isabelle strung the names into a fabrication of gaiety that would have dazzled a Viennese nobleman. Such is the power of young contralto voices on sink-down sofas.

He asked her if she thought he was conceited. She said there was a difference between conceit and self-confidence. She adored self-confidence in men.

'Is Froggy a good friend of yours ?' she asked.

'Rather – why ?'

'He's a bum dancer.'

Amory laughed.

'He dances as if the girl were on his back instead of in his arms.'

She appreciated this.

'You're awfully good at sizing people up.'

Amory denied this painfully. However, he sized up several people for her. Then they talked about hands.

'You've got awfully nice hands,' she said. 'They look as if you played the piano. Do you ?'

I have said they had reached a very definite stage – nay, more, a very critical stage. Amory had stayed over a day to see her, and his train left at twelve-eighteen that night. His trunk and suitcase awaited him at the station; his watch was beginning to hang heavy in his pocket.

'Isabelle,' he said suddenly, 'I want to tell you something.' They had been talking lightly about 'that funny look in her eyes,' and Isabelle knew from the change in his manner what was coming – indeed, she had been wondering how soon it would come. Amory reached above their heads and turned out the electric light, so that they were in the dark, except for the red glow that fell through the door from the reading-room lamps. Then he began:

'I don't know whether or not you know what you – what I'm going to say. Lordy, Isabelle – this *sounds* like a line, but it isn't.'

'I know,' said Isabelle softly.

'Maybe we'll never meet again like this – I have darned hard luck sometimes.' He was leaning away from her on the other arm of the lounge, but she could see his eyes plainly in the dark.

'You'll meet me again – silly.' There was just the slightest emphasis on the last word – so that it became almost a term of endearment. He continued a bit huskily:

'I've fallen for a lot of people – girls – and I guess you have, too – boys, I mean, but, honestly, you –' he broke off suddenly and leaned forward, chin on his hands: 'Oh, what's the use – you'll go your way and I suppose I'll go mine.'

Silence for a moment. Isabelle was quite stirred; she wound her handkerchief into a tight ball, and by the faint light that streamed over her, dropped it deliberately on the floor. Their hands touched for an instant, but neither spoke. Silences were becoming more frequent and more delicious. Outside another stray couple had come up and were experimenting on the piano in the next room. After the usual preliminary of 'chopsticks,' one of them started 'Babes in the Woods' and a light tenor carried the words into the den:

> '*Give me your hand –*
> *I'll understand*
> *We're off to slumberland.*'

Isabelle hummed it softly and trembled as she felt Amory's hand close over hers.

'Isabelle,' he whispered. 'You know I'm mad about you. You *do* give a darn about me.'

'Yes.'

'How much do you care – do you like any one better?'

'No.' He could scarcely hear her, although he bent so near that he felt her breath against his cheek.

'Isabelle, I'm going back to college for six long months, and why shouldn't we – if I could only just have one thing to remember you by——'

'Close the door. . . .' Her voice had just stirred so that he half wondered whether she had spoken at all. As he swung the door softly shut, the music seemed quivering just outside.

> '*Moonlight is bright,*
> *Kiss me good night.*'

What a wonderful song, she thought – everything was wonderful to-night, most of all this romantic scene in the den, with their hands clinging and the inevitable looming charmingly close. The future vista of her life seemed an unending succession of scenes like this: under moonlight and pale starlight, and in the backs of warm limousines and in low, cosy roadsters stopped under sheltering trees – only the boy might change, and this one was *so* nice. He took her hand softly. With a sudden movement he turned it and, holding it to his lips, kissed the palm.

'Isabelle!' His whisper blended in the music, and they seemed to float nearer together. Her breath came faster. 'Can't I kiss you, Isabelle – Isabelle?' Lips half parted, she turned her head to him in the dark. Suddenly the ring of voices, the sound of running footsteps surged toward them. Quick as a flash Amory reached up and turned on the light, and when the door opened and three boys, the wrathy and dance-craving Froggy among them, rushed in, he was turning over the magazines on the table, while she sat without moving, serene and unembarrassed, and even greeted them with a welcoming smile. But her heart was beating wildly, and she felt somehow as if she had been deprived.

It was evidently over. There was a clamour for a dance, there was a glance that passed between them – on his side despair, on hers regret, and then the evening went on, with the reassured beaux and the eternal cutting in.

At quarter to twelve Amory shook hands with her gravely, in the midst of a small crowd assembled to wish him good-speed. For an instant he lost his poise, and she felt a bit rattled when a satirical voice from a concealed wit cried: 'Take her outside, Amory!' As he took her hand he pressed it a little, and she returned the pressure as she had done to twenty hands that evening – that was all.

At two o'clock back at the Weatherbys' Sally asked her if she and Amory had had a 'time' in the den. Isabelle turned to her quietly. In her eyes was the light of the idealist, the inviolate dreamer of Joan-like dreams.

'No,' she answered. 'I don't do that sort of thing any more; he asked me to, but I said no.'

As she crept in bed she wondered what he'd say in his special delivery to-morrow. He had such a good-looking mouth – would she ever—— ?

'Fourteen angels were watching o'er them,' sang Sally sleepily from the next room.

'Damn!' muttered Isabelle, punching the pillow into a luxurious lump and exploring the cold sheets cautiously. 'Damn!'

Carnival

Amory, by way of the *Princetonian*, had arrived. The minor snobs, finely balanced thermometers of success, warmed to him as the club elections grew nigh, and he and Tom were visited by groups of upper classmen who arrived awkwardly, balanced on the edge of the furniture and talked of all subjects except the one of absorbing interest. Amory was amused at the intent eyes upon him, and, in case the visitors represented some club in which he was not interested, took great pleasure in shocking them with unorthodox remarks.

'Oh, let me see –' he said one night to a flabbergasted delegation, 'what club do you represent?'

With visitors from Ivy and Cottage and Tiger Inn he played the 'nice, unspoilt, ingenuous boy' very much at ease and quite unaware of the object of the call.

When the fatal morning arrived, early in March, and the campus became a document in hysteria, he slid smoothly into Cottage with Alec Connage and watched his suddenly neurotic class with much wonder.

There were fickle groups that jumped from club to club; there were friends of two or three days who announced tearfully and wildly that they must join the same club, nothing should separate them; there were snarling disclosures of long-hidden grudges as the Suddenly Prominent remembered snubs of freshman year. Unknown men were elevated into importance when they received certain coveted bids; others who were considered 'all set' found that they had made unexpected enemies, felt themselves stranded and deserted, talked wildly of leaving college.

In his own crowd Amory saw men kept out for wearing green hats, for being 'a damn tailor's dummy,' for having 'too much pull in heaven,' for getting drunk one night 'not like a gentleman, by God,' or for unfathomable secret reasons known to no one but the wielders of the black balls.

This orgy of sociability culminated in a gigantic party at the Nassau Inn, where punch was dispensed from immense bowls, and the whole downstairs became a delirious, circulating, shouting pattern of faces and voices.

'Hi, Dibby – 'gratulations!'

'Goo' boy, Tom, you got a good bunch in Cap.'

'Say, Kerry –'

'Oh, Kerry – I hear you went Tiger with all the weight-lifters!'

'Well, I didn't go Cottage – the parlour-snakes' delight.'

'They say Overton fainted when he got his Ivy bid – Did he sign up the first day? – oh, *no*. Tore over to Murray-Dodge on a bicycle – afraid it was a mistake.'

'How'd you get into Cap – you old roué?'

"Gratulations!'

"Gratulations yourself. Hear you got a good crowd.'

When the bar closed, the party broke up into groups and streamed, singing, over the snow-clad campus, in a weird delusion that snobbishness and strain were over at last, and that they could do what they pleased for the next two years.

Long afterward Amory thought of sophomore spring as the happiest time of his life. His ideas were in tune with life as he found it; he wanted no more than to drift and dream and enjoy a dozen new-found friendships through the April afternoons.

Alec Connage came into his room one morning and woke him up into the sunshine and peculiar glory of Campbell Hall shining in the window.

'Wake up, Original Sin, and scrape yourself together. Be in front of Renwick's in half an hour. Somebody's got a car.' He took the bureau cover and carefully deposited it, with its load of small articles, upon the bed.

'Where'd you get the car ?' demanded Amory cynically.

'Sacred trust, but don't be a critical goopher or you can't go!'

'I think I'll sleep,' Amory said calmly, resettling himself and reaching beside the bed for a cigarette.

'Sleep!'

'Why not ? I've got a class at eleven-thirty.'

'You damned gloom! Of course, if you don't want to go to the coast——'

With a bound Amory was out of bed, scattering the bureau cover's burden on the floor. The coast . . . he hadn't seen it for years, since he and his mother were on their pilgrimage.

'Who's going ?' he demanded as he wriggled into his B. V. Ds.

'Oh, Dick Humbird and Kerry Holiday and Jesse Ferrenby and – oh about five or six. Speed it up, kid!'

In ten minutes Amory was devouring cornflakes in Renwick's, and at nine-thirty they bowled happily out of town, headed for the sands of Deal Beach.

'You see,' said Kerry, 'the car belongs down there. In fact, it was stolen from Asbury Park by persons unknown, who deserted it in Princeton and left for the West. Heartless Humbird here got permission from the city council to deliver it.'

'Anybody got any money?' suggested Ferrenby, turning around from the front seat.

There was an emphatic negative chorus.

'That makes it interesting.'

'Money – what's money? We can sell the car.'

'Charge him salvage or something.'

'How're we going to get food?' asked Amory.

'Honestly,' answered Kerry, eying him reprovingly, 'do you doubt Kerry's ability for three short days? Some people have lived on nothing for years at a time. Read the Boy Scout Monthly.'

'Three days,' Amory mused, 'and I've got classes.'

'One of the days is the Sabbath.'

'Just the same, I can only cut six more classes, with over a month and half to go.'

'Throw him out!'

'It's a long walk back.'

'Amory, you're running it out, if I may coin a new phrase.'

'Hadn't you better get some dope on yourself, Amory?'

Amory subsided resignedly and drooped into a contemplation of the scenery. Swinburne seemed to fit in somehow.

> '*Oh, winter's rains and ruins are over,*
>   *And all the seasons of snows and sins;*
> *The days dividing lover and lover,*
>   *The light that loses, the night that wins;*
> *And time remembered is grief forgotten,*
> *And frosts are slain and flowers begotten,*
> *And in green underwood and cover,*
>   *Blossom by blossom the spring begins.*

> '*The full streams feed on flower of——*'

'What's the matter, Amory? Amory's thinking about poetry, about the pretty birds and flowers. I can see it in his eye.'

'No, I'm not,' he lied. 'I'm thinking about the *Princetonian*. I ought to make up to-night; but I can telephone back, I suppose.'

'Oh,' said Kerry respectfully, 'these important men——'

Amory flushed and it seemed to him that Ferrenby, a defeated competitor, winced a little. Of course, Kerry was only kidding, but he really mustn't mention the *Princetonian*.

It was a halcyon day, and as they neared the shore and the salt breezes scurried by, he began to picture the ocean and long, level stretches of sand and red roofs over blue sea. Then they hurried through the little town and it all flashed upon his consciousness to a mighty pæan of emotion. . . .

'Oh, good Lord! *Look* at it!' he cried.

'What?'

'Let me out, quick – I haven't seen it for eight years! Oh, gentlefolk, stop the car!'

'What an odd child!' remarked Alec.

'I do believe he's a bit eccentric.'

The car was obligingly drawn up at a curb, and Amory ran for the boardwalk. First, he realized that the sea was blue and that there was an enormous quantity of it, and that it roared and roared – really all the banalities about the ocean that one could realize, but if any one had told him then that these things were banalities, he would have gaped in wonder.

'Now we'll get lunch,' ordered Kerry, wandering up with the crowd. 'Come on, Amory, tear yourself away and get practical.'

'We'll try the best hotel first,' he went on, 'and thence and so forth.'

They strolled along the boardwalk to the most imposing hostelry in sight, and, entering the dining-room, scattered about a table.

'Eight Bronxes,' commanded Alec, 'and a club sandwich and Juliennes. The food for one. Hand the rest around.'

Amory ate little, having seized a chair where he could watch the sea and feel the rock of it. When luncheon was over they sat and smoked quietly.

'What's the bill?'

Some one scanned it.

'Eight twenty-five.'

'Rotten overcharge. We'll give them two dollars and one for the waiter. Kerry, collect the small change.'

The waiter approached, and Kerry gravely handed him a dollar, tossed two dollars on the check, and turned away. They sauntered leisurely toward the door, pursued in a moment by the suspicious Ganymede.

'Some mistake, sir.'

Kerry took the bill and examined it critically.

'No mistake!' he said, shaking his head gravely, and, tearing it into four pieces, he handed the scraps to the waiter, who was so dumbfounded that he stood motionless and expressionless while they walked out.

'Won't he send after us?'

'No,' said Kerry; 'for a minute he'll think we're the proprietor's sons or something; then he'll look at the check again and call the manager, and in the meantime——'

They left the car at Asbury and street-car'd to Allenhurst, where they investigated the crowded pavilions for beauty. At four there were refreshments in a lunch-room, and this time they paid an even smaller per cent on the total cost; something about the appearance and savoir-faire of the crowd made the thing go, and they were not pursued.

'You see, Amory, we're Marxian Socialists,' explained Kerry. 'We don't believe in property and we're putting it to the great test.'

'Night will descend,' Amory suggested.

'Watch, and put your trust in Holiday.'

They became jovial about five-thirty and, linking arms, strolled up and down the boardwalk in a row, chanting a monotonous ditty about the sad sea waves. Then Kerry saw a face in the crowd that attracted him and, rushing off, reappeared in a moment with one of the homeliest girls

Amory had ever set eyes on. Her pale mouth extended from
ear to ear, her teeth projected in a solid wedge, and she had
little, squinty eyes that peeped ingratiatingly over the side
sweep of her nose. Kerry presented them formally.

'Name of Kaluka, Hawaiian queen! Let me present
Messrs. Connage, Sloane, Humbird, Ferrenby, and Blaine.'

The girl bobbed courtesies all around. Poor creature;
Amory supposed she had never before been noticed in her
life – possibly she was half-witted. While she accompanied
them (Kerry had invited her to supper) she said nothing
which could discountenance such a belief.

'She prefers her native dishes,' said Alec gravely to the
waiter, 'but any coarse food will do.'

All through supper he addressed her in the most respect-
ful language, while Kerry made idiotic love to her on the
other side, and she giggled and grinned. Amory was content
to sit and watch the by-play, thinking what a light touch
Kerry had, and how he could transform the barest incident
into a thing of curve and contour. They all seemed to have
the spirit of it more or less, and it was a relaxation to be with
them. Amory usually liked men individually, yet feared
them in crowds unless the crowd was around *him*. He
wondered how much each one contributed to the party, for
there was somewhat of a spiritual tax levied. Alec and Kerry
were the life of it, but not quite the centre. Somehow the
quiet Humbird, and Sloane, with his impatient super-
ciliousness, were the centre.

Dick Humbird had, ever since freshman year, seemed to
Amory a perfect type of aristocrat. He was slender but well-
built – black curly hair, straight features, and rather a dark
skin. Everything he said sounded intangibly appropriate. He
possessed infinite courage, an averagely good mind, and a
sense of honour with a clear charm and noblesse oblige that
varied it from righteousness. He could dissipate without
going to pieces, and even his most bohemian adventures
never seemed 'running it out.' People dressed like him, tried
to talk as he did . . . Amory decided that he probably held
the world back, but he wouldn't have changed him. . . .

He differed from the healthy type that was essentially middle-class – he never seemed to perspire. Some people couldn't be familiar with a chauffeur without having it returned; Humbird could have lunched at Sherry's with a coloured man, yet people would have somehow known that it was all right. He was not a snob, though he knew only half his class. His friends ranged from the highest to the lowest, but it was impossible to 'cultivate' him. Servants worshipped him, and treated him like a god. He seemed the eternal example of what the upper class tries to be.

'He's like those pictures in the Illustrated London News of the English officers who have been killed,' Amory had said to Alec.

'Well,' Alec had answered, 'if you want to know the shocking truth, his father was a grocery clerk who made a fortune in Tacoma real estate and came to New York ten years ago.'

Amory had felt a curious sinking sensation.

This present type of party was made possible by the surging together of the class after club elections – as if to make a last desperate attempt to know itself, to keep together, to fight off the tightening spirit of the clubs. It was a let-down from the conventional heights they had all walked so rigidly.

After supper they saw Kaluka to the boardwalk, and then strolled back along the beach to Asbury. The evening sea was a new sensation, for all its colour and mellow age was gone, and it seemed the bleak waste that made the Norse sagas sad; Amory thought of Kipling's

'Beaches of Lukanon before the sealers came.'

It was still a music, though, infinitely sorrowful.

Ten o'clock found them penniless. They had suppered greatly on their last eleven cents and, singing, strolled up through the casinos and lighted arches on the boardwalk, stopping to listen approvingly to all band concerts. In one place Kerry took up a collection for the French War Orphans which netted a dollar and twenty cents, and with this they bought some brandy in case they caught cold in the night. They finished the day in a moving-picture show and went into solemn systematic roars of laughter at an ancient comedy, to the startled annoyance of the rest of the audience. Their entrance was distinctly strategic, for each man as he entered pointed reproachfully at the one just behind him. Sloane, bringing up the rear, disclaimed all knowledge and responsibility as soon as the others were scattered inside; then as the irate ticket-taker rushed in he followed nonchalantly.

They reassembled later by the Casino and made arrangements for the night. Kerry wormed permission from the watchman to sleep on the platform and, having collected a huge pile of rugs from the booths to serve as mattresses and blankets, they talked until midnight, and then fell into a dreamless sleep, though Amory tried hard to stay awake and watch that marvellous moon settle on the sea.

So they progressed for two happy days, up and down the shore by street-car or machine, or by shoe-leather on the crowded boardwalk; sometimes eating with the wealthy, more frequently dining frugally at the expense of an unsuspecting restaurateur. They had their photos taken, eight poses, in a quick-development store. Kerry insisted on grouping them as a 'varsity' football team, and then as a tough gang from the East Side, with their coats inside out, and himself sitting in the middle on a cardboard moon. The photographer probably has them yet – at least, they never called for them. The weather was perfect, and again they slept outside, and again Amory fell unwillingly asleep.

Sunday broke stolid and respectable, and even the sea seemed to mumble and complain, so they returned to Princeton via the Fords of transient farmers, and broke up with colds in their heads, but otherwise none the worse for wandering.

Even more than in the year before, Amory neglected his work, not deliberately but lazily and through a multitude of other interests. Co-ordinate geometry and the melancholy hexameters of Corneille and Racine held forth small allurements, and even psychology, which he had eagerly awaited, proved to be a dull subject full of muscular reactions and biological phrases rather than the study of personality and influence. That was a noon class, and it always sent him dozing. Having found that 'subjective and objective, sir,' answered most of the questions, he used the phrase on all occasions, and it became the class joke when, on a query being levelled at him, he was nudged awake by Ferrenby or Sloane to gasp it out.

Mostly there were parties – to Orange or the Shore, more rarely to New York and Philadelphia, though one night they marshalled fourteen waitresses out of Childs' and took them to ride down Fifth Avenue on top of an auto bus. They all cut more classes than were allowed, which meant an additional course the following year, but spring was too rare to let anything interfere with their colourful ramblings. In May Amory was elected to the Sophomore Prom Committee, and when after a long evening's discussion with Alec they made out a tentative list of class probabilities for the senior council, they placed themselves among the surest. The senior council was composed presumably of the eighteen most representative seniors, and in view of Alec's football managership and Amory's chance of nosing out Burne Holiday as *Princetonian* chairman, they seemed fairly justified in this presumption. Oddly enough, they both placed D'Invilliers as among the possibilities, a guess that a year before the class would have gaped at.

All through the spring Amory had kept up an intermittent correspondence with Isabelle Borgé, punctuated by violent squabbles and chiefly enlivened by his attempts to find new words for love. He discovered Isabelle to be discreetly and aggravatingly unsentimental in letters, but he hoped against hope that she would prove not too exotic a bloom to fit the large spaces of spring as she had fitted the den in the Minnehaha Club. During May he wrote thirty-page documents almost nightly, and sent them to her in bulky envelopes exteriorly labelled 'Part I' and 'Part II.'

'Oh, Alec, I believe I'm tired of college,' he said sadly, as they walked the dusk together.

'I think I am, too, in a way.'

'All I'd like would be a little home in the country, some warm country, and a wife, and just enough to do to keep from rotting.'

'Me, too.'

'I'd like to quit.'

'What does your girl say ?'

'Oh!' Amory gasped in horror. 'She wouldn't *think* of marrying . . . that is, not now. I mean the future, you know.'

'My girl would. I'm engaged.'

'Are you really ?'

'Yes. Don't say a word to anybody, please, but I am. I may not come back next year.'

'But you're only twenty! Give up college ?'

'Why, Amory, you were saying a minute ago——'

'Yes,' Amory interrupted, 'but I was just wishing. I wouldn't think of leaving college. It's just that I feel so sad these wonderful nights. I sort of feel they're never coming again, and I'm not really getting all I could out of them. I wish my girl lived here. But marry – not a chance. Especially as father says the money isn't forthcoming as it used to be."

'What a waste these nights are!' agreed Alec.

But Amory sighed and made use of the nights. He had a snap-shot of Isabelle, enshrined in an old watch, and at eight almost every night he would turn off all the lights except the desk lamp and, sitting by the open windows with the picture before him, write her rapturous letters.

. . . Oh, it's so hard to write you what I really *feel* when I think about you so much; you've gotten to mean to me a *dream* that I can't put on paper any more. Your last letter came and it was wonderful! I read it over about six times, especially the *last* part, but I do wish, sometimes, you'd be more *frank* and tell me what you really do think of me, yet your last letter was too good to be true, and I can hardly wait until June! Be sure and be able to come to the prom. It'll be fine, I think, and I want to bring *you* just at the end of a wonderful year. I often think over what you said on that night and wonder how much you meant. If it were any one but you – but you see I *thought* you were fickle the first time I saw you and you are so popular and everything that I can't imagine your really liking me *best*.

Oh, Isabelle, dear – it's a wonderful night. Somebody is playing 'Love Moon' on a mandolin far across the campus, and the music seems to bring you into the window. Now he's playing 'Good-by, Boys, I'm Through,' and how well it suits me. For I *am* through with everything. I have decided never to take a cocktail again, and I know I'll never again fall in love – I couldn't – you've been too much a part of my days and nights to ever let me think of another girl. I meet them all the time and they don't interest me. I'm not pretending to be blasé, because it's not that. It's just that I'm in love. Oh, *dearest* Isabelle (somehow I can't call you just Isabelle, and I'm afraid I'll come out with the 'dearest' before your family this June), you've *got* to come to the prom, and then I'll come up to your house for a day and everything'll be perfect. . . .

And so on in an eternal monotone that seemed to both of them infinitely charming, infinitely new.

June came and the days grew so hot and lazy that they could not worry even about exams, but spent dreamy evenings on the court of Cottage, talking of long subjects until the sweep of country toward Stony Brook became a blue haze and the lilacs were white around tennis-courts, and words gave way to silent cigarettes. . . . Then down deserted Prospect and along McCosh with song everywhere around them, up to the hot joviality of Nassau Street.

Tom D'Invilliers and Amory walked late in those days. A gambling fever swept through the sophomore class and they bent over the bones till three o'clock many a sultry night. After one session they came out of Sloane's room to find the dew fallen and the stars old in the sky.

'Let's borrow bicycles and take a ride,' Amory suggested.

'All right. I'm not a bit tired and this is almost the last night of the year, really, because the prom stuff starts Monday.'

They found two unlocked bicycles in Holder Court and rode out about half-past three along the Lawrenceville Road.

'What are you going to do this summer, Amory?'

'Don't ask me – same old things, I suppose. A month or two in Lake Geneva – I'm counting on you to be there in July, you know – then there'll be Minneapolis, and that means hundreds of summer hops, parlour-snaking, getting bored – But oh, Tom,' he added suddenly, 'hasn't this year been slick!'

'No,' declared Tom emphatically, a new Tom, clothed by Brooks, shod by Franks, 'I've won this game, but I feel as if I never want to play another. You're all right – you're a rubber ball, and somehow it suits you, but I'm sick of adapting myself to the local snobbishness of this corner of the world. I want to go where people aren't barred because of the colour of their neckties and the roll of their coats.'

'You can't, Tom,' argued Amory, as they rolled along through the scattering night; 'wherever you go now you'll always unconsciously apply these standards of "having it" or "lacking it." For better or worse we've stamped you; you're a Princeton type!'

'Well, then,' complained Tom, his cracked voice rising plaintively, 'why do I have to come back at all? I've learned all that Princeton has to offer. Two years more of mere pedantry and lying around a club aren't going to help. They're just going to disorganize me, conventionalize me completely. Even now I'm so spineless that I wonder how I get away with it.'

'Oh, but you're missing the real point, Tom,' Amory interrupted. 'You've just had your eyes opened to the snobbishness of the world in a rather abrupt manner. Princeton invariably gives the thoughtful man a social sense.'

'You consider you taught me that, don't you?' he asked quizzically, eying Amory in the half dark.

Amory laughed quietly.

'Didn't I?'

'Sometimes,' he said slowly, 'I think you're my bad angel. I might have been a pretty fair poet.'

'Come on, that's rather hard. You chose to come to an Eastern college. Either your eyes were opened to the mean scrambling quality of people, or you'd have gone through blind, and you'd hate to have done that – been like Marty Kaye.'

'Yes,' he agreed, 'you're right. I wouldn't have liked it. Still, it's hard to be made a cynic at twenty.'

'I was born one,' Amory murmured. 'I'm a cynical idealist.' He paused and wondered if that meant anything.

They reached the sleeping school of Lawrenceville, and turned to ride back.

'It's good, this ride, isn't it?' Tom said presently.

'Yes; it's a good finish, it's knock-out; everything's good to-night. Oh, for a hot, languorous summer and Isabelle!'

'Oh, you and your Isabelle! I'll bet she's a simple one . . . let's say some poetry.'

So Amory declaimed 'The Ode to a Nightingale' to the bushes they passed.

'I'll never be a poet,' said Amory as he finished. 'I'm not enough of a sensualist really; there are only a few obvious things that I notice as primarily beautiful: women, spring evenings, music at night, the sea; I don't catch the subtle things like "silver-snarling trumpets." I may turn out an intellectual, but I'll never write anything but mediocre poetry.'

They rode into Princeton as the sun was making coloured maps of the sky behind the graduate school, and hurried to the refreshment of a shower that would have to serve in place of sleep. By noon the bright-costumed alumni crowded the streets with their bands and choruses, and in the tents there was great reunion under the orange-and-black banners that curled and strained in the wind. Amory looked long at one house which bore the legend 'Sixty-nine.' There a few grey-haired men sat and talked quietly while the classes swept by in panorama of life.

Under the Arc-Light

Then tragedy's emerald eyes glared suddenly at Amory over the edge of June. On the night after his ride to Lawrence-ville a crowd sallied to New York in quest of adventure, and started back to Princeton about twelve o'clock in two mach-ines. It had been a gay party and different stages of sobriety were represented. Amory was in the car behind; they had taken the wrong road and lost the way, and so were hurrying to catch up.

It was a clear night and the exhilaration of the road went to Amory's head. He had the ghost of two stanzas of a poem forming in his mind. . . .

So the grey car crept nightward in the dark and there was no life stirred as it went by. . . . As the still ocean paths before the shark in starred and glittering waterways, beauty-high, the moon-swathed trees divided, pair on pair, while flapping night-birds cried across the air. . . .

A moment by an inn of lamps and shades, a yellow inn under a yellow moon – then silence, where crescendo laughter fades . . . the car swung out again to the winds of June, mellowed the shadows where the distance grew, then crushed the yellow shadows into blue. . . .

They jolted to a stop, and Amory peered up, startled. A woman was standing beside the road, talking to Alec at the wheel. Afterward he remembered the harpy effect that her old kimono gave her, and the cracked hollowness of her voice as she spoke:

'You Princeton boys?'

'Yes.'

'Well, there's one of you killed here, and two others about dead.'

'*My God!*'

'Look!' She pointed and they gazed in horror. Under the full light of a roadside arc-light lay a form, face downward in a widening circle of blood.

They sprang from the car. Amory thought of the back of

that head – that hair – that hair . . . and then they turned the form over.

'It's Dick – Dick Humbird!'

'Oh, Christ!'

'Feel his heart!'

Then the insistent voice of the old crone in a sort of croaking triumph:

'He's quite dead, all right. The car turned over. Two of the men that weren't hurt just carried the others in, but this one's no use.'

Amory rushed into the house and the rest followed with a limp mass that they laid on the sofa in the shoddy little front parlour. Sloane, with his shoulder punctured, was on another lounge. He was half delirious, and kept calling something about a chemistry lecture at 8:10.

'I don't know what happened,' said Ferrenby in a strained voice. 'Dick was driving and he wouldn't give up the wheel; we told him he'd been drinking too much – then there was this damn curve – oh, my *God! . . .*' He threw himself face downward on the floor and broke into dry sobs.

The doctor had arrived, and Amory went over to the couch, where some one handed him a sheet to put over the body. With a sudden hardness, he raised one of the hands and let it fall back inertly. The brow was cold but the face not expressionless. He looked at the shoe-laces – Dick had tied them that morning. *He* had tied them – and now he was this heavy white mass. All that remained of the charm and personality of the Dick Humbird he had known – oh, it was all so horrible and unaristocratic and close to the earth. All tragedy has that strain of the grotesque and squalid – so useless, futile . . . the way animals die. . . . Amory was reminded of a cat that had lain horribly mangled in some alley of his childhood.

'Some one go to Princeton with Ferrenby.'

Amory stepped outside the door and shivered slightly at the late night wind – a wind that stirred a broken fender on the mass of bent metal to a plaintive, tinny sound.

Crescendo!

Next day, by a merciful chance, passed in a whirl. When Amory was by himself his thoughts zigzagged inevitably to the picture of that red mouth yawning incongruously in the white face, but with a determined effort he piled present excitement upon the memory of it and shut it coldly away from his mind.

Isabelle and her mother drove into town at four, and they rode up smiling Prospect Avenue, through the gay crowd, to have tea at Cottage. The clubs had their annual dinners that night, so at seven he loaned her to a freshman and arranged to meet her in the gymnasium at eleven, when the upper classmen were admitted to the freshmen dance. She was all he had expected, and he was happy and eager to make that night the centre of every dream. At nine the upper classes stood in front of the clubs as the freshmen torchlight parade rioted past, and Amory wondered if the dress-suited groups against the dark, stately backgrounds and under the flare of the torches made the night as brilliant to the staring, cheering freshmen as it had been to him the year before.

The next day was another whirl. They lunched in a gay party of six in a private dining-room at the club, while Isabelle and Amory looked at each other tenderly over the fried chicken and knew that their love was to be eternal. They danced away the prom until five, and the stags cut in on Isabelle with joyous abandon, which grew more and more enthusiastic as the hour grew late, and their wines, stored in overcoat pockets in the coat room, made old weariness wait until another day. The stag line is a most homogeneous mass of men. It fairly sways with a single soul. A dark-haired beauty dances by and there is a half-gasping sound as the ripple surges forward and some one sleeker than the rest darts out and cuts in. Then when the six-foot girl (brought by Kaye in your class, and to whom he has been trying to introduce you all evening) gallops by, the line surges back and the groups face about and become intent on far corners of the hall, for Kaye, anxious and perspiring, appears elbowing through the crowd in search of familiar faces.

'I say, old man, I've got an awfully nice——'

'Sorry, Kaye, but I'm set for this one. I've got to cut in on a fella.'

'Well, the next one?'

'What – ah – er – I swear I've got to go cut in – look me up when she's got a dance free.'

It delighted Amory when Isabelle suggested that they leave for a while and drive around in her car. For a delicious hour that passed too soon they glided the silent roads about Princeton and talked from the surface of their hearts in shy excitement. Amory felt strangely ingenuous and made no attempt to kiss her.

Next day they rode up through the Jersey country, had luncheon in New York, and in the afternoon went to see a problem play at which Isabelle wept all through the second act, rather to Amory's embarrassment – though it filled him with tenderness to watch her. He was tempted to lean over and kiss away her tears, and she slipped her hand into his under cover of darkness to be pressed softly.

Then at six they arrived at the Borgés' summer place on Long Island, and Amory rushed upstairs to change into a dinner coat. As he put in his studs he realized that he was enjoying life as he would probably never enjoy it again. Everything was hallowed by the haze of his own youth. He had arrived, abreast of the best in his generation at Princeton. He was in love and his love was returned. Turning on all the lights, he looked at himself in the mirror, trying to find in his own face the qualities that made him see clearer than the great crowd of people, that made him decide firmly, and able to influence and follow his own will. There was little in his life now that he would have changed. . . . Oxford might have been a bigger field.

Silently he admired himself. How conveniently well he looked, and how well a dinner coat became him. He stepped into the hall and then waited at the top of the stairs, for he heard footsteps coming. It was Isabelle and from the top of her shining hair to her little golden slippers she had never seemed so beautiful.

'Isabelle!' he cried, half involuntarily, and held out his arms. As in the story-books, she ran into them, and on that half-minute, as their lips first touched, rested the high point of vanity, the crest of his young egotism.

III. THE EGOTIST CONSIDERS

'Ouch! Let me go!'

He dropped his arms to his sides.

'What's the matter?'

'Your shirt stud – it hurt me – look!' She was looking down at her neck, where a little blue spot about the size of a pea marred its pallor.

'Oh, Isabelle,' he reproached himself, 'I'm a goopher. Really, I'm sorry – I shouldn't have held you so close.'

She looked up impatiently.

'Oh, Amory, of course you couldn't help it, and it didn't hurt much; but what *are* we going to do about it?'

'*Do* about it?' he asked. 'Oh – that spot; it'll disappear in a second.'

'It isn't,' she said, after a moment of concentrated gazing, 'it's still there – and it looks like Old Nick – oh, Amory, what'll we do! It's *just* the height of your shoulder.'

'Massage it,' he suggested, repressing the faintest inclination to laugh.

She rubbed it delicately with the tips of her fingers, and then a tear gathered in the corner of her eye, and slid down her cheek.

'Oh, Amory,' she said despairingly, lifting up a most pathetic face, 'I'll just make my whole neck *flame* if I rub it. What'll I do?'

A quotation sailed into his head and he couldn't resist repeating it aloud.

'All the perfumes of Arabia will not whiten this little hand.'

She looked up and the sparkle of the tear in her eye was like ice.

'You're not very sympathetic.'

Amory mistook her meaning.

'Isabelle, darling, I think it'll——'

'Don't touch me!' she cried. 'Haven't I enough on my mind and you stand there and *laugh!*'

Then he slipped again.

'Well, it *is* funny, Isabelle, and we were talking the other day about a sense of humour being——'

She was looking at him with something that was not a smile, rather the faint, mirthless echo of a smile, in the corners of her mouth.

'Oh, shut up!' she cried suddenly, and fled down the hallway toward her room. Amory stood there, covered with remorseful confusion.

'Damn!'

When Isabelle reappeared she had thrown a light wrap about her shoulders, and they descended the stairs in a silence that endured through dinner.

'Isabelle,' he began rather testily, as they arranged themselves in the car, bound for a dance at the Greenwich Country Club, 'you're angry, and I'll be, too, in a minute. Let's kiss and make up.'

Isabelle considered glumly.

'I hate to be laughed at,' she said finally.

'I won't laugh any more. I'm not laughing now, am I?'

'You did.'

'Oh, don't be so darned feminine.'

Her lips curled slightly.

'I'll be anything I want.'

Amory kept his temper with difficulty. He became aware that he had not an ounce of real affection for Isabelle, but her coldness piqued him. He wanted to kiss her, kiss her a lot, because then he knew he could leave in the morning and not care. On the contrary, if he didn't kiss her, it would worry him. ... It would interfere vaguely with his idea of himself as a conqueror. It wasn't dignified to come off second best, *pleading*, with a doughty warrior like Isabelle.

Perhaps she suspected this. At any rate, Amory watched the night that should have been the consummation of romance glide by with great moths overhead and the heavy fragrance of roadside gardens, but without those broken words, those little sighs. . . .

Afterwards they supped on ginger ale and devil's food in the pantry, and Amory announced a decision.

'I'm leaving early in the morning.'

'Why?'

'Why not?' he countered.

'There's no need.'

'However, I'm going.'

'Well, if you insist on being ridiculous——'

'Oh, don't put it that way,' he objected.

'——just because I won't let you kiss me. Do you think——'

'Now, Isabelle,' he interrupted, 'you know it's not that – even suppose it is. We've reached the stage where we either ought to kiss – or – or – nothing. It isn't as if you were re- fusing on moral grounds.'

She hesitated.

'I really don't know what to think about you,' she began, in a feeble, perverse attempt at conciliation. 'You're so funny.'

'How?'

'Well, I thought you had a lot of self-confidence and all that; remember you told me the other day that you could do anything you wanted, or get anything you wanted?'

Amory flushed. He *had* told her a lot of things.

'Yes.'

'Well, you didn't seem to feel so self-confident tonight. Maybe you're just plain conceited.'

'No, I'm not,' he hesitated. 'At Princeton——'

'Oh, you and Princeton! You'd think that was the world, the way you talk! Perhaps you *can* write better than any-

4

body else on your old Princetonian; maybe the freshmen *do* think you're important——'

'You don't understand——'

'Yes, I do,' she interrupted. 'I *do*, because you're always talking about yourself and I used to like it; now I don't.'

'Have I to-night?'

'That's just the point,' insisted Isabelle. 'You got all upset to-night. You just sat and watched my eyes. Besides, I have to think all the time I'm talking to you – you're so critical.'

'I make you think, do I?' Amory repeated with a touch of vanity.

'You're a nervous strain' – this emphatically – 'and when you analyze every little emotion and instinct I just don't have 'em.'

'I know.' Amory admitted her point and shook his head helplessly.

'Let's go.' She stood up.

He rose abstractedly and they walked to the foot of the stairs.

'What train can I get?'

'There's one about 9:11 if you really must go.'

'Yes, I've got to go, really. Good night.'

'Good night.'

They were at the head of the stairs, and as Amory turned into his room he thought he caught just the faintest cloud of discontent in her face. He lay awake in the darkness and wondered how much he cared – how much of his sudden unhappiness was hurt vanity – whether he was, after all, temperamentally unfitted for romance.

When he awoke, it was with a glad flood of consciousness. The early wind stirred the chintz curtains at the windows and he was idly puzzled not to be in his room at Princeton with his school football picture over the bureau and the Triangle Club on the wall opposite. Then the grandfather's clock in the hall outside struck eight, and the memory of the night before came to him. He was out of bed, dressing, like the wind; he must get out of the house before he saw Isabelle. What had seemed a melancholy happening, now seemed a tiresome anticlimax. He was dressed at half past, so he sat down by the window; felt that the sinews of his heart were twisted somewhat more than he had thought. What an ironic mockery the morning seemed! – bright and sunny, and full of the smell of the garden; hearing Mrs. Borgé's voice in the sun-parlour below, he wondered where was Isabelle.

There was a knock at the door.

'The car will be around at ten minutes of nine, sir.'

He returned to his contemplation of the outdoors, and began repeating over and over, mechanically, a verse from Browning, which he had once quoted to Isabelle in a letter:

> *'Each life unfulfilled, you see,*
> *It hangs still, patchy and scrappy;*
> *We have not sighed deep, laughed free,*
> *Starved, feasted, despaired – been happy.'*

But his life would not be unfulfilled. He took a sombre satisfaction in thinking that perhaps all along she had been nothing except what he had read into her; that this was her high point, that no one else would ever make her think. Yet that was what she had objected to in him; and Amory was suddenly tired of thinking, thinking!

'Damn her!' he said bitterly, 'she's spoiled my year!'

The Superman Grows Careless

On a dusty day in September Amory arrived in Princeton and joined the sweltering crowd of conditioned men who thronged the streets. It seemed a stupid way to commence his upper-class years, to spend four hours a morning in the stuffy room of a tutoring school, imbibing the infinite boredom of conic sections. Mr. Rooney, pander to the dull, conducted the class and smoked innumerable Pall Malls as he drew diagrams and worked equations from six in the morning until midnight.

'Now, Langueduc, if I used that formula, where would my *A* point be?'

Langueduc lazily shifts his six-foot-three of football material and tries to concentrate.

'Oh – ah – I'm damned if I know, Mr. Rooney.'

'Oh, why of course, of course you can't *use* that formula. *That's* what I wanted you to say.'

'Why, sure, of course.'

'Do you see why?'

'You bet – I suppose so.'

'If you don't see, tell me. I'm here to show you.'

'Well, Mr. Rooney, if you don't mind, I wish you'd go over that again.'

'Gladly. Now here's "*A*" . . .'

The room was a study in stupidity – two huge stands for paper, Mr. Rooney in his shirt-sleeves in front of them, and slouched around on chairs, a dozen men: Fred Sloane, the pitcher, who absolutely *had* to get eligible; 'Slim' Langueduc, who would beat Yale this fall, if only he could master a poor fifty per cent; McDowell, gay young sophomore, who thought it was quite a sporting thing to be tutoring here with all these prominent athletes.

'Those poor birds who haven't a cent to tutor, and have to study during the term are the ones I pity,' he announced to Amory one day, with a flaccid camaraderie in the droop of the cigarette from his pale lips. 'I should think it would be such a bore, there's so much else to do in New York during the term. I suppose they don't know what they miss, any-how.' There was such an air of 'you and I' about Mr. Mc-Dowell that Amory very nearly pushed him out of the open window when he said this . . . Next February his mother would wonder why he didn't make a club and increase his allowance . . . simple little nut. . . .

Through the smoke and the air of solemn, dense earnest-ness that filled the room would come the inevitable helpless cry:

'I don't get it! Repeat that, Mr. Rooney!' Most of them were so stupid or careless that they wouldn't admit when they didn't understand, and Amory was of the latter. He found it impossible to study conic sections; something in their calm and tantalizing respectability breathing defiantly through Mr. Rooney's fetid parlours distorted their equations into insoluble anagrams. He made a last night's effort with the proverbial wet towel, and then blissfully took the exam, wondering unhappily why all the colour and ambition of the spring before had faded out. Somehow, with the defection of Isabelle the idea of undergraduate success had loosed its grasp on his imagination, and he contemplated a possible failure to pass off his condition with equanimity, even though it would arbitrarily mean his removal from the *Princetonian* board and the slaughter of his chances for the Senior Council.

There was always his luck.

He yawned, scribbled his honour pledge on the cover, and sauntered from the room.

'If you don't pass it,' said the newly arrived Alec as they sat on the window-seat of Amory's room and mused upon a scheme of wall decoration, 'you're the world's worst goopher. Your stock will go down like an elevator at the club and on the campus.'

'Oh, hell, I know it. Why rub it in?'

"Cause you deserve it. Anybody that'd risk what you were in line for *ought* to be ineligible for Princetonian chairman.'

'Oh, drop the subject,' Amory protested. 'Watch and wait and shut up. I don't want every one at the club asking me about it, as if I were a prize potato being fattened for a vegetable show.'

One evening a week later Amory stopped below his own window on the way to Renwick's, and, seeing a light, called up:

'Oh, Tom, any mail?'

Alec's head appeared against the yellow square of light.

'Yes, your result's here.'

His heart clamoured violently.

'What is it, blue or pink?'

'Don't know. Better come up.'

He walked into the room and straight over to the table, and then suddenly noticed that there were other people in the room.

"Lo, Kerry.' He was most polite. 'Ah, men of Princeton.' They seemed to be mostly friends, so he picked up the envelope marked 'Registrar's Office,' and weighed it nervously.

'We have here quite a slip of paper.'

'Open it, Amory.'

'Just to be dramatic, I'll let you know that if it's blue, my name is withdrawn from the editorial board of the Prince, and my short career is over.'

He paused, and then saw for the first time Ferrenby's eyes, wearing a hungry look and watching him eagerly. Amory returned the gaze pointedly.

'Watch my face, gentlemen, for the primitive emotions.'

He tore it open and held the slip up to the light.

'Well?'

'Pink or blue?'

'Say what it is.'

'We're all ears, Amory.'

'Smile or swear – or something.'

There was a pause . . . a small crowd of seconds swept by . . . then he looked again and another crowd went on into time.

'Blue as the sky, gentlemen. . . .'

Aftermath

What Amory did that year from early September to late in the spring was so purposeless and inconsecutive that it seems scarcely worth recording. He was, of course, immediately sorry for what he had lost. His philosophy of success had tumbled down upon him, and he looked for the reasons.

'Your own laziness,' said Alec later.

'No – something deeper than that. I've begun to feel that I was meant to lose this chance.'

'They're rather off you at the club, you know; every man that doesn't come through makes our crowd just so much weaker.'

'I hate that point of view.'

'Of course, with a little effort you could still stage a comeback.'

'No – I'm through – as far as ever being a power in college is concerned.'

'But, Amory, honestly, what makes me the angriest isn't the fact that you won't be chairman of the Prince and on the Senior Council, but just that you didn't get down and pass that exam.'

'Not me,' said Amory slowly; 'I'm mad at the concrete thing. My own idleness was quite in accord with my system, but the luck broke.'

'Your system broke, you mean.'

'Maybe.'

'Well, what are you going to do? Get a better one quick, or just bum around for two more years as a has-been?'

'I don't know yet . . .'

'Oh, Amory, buck up!'

'Maybe.'

Amory's point of view, though dangerous, was not far from the true one. If his reactions to his environment could be tabulated, the chart would have appeared like this, beginning with his earliest years:

1. The fundamental Amory.
2. Amory plus Beatrice.
3. Amory plus Beatrice plus Minneapolis.

Then St. Regis' had pulled him to pieces and started him over again:

4. Amory plus St. Regis'.
5. Amory plus St. Regis' plus Princeton.

That had been his nearest approach to success through conformity. The fundamental Amory, idle, imaginative, rebellious, had been nearly snowed under. He had conformed, he had succeeded, but as his imagination was neither satisfied nor grasped by his own success, he had list-lessly, half-accidentally chucked the whole thing and be-come again:

6. The fundamental Amory.

Financial

His father died quietly and inconspicuously at Thanks-giving. The incongruity of death with either the beauties of Lake Geneva or with his mother's dignified, reticent atti-tude diverted him, and he looked at the funeral with an amused tolerance. He decided that burial was after all pref-erable to cremation, and he smiled at his old boyhood choice, slow oxidation in the top of a tree. The day after the ceremony he was amusing himself in the great library by sinking back on a couch in graceful mortuary attitudes, trying to determine whether he would, when his day came, be found with his arms crossed piously over his chest (Monsignor Darcy had once advocated this posture as being the most distinguished), or with his hands clasped behind his head, a more pagan and Byronic attitude.

What interested him much more than the final departure of his father from things mundane was a tri-cornered con-versation between Beatrice, Mr. Barton, of Barton and Krogman, their lawyers, and himself, that took place several days after the funeral. For the first time he came into actual cognizance of the family finances, and realized what a tidy fortune had once been under his father's management. He took a ledger labelled '1906' and ran through it rather carefully. The total expenditure that year had come to something over one hundred and ten thousand dollars. Forty thousand of this had been Beatrice's own income, and there had been no attempt to account for it: it was all under the heading, 'Drafts, cheques, and letters of credit forwarded to Beatrice Blaine.' The dispersal of the rest was rather minutely itemized: the taxes and improvements on the Lake Geneva estate had come to almost nine thousand dollars;

the general up-keep, including Beatrice's electric and a French car, bought that year, was over thirty-five thousand dollars. The rest was fully taken care of, and there were invariably items which failed to balance on the right side of the ledger.

In the volume for 1912 Amory was shocked to discover the decrease in the number of bond holdings and the great drop in the income. In the case of Beatrice's money this was not so pronounced, but it was obvious that his father had devoted the previous year to several unfortunate gambles in oil. Very little of the oil had been burned, but Stephen Blaine had been rather badly singed. The next year and the next and the next showed similar decreases, and Beatrice had for the first time begun using her own money for keeping up the house. Yet her doctor's bill for 1913 had been over nine thousand dollars.

About the exact state of things Mr. Barton was quite vague and confused. There had been recent investments, the outcome of which was for the present problematical, and he had an idea there were further speculations and exchanges concerning which he had not been consulted.

It was not for several months that Beatrice wrote Amory the full situation. The entire residue of the Blaine and O'Hara fortunes consisted of the place at Lake Geneva and approximately a half million dollars, invested now in fairly conservative six-per-cent holdings. In fact, Beatrice wrote that she was putting the money into railroad and street-car bonds as fast as she could conveniently transfer it.

'I am quite sure,' she wrote to Amory, 'that if there is one thing we can be positive of, it is that people will not stay in one place. This Ford person has certainly made the most of that idea. So I am instructing Mr. Barton to specialize on such things as Northern Pacific and these Rapid Transit Companies, as they call the street-cars. I shall never forgive myself for not buying Bethlehem Steel. I've heard the most *fascinating* stories. You must go into finance, Amory. I'm sure you would revel in it. You start as a messenger or a

teller, I believe, and from that you go up – almost indefinitely. I'm sure if I were a man I'd love the handling of
money; it has become quite a senile passion with me. Before
I get any farther I want to discuss something. A Mrs. Bispam
an overcordial little lady whom I met at a tea the other day,
told me that her son, he is at Yale, wrote her that all the
boys there wore their summer underwear *all during the
winter*, and also went about with their heads wet and in low
shoes on the *coldest days*. Now, Amory, I don't know whether
that is a fad at Princeton too, but I don't want you to be so
foolish. It not only inclines a young man to *pneumonia* and
infantile paralysis, but to all forms of lung trouble, to which
you are particularly *inc ined*. You cannot experiment with
your health. I have found that out. I will not make myself
ridiculous as some mothers no doubt do, by insisting that
you wear overshoes, though I remember one Christmas you
wore them around *constantly* without a single buckle
latched, making such a curious swishing sound, and you refused to buckle them because it was not the thing to do. The
very *next* Christmas you would not wear even *rubbers*,
though I begged you. You are nearly twenty years old now,
dear, and I can't be with you constantly to find whether you
are doing the sensible thing.

'This has been a very *practical* letter. I warned you in my
last that the lack of money to do the things one wants to
makes one quite prosy and domestic, but there is still plenty
for everything if we are not too extravagant. Take care of
yourself, my dear boy, and do try to write at least *once* a
week, because I imagine all sorts of horrible things if I don't
hear from you.

Affectionately,   MOTHER.'

First Appearance of the Term 'Personage'

Monsignor Darcy invited Amory up to the Stuart palace
on the Hudson for a week at Christmas, and they had
enormous conversations around the open fire. Monsignor
was growing a trifle stouter and his personality had expanded

even with that, and Amory felt both rest and security in sinking into a squat, cushioned chair and joining him in the middle-aged sanity of a cigar.

'I've felt like leaving college, Monsignor.'

'Why?'

'All my career's gone up in smoke; you think it's petty and all that, but——'

'Not at all petty. I think it's most important. I want to hear the whole thing. Everything you've been doing since I saw you last.'

Amory talked; he went thoroughly into the destruction of his egotistic highways, and in a half-hour the listless quality had left his voice.

'What would you do if you left college?' asked Monsignor.

'Don't know. I'd like to travel, but of course this tiresome war prevents that. Anyways, mother would hate not having me graduate. I'm just at sea. Kerry Holiday wants me to go over with him and join the Lafayette Esquadrille.'

'You know you wouldn't like to go.'

'Sometimes I would – to-night I'd go in a second.'

'Well, you'd have to be very much more tired of life than I think you are. I know you.'

'I'm afraid you do,' agreed Amory reluctantly. 'It just seemed an easy way out of everything – when I think of another useless, draggy year.'

'Yes, I know; but to tell you the truth, I'm not worried about you; you seem to me to be progressing perfectly naturally.'

'No,' Amory objected. 'I've lost half my personality in a year.'

'Not a bit of it!' scoffed Monsignor. 'You've lost a great amount of vanity and that's all.'

'Lordy! I feel, anyway, as if I've gone through another fifth form at St. Regis's.'

'No.' Monsignor shook his head. 'That was a misfortune; this has been a good thing. Whatever worth while comes to you, won't be through the channels you were searching last year.'

'What could be more unprofitable than my present lack of pep?'

'Perhaps in itself . . . but you're developing. This has given you time to think and you're casting off a lot of your old luggage about success and the superman and all. People like us can't adopt whole theories, as you did. If we can do the next thing, and have an hour a day to think in, we can accomplish marvels, but as far as any high-handed scheme of blind dominance is concerned – we'd just make asses of ourselves.'

'But, Monsignor, I can't do the next thing.'

'Amory, between you and me, I have only just learned to do it myself. I can do the one hundred things beyond the next thing, but I stub my toe on that, just as you stubbed your toe on mathematics this fall.'

'Why do we have to do the next thing? It never seems the sort of thing I should do.'

'We have to do it because we're not personalities, but personages.'

'That's a good line – what do you mean?'

'A personality is what you thought you were, what this Kerry and Sloane you tell me of evidently are. Personality is a physical matter almost entirely; it lowers the people it acts on – I've seen it vanish in a long sickness. But while a personality is active, it overrides "the next thing." Now a personage, on the other hand, gathers. He is never thought of apart from what he's done. He's a bar on which a thous- and things have been hung – glittering things sometimes, as ours are; but he uses those things with a cold mentality back of them.'

'And several of my most glittering possessions had fallen off when I needed them.' Amory continued the simile eagerly.

'Yes, that's it; when you feel that your garnered prestige and talents and all that are hung out, you need never bother about anybody; you can cope with them without difficulty.'

'But, on the other hand, if I haven't my possessions, I'm helpless!'

'Absolutely.'

'That's certainly an idea.'

'Now you've a clean start – a start Kerry or Sloane can constitutionally never have. You brushed three or four ornaments down, and, in a fit of pique, knocked off the rest of them. The thing now is to collect some new ones, and the farther you look ahead in the collecting the better. But remember, do the next thing!'

'How clear you can make things!'

So they talked, often about themselves, sometimes of philosophy and religion, and life as respectively a game or a mystery. The priest seemed to guess Amory's thoughts before they were clear in his own head, so closely related were their minds in form and groove.

'Why do I make lists?' Amory asked him one night. 'Lists of all sorts of things?'

'Because you're a mediævalist,' Monsignor answered. 'We both are. It's the passion for classifying and finding a type.'

'It's a desire to get something definite.'

'It's the nucleus of scholastic philosophy.'

'I was beginning to think I was growing eccentric till I came up here. It was a pose, I guess.'

'Don't worry about that; for you not posing may be the biggest pose of all. Pose——'

'Yes?'

'But do the next thing.'

After Amory returned to college he received several letters from Monsignor which gave him more egotistic food for consumption.

I am afraid that I gave you too much assurance of your inevitable safety, and you must remember that I did that through faith in your springs of effort; not in the silly conviction that you will arrive without struggle. Some nuances of character you will have to take for granted in yourself, though you must be careful in confessing them to others.

You are unsentimental, almost incapable of affection, astute without being cunning and vain without being proud.

Don't let yourself feel worthless; often through life you will really be at your worst when you seem to think best of yourself; and don't worry about losing your 'personality,' as you persist in calling it; at fifteen you had the radiance of early morning, at twenty you will begin to have the melancholy brilliance of the moon, and when you are my age you will give out, as I do, the genial golden warmth of 4 p.m.

If you write me letters, please let them be natural ones. Your last, that dissertation on architecture, was perfectly awful – so 'highbrow' that I picture you living in an intellectual and emotional vacuum; and beware of trying to classify people too definitely into types; you will find that all through their youth they will persist annoyingly in jumping from class to class, and by pasting a supercilious label on every one you meet you are merely packing a Jack-in-the-box that will spring up and leer at you when you begin to come into really antagonistic contact with the world. An idealization of some such man as Leonardo da Vinci would be a more valuable beacon to you at present.

You are bound to go up and down, just as I did in my youth, but do keep your clarity of mind, and if fools or sages dare to criticise don't blame yourself too much.

You say that convention is all that really keeps you straight in this 'woman proposition'; but it's more than that, Amory; it's the fear that what you begin you can't stop; you would run amuck, and I know whereof I speak; it's that half-miraculous sixth sense by which you detect evil, it's the half-realized fear of God in your heart.

Whatever your métier proves to be – religion, architecture, literature – I'm sure you would be much safer anchored to the Church, but I won't risk my influence by arguing with you even though I am secretly sure that the 'black chasm of Romanism' yawns beneath you. Do write me soon.

With affectionate regards,

THAYER DARCY.

Even Amory's reading paled during this period; he delved further into the misty side streets of literature: Huysmans, Walter Pater, Theophile Gautier, and the racier sections of Rabelais, Boccaccio, Petronius, and Suetonius. One week, through general curiosity, he inspected the private libraries of his classmates and found Sloane's as typical as any: sets of Kipling, O. Henry, John Fox, Jr., and Richard Harding Davis; 'What Every Middle-Aged Woman Ought to Know,' 'The Spell of the Yukon'; a 'gift' copy of James Whitcomb Riley, an assortment of battered, annotated school-books, and, finally, to his surprise, one of his own late discoveries, the collected poems of Rupert Brooke.

Together with Tom D'Invilliers, he sought among the lights of Princeton for some one who might found the Great American Poetic Tradition.

The undergraduate body itself was rather more interesting that year than had been the entirely Philistine Princeton of two years before. Things had livened surprisingly, though at the sacrifice of much of the spontaneous charm of freshman year. In the old Princeton they would never have discovered Tanaduke Wylie. Tanaduke was a sophomore, with tremendous ears and a way of saying, 'The earth swirls down through the ominous moons of preconsidered generations!' that made them vaguely wonder why it did not sound quite clear, but never question that it was the utterance of a supersoul. At least so Tom and Amory took him. They told him in all earnestness that he had a mind like Shelley's, and featured his ultrafree free verse and prose poetry in the *Nassau Literary Magazine*. But Tanaduke's genius absorbed the many colours of the age, and he took to the Bohemian life, to their great disappointment. He talked of Greenwich Village now instead of 'noon-swirled moons,' and met winter muses, unacademic, and cloistered by Forty-second Street and Broadway, instead of the Shelleyan dream-children with whom he had regaled their expectant appreciation. So they surrendered Tanaduke to the futurists, deciding that he and his flaming ties would do better there.

Tom gave him the final advice that he should stop writing
for two years and read the complete works of Alexander
Pope four times, but on Amory's suggestion that Pope for
Tanaduke was like foot-ease for stomach trouble, they withdrew in laughter, and called it a coin's toss whether this
genius was too big or too petty for them.

Amory rather scornfully avoided the popular professors
who dispensed easy epigrams and thimblefuls of Chart-
reuse to groups of admirers every night. He was disappointed, too, at the air of general uncertainty on every
subject that seemed linked with the pedantic temperament;
his opinions took shape in a miniature satire called 'In a
Lecture-Room,' which he persuaded Tom to print in the
Nassau Lit.

> 'Good-morning, Fool . . .
>   Three times a week
> You hold us helpless while you speak,
> Teasing our thirsty souls with the
> Sleek "yeas" of your philosophy . . .
> Well, here we are, your hundred sheep,
> Tune up, play on, pour forth . . . we sleep . . .
> You are a student, so they say;
> You hammered out the other day
> A syllabus, from what we know
> Of some forgotten folio;
> You'd sniffled through an era's must,
> Filling your nostrils up with dust,
> And then, arising from your knees,
> Published, in one gigantic sneeze . . .
> But here's a neighbour on my right,
> An *Eager Ass*, considered bright;
> Asker of questions. . . . How he'll stand,
> With earnest air and fidgy hand,
> After this hour, telling you
> He sat all night and burrowed through
> Your book. . . . Oh, you'll be coy and he
> Will simulate precosity,

And pedants both, you'll smile and smirk,
And leer, and hasten back to work. . . .

'Twas this day week, sir, you returned
A theme of mine, from which I learned
(Through various comment on the side
Which you had scrawled) that I defied
The *highest rules of criticism*
For *cheap* and *careless* witticism. . . .
    "Are you quite sure that this could be?"
And
    "Shaw is no authority!"
But *Eager Ass*, with what he's sent,
Plays havoc with your best per cent.

Still – still I meet you here and there . . .
When Shakespeare's played you hold a chair,
And some defunct, moth-eaten star
Enchants the mental prig you are . . .
A radical comes down and shocks
The *atheistic orthodox?*—
You're representing *Common Sense*,
Mouth open, in the audience.

And, sometimes, even chapel lures
That conscious tolerance of yours,
That broad and beaming view of truth
(Including *Kant* and *General Booth* . . .)
And so from shock to shock you live,
A hollow, pale affirmative . . .

The hour's up . . . and roused from rest
One hundred children of the blest
Cheat you a word or two with feet
That down the noisy aisle-ways beat . . .
Forget on *narrow-minded earth*
The Mighty Yawn that gave you birth.'

In April, Kerry Holiday left college and sailed for France
to enroll in the Lafayette Esquadrille. Amory's envy and

admiration of this step was drowned in an experience of his own to which he never succeeded in giving an appropriate value, but which, nevertheless, haunted him for three years afterwards.

The Devil

Healy's they left at twelve and taxied to Bistolary's. There were Axia Marlowe and Phœbe Column, from the Summer Garden show, Fred Sloane and Amory. The evening was so very young that they felt ridiculous with surplus energy, and burst into the café like Dionysian revellers.

'Table for four in the middle of the floor,' yelled Phœbe. 'Hurry, old dear, tell 'em we're here!'

'Tell 'em to play "Admiration"!' shouted Sloane. 'You two order; Phœbe and I are going to shake a wicked calf,' and they sailed off in the muddled crowd. Axia and Amory, acquaintances of an hour, jostled behind a waiter to a table at a point of vantage; there they took seats and watched.

'There's Findle Margotson, from New Haven!' she cried above the uproar. "Lo, Findle! Whoo-ee!'

'Oh, Axia!' he shouted in salutation. 'C'mon over to our table.'

'No!' Amory whispered.

'Can't do it, Findle; I'm with somebody else! Call me up to-morrow about one o'clock!'

Findle, a nondescript man-about-Bisty's, answered incoherently, and turned back to the brilliant blonde whom he was endeavouring to steer around the room.

'There's a natural damn fool,' commented Amory.

'Oh, he's all right. Here's the old jitney waiter. If you ask me, I want a double Daiquiri.'

'Make it four.'

The crowd whirled and changed and shifted. They were mostly from the colleges, with a scattering of the male refuse of Broadway, and women of two types, the higher of which was the chorus girl. On the whole it was a typical crowd, and their party as typical as any. About three-fourths of the whole business was for effect and therefore harmless, ended at the door of the café, soon enough for the five-o'clock train back to Yale or Princeton; about one-fourth continued on into the dimmer hours and gathered strange dust from strange places. Their party was scheduled to be one of the harmless kind. Fred Sloane and Phœbe Column were old friends; Axia and Amory new ones. But strange things are prepared even in the dead of night, and the unusual, which lurks least in the café, home of the pro-saic and inevitable, was preparing to spoil for him the wan-ing romance of Broadway. The way it took was so inex-pressibly terrible, so unbelievable, that afterwards he never thought of it as experience; but it was a scene from a misty tragedy, played far behind the veil, and that it meant some-thing definite he knew.

About one o'clock they moved to Maxim's, and two found them in Devinière's. Sloane had been drinking consecu-tively and was in a state of unsteady exhilaration, but Amory was quite tiresomely sober; they had run across none of those ancient, corrupt buyers of champagne who usually assisted their New York parties.

They were just through dancing and were making their way back to their chairs when Amory became aware that some one at a near-by table was looking at him. He turned and glanced casually . . . a middle-aged man dressed in a brown sack suit, it was, sitting a little apart at a table by himself and watching their party intently. At Amory's glance he smiled faintly. Amory turned to Fred, who was just sitting down.

'Who's that pale fool watching us?' he complained in-dignantly.

'Where?' cried Sloane. 'We'll have him thrown out!' He rose to his feet and swayed back and forth, clinging to his chair. 'Where is he?'

Axia and Phœbe suddenly leaned and whispered to each other across the table, and before Amory realized it they found themselves on their way to the door.

'Where now?'

'Up to the flat,' suggested Phœbe. 'We've got brandy and fizz – and everything's slow down here tonight.'

Amory considered quickly. He hadn't been drinking, and decided that if he took no more, it would be reasonably discreet for him to trot along in the party. In fact, it would be, perhaps, the thing to do in order to keep an eye on Sloane, who was not in a state to do his own thinking. So he took Axia's arm and, piling intimately into a taxicab, they drove out over the hundreds and drew up at a tall, white-stone apartment-house. . . . Never would he forget that street. . . . It was a broad street, lined on both sides with just such tall, white-stone buildings, dotted with dark windows; they stretched along as far as the eye could see, flooded with a bright moonlight that gave them a calcium pallor. He imagined each one to have an elevator and a coloured hall-boy and a key-rack; each one to be eight stories high and full of three and four room suites. He was rather glad to walk into the cheeriness of Phœbe's living-room and sink on to a sofa, while the girls went rummaging for food.

'Phœbe's great stuff,' confided Sloane, sotto voce.

'I'm only going to stay half an hour,' Amory said sternly. He wondered if it sounded priggish.

'Hell y' say,' protested Sloane. 'We're here now – don't le's rush.'

'I don't like this place,' Amory said sulkily, 'and I don't want any food.'

Phœbe reappeared with sandwiches, brandy bottle, siphon, and four glasses.

'Amory, pour 'em out,' she said, 'and we'll drink to Fred Sloane, who has a rare, distinguished edge.'

'Yes,' said Axia, coming in, 'and Amory. I like Amory.' She sat down beside him and laid her yellow head on his shoulder.

'I'll pour,' said Sloane; 'you use siphon, Phœbe.'

They filled the tray with glasses.

'Ready, here she goes!'

Amory hesitated, glass in hand.

There was a minute while temptation crept over him like a warm wind, and his imagination turned to fire, and he took the glass from Phœbe's hand. That was all; for at the second that his decision came, he looked up and saw, ten yards from him, the man who had been in the café, and with his jump of astonishment the glass fell from his uplifted hand. There the man half sat, half leaned against a pile of pillows on the corner divan. His face was cast in the same yellow wax as in the café, neither the dull, pasty colour of a dead man – rather a sort of virile pallor – nor unhealthy, you'd have called it; but like a strong man who'd worked in a mine or done night shifts in a damp climate. Amory looked him over carefully and later he could have drawn him after a fashion, down to the merest details. His mouth was the kind that is called frank, and he had steady grey eyes that moved slowly from one to the other of their group, with just the shade of a questioning expression. Amory noticed his hands; they weren't fine at all, but they had versatility and a tenuous strength . . . they were nervous hands that sat lightly along the cushions and moved constantly with little jerky openings and closings. Then, suddenly, Amory perceived the feet, and with a rush of blood to the head he realized he was afraid. The feet were all wrong . . . with a sort of wrongness that he felt rather than knew. . . . It was like weakness in a good woman, or blood on satin; one of those terrible incongruities that shake little things in the back of the brain. He wore no shoes, but, instead, a sort of half moccasin, pointed, though, like the shoes they wore in the fourteenth century, and with the little ends curling up. They were a darkish brown and his toes seemed to fill them to the end. . . . They were unutterably terrible. . . .

He must have said something, or looked something, for Axia's voice came out of the void with a strange goodness.

'Well, look at Amory! Poor old Amory's sick – old head going 'round?'

'Look at that man!' cried Amory, pointing toward the corner divan.

'You mean that purple zebra!' shrieked Axia facetiously. 'Ooo-ee! Amory's got a purple zebra watching him!'

Sloane laughed vacantly.

'Ole zebra gotcha, Amory?'

There was a silence. . . . The man regarded Amory quizzically. . . . Then the human voices fell faintly on his ear:

'Thought you weren't drinking,' remarked Axia sardonically, but her voice was good to hear; the whole divan that held the man was alive; alive like heat waves over asphalt, like wriggling worms. . . .

'Come back! Come back!' Axia's arm fell on his. 'Amory, dear, you aren't going, Amory!' He was half-way to the door.

'Come on, Amory, stick 'th us!'

'Sick, are you?'

'Sit down a second!'

'Take some water.'

'Take a little brandy. . . .'

The elevator was close, and the coloured boy was half asleep, paled to a livid bronze . . . Axia's beseeching voice floated down the shaft. Those feet . . . those feet. . . .

As they settled to the lower floor the feet came into view in the sickly electric light of the paved hall.

In the Alley

Down the long street came the moon, and Amory turned his back on it and walked. Ten, fifteen steps away sounded the footsteps. They were like a slow dripping, with just the slightest insistence in their fall. Amory's shadow lay, perhaps, ten feet ahead of him, and soft shoes was presumably that far behind. With the instinct of a child Amory edged in under the blue darkness of the white buildings, cleaving the moonlight for haggard seconds, once bursting into a slow run with clumsy stumblings. After that he stopped suddenly; he must keep hold, he thought. His lips were dry and he licked them.

If he met any one good – were there any good people left

in the world or did they all live in white apartment-houses now? Was every one followed in the moonlight? But if he met some one good who'd know what he meant and hear this damned scuffle . . . then the scuffling grew suddenly nearer, and a black cloud settled over the moon. When again the pale sheen skimmed the cornices, it was almost beside him, and Amory thought he heard a quiet breathing. Suddenly he realized that the footsteps were not behind, had never been behind, they were ahead and he was not eluding but following . . . following. He began to run, blindly, his heart knocking heavily, his hands clenched. Far ahead a black dot showed itself, resolved slowly into a human shape. But Amory was beyond that now; he turned off the street and darted into an alley, narrow and dark and smelling of old rottenness. He twisted down a long, sinuous blackness, where the moonlight was shut away except for tiny glints and patches . . . then suddenly sank panting into a corner by a fence, exhausted. The steps ahead stopped, and he could hear them shift slightly with a continuous motion, like waves around a dock.

He put his face in his hands and covered eyes and ears as well as he could. During all this time it never occurred to him that he was delirious or drunk. He had a sense of reality such as material things could never give him. His intellectual content seemed to submit passively to it, and it fitted like a glove everything that had ever preceded it in his life. It did not muddle him. It was like a problem whose answer he knew on paper, yet whose solution he was unable to grasp. He was far beyond horror. He had sunk through the thin surface of that, now moved in a region where the feet and the fear of white walls were real, living things, things he must accept. Only far inside his soul a little fire leaped and cried that something was pulling him down, trying to get him inside a door and slam it behind him. After that door was slammed there would be only footfalls and white buildings in the moonlight, and perhaps he would be one of the footfalls.

During the five or ten minutes he waited in the shadow of

the fence, there was somehow this fire . . . that was as near
as he could name it afterward. He remembered calling
aloud:

'I want some one stupid. Oh, send some one stupid!'
This to the black fence opposite him, in whose shadows the
footsteps shuffled . . . shuffled. He supposed 'stupid' and
'good' had become somehow intermingled through previous
association. When he called thus it was not an act of will at
all – will had turned him away from the moving figure in
the street; it was almost instinct that called, just the pile on
pile of inherent tradition or some wild prayer from way over
the night. Then something clanged like a low gong struck
at a distance, and before his eyes a face flashed over the two
feet, a face pale and distorted with a sort of infinite evil that
twisted it like flame in the wind; *but he knew, for the half
instant that the gong tanged and hummed, that it was the face
of Dick Humbird.*

Minutes later he sprang to his feet, realizing dimly that
there was no more sound, and that he was alone in the greying alley. It was cold, and he started on a steady run for the
light that showed the street at the other end.

At the Window

It was late morning when he woke and found the telephone beside his bed in the hotel tolling frantically, and
remembered that he had left word to be called at eleven.
Sloane was snoring heavily, his clothes in a pile by his bed.
They dressed and ate breakfast in silence, and then sauntered out to get some air. Amory's mind was working slowly,
trying to assimilate what had happened and separate from
the chaotic imagery that stacked his memory the bare shreds
of truth. If the morning had been cold and grey he could
have grasped the reins of the past in an instant, but it was
one of those days that New York gets sometimes in May,
when the air on Fifth Avenue is a soft, light wine. How
much or how little Sloane remembered Amory did not care
to know; he apparently had none of the nervous tension that

was gripping Amory and forcing his mind back and forth like a shrieking saw.

Then Broadway broke upon them, and with the babel of noise and the painted faces a sudden sickness rushed over Amory.

'For God's sake, let's go back! Let's get off of this – this place!'

Sloane looked at him in amazement.

'What do you mean?'

'This street, it's ghastly! Come on! let's get back to the Avenue!'

'Do you mean to say,' said Sloane stolidly, 'that 'cause you had some sort of indigestion that made you act like a maniac last night, you're never coming on Broadway again?'

Simultaneously Amory classed him with the crowd, and he seemed no longer Sloane of the debonair humour and the happy personality, but only one of the evil faces that whirled along the turbid stream.

'Man!' he shouted so loud that the people on the corner turned and followed them with their eyes, 'it's filthy, and if you can't see it, you're filthy, too!'

'I can't help it,' said Sloane doggedly. 'What's the matter with you? Old remorse getting you? You'd be in a fine state if you'd gone through with our little party.'

'I'm going, Fred,' said Amory slowly. His knees were shaking under him, and he knew that if he stayed another minute on this street he would keel over where he stood. 'I'll be at the Vanderbilt for lunch.' And he strode rapidly off and turned over to Fifth Avenue. Back at the hotel he felt better, but as he walked into the barber-shop, intending to get a head massage, the smell of the powders and tonics brought back Axia's sidelong, suggestive smile, and he left hurriedly. In the doorway of his room a sudden blackness flowed around him like a divided river.

When he came to himself he knew that several hours had passed. He pitched on to the bed and rolled over on his face with a deadly fear that he was going mad. He wanted people,

people, some one sane and stupid and good. He lay for he knew not how long without moving. He could feel the little hot veins on his forehead standing out, and his terror had hardened on him like plaster. He felt he was passing up again through the thin crust of horror, and now only could he distinguish the shadowy twilight he was leaving. He must have fallen asleep again, for when he next recollected himself he had paid the hotel bill and was stepping into a taxi at the door. It was raining torrents.

On the train for Princeton he saw no one he knew, only a crowd of fagged-looking Philadelphians. The presence of a painted woman across the aisle filled him with a fresh burst of sickness and he changed to another car, tried to concentrate on an article in a popular magazine. He found himself reading the same paragraphs over and over, so he abandoned this attempt and leaning over wearily pressed his hot forehead against the damp window-pane. The car, a smoker, was hot and stuffy with most of the smells of the state's alien population; he opened a window and shivered against the cloud of fog that drifted in over him. The two hours' ride were like days, and he nearly cried aloud with joy when the towers of Princeton loomed up beside him and the yellow squares of light filtered through the blue rain.

Tom was standing in the centre of the room, pensively relighting a cigar-stub. Amory fancied he looked rather relieved on seeing him.

'Had a hell of a dream about you last night,' came in the cracked voice through the cigar smoke. 'I had an idea you were in some trouble.'

'Don't tell me about it!' Amory almost shrieked. 'Don't say a word; I'm tired and pepped out.'

Tom looked at him queerly and then sank into a chair and opened his Italian note-book. Amory threw his coat and hat on the floor, loosened his collar, and took a Wells novel at random from the shell. 'Wells is sane,' he thought, 'and if he won't do I'll read Rupert Brooke.'

Half an hour passed. Outside the wind came up, and Amory started as the wet branches moved and clawed with

their finger-nails at the window-pane. Tom was deep in his
work, and inside the room only the occasional scratch of a
match or the rustle of leather as they shifted in their chairs
broke the stillness. Then like a zigzag of lightning came the
change. Amory sat bolt upright, frozen cold in his chair.
Tom was looking at him with his mouth drooping, eyes
fixed.

'God help us!' Amory cried.

'Oh, my heavens!' shouted Tom, 'look behind!' Quick as
a flash Amory whirled around. He saw nothing but the dark
window-pane.

'It's gone now,' came Tom's voice after a second in a still
terror. 'Something was looking at you.'

Trembling violently, Amory dropped into his chair again.

'I've got to tell you,' he said. 'I've had one hell of an
experience. I think I've – I've seen the devil or – something
like him. What face did you just see? – or no,' he added
quickly, 'don't tell me!'

And he gave Tom the story. It was midnight when he
finished, and after that, with all lights burning, two sleepy,
shivering boys read to each other from 'The New Machiavelli,' until dawn came up out of Witherspoon Hall, and the
Princetonian fell against the door, and the May birds hailed
the sun on last night's rain.

IV. NARCISSUS OFF DUTY

DURING Princeton's transition period, that is, during
Amory's last two years there, while he saw it change and
broaden and live up to its Gothic beauty by better means
than night parades, certain individuals arrived who stirred
it to its plethoric depths. Some of them had been freshmen,
and wild freshmen, with Amory; some were in the class
below; and it was in the beginning of his last year and
around small tables at the Nassau Inn that they began

questioning aloud the institutions that Amory and countless others before him had questioned so long in secret. First, and partly by accident, they struck on certain books, a definite type of biographical novel that Amory christened 'quest' books. In the 'quest' book the hero set off in life armed with the best weapons and avowedly intending to use them as such weapons are usually used, to push their possessors ahead as selfishly and blindly as possible, but the heroes of the 'quest' books discovered that there might be a more magnificent use for them. 'None Other Gods,' 'Sinister Street,' and 'The Research Magnificent' were examples of such books; it was the latter of these three that gripped Burne Holiday and made him wonder in the beginning of senior year how much it was worth while being a diplomatic autocrat around his club on Prospect Avenue and basking in the high lights of class office. It was distinctly through the channels of aristocracy that Burne found his way. Amory, through Kerry, had had a vague drifting acquaintance with him, but not until January of senior year did their friendship commence.

'Heard the latest?' said Tom, coming in late one drizzly evening with that triumphant air he always wore after a successful conversational bout.

'No. Somebody flunked out? Or another ship sunk?'

'Worse than that. About one-third of the junior class are going to resign from their clubs.'

'What!'

'Actual fact!'

'Why!'

'Spirit of reform and all that. Burne Holiday is behind it. The club presidents are holding a meeting to-night to see if they can find a joint means of combating it.'

'Well, what's the idea of the thing?'

'Oh, clubs injurious to Princeton democracy; cost a lot; draw social lines, take time; the regular line you get sometimes from disappointed sophomores. Woodrow thought they should be abolished and all that.'

'But this is the real thing?'

'Absolutely. I think it'll go through.'

'For Pete's sake, tell me more about it.'

'Well,' began Tom, 'it seems that the idea developed simultaneously in several heads. I was talking to Burne awhile ago, and he claims that it's a logical result if an intelligent person thinks long enough about the social system. They had a "discussion crowd" and the point of abolishing the clubs was brought up by some one – everybody there leaped at it – it had been in each one's mind, more or less, and it just needed a spark to bring it out.'

'Fine! I swear I think it'll be most entertaining. How do they feel up at Cap and Gown?'

'Wild, of course. Every one's been sitting and arguing and swearing and getting mad and getting sentimental and getting brutal. It's the same at all the clubs; I've been the rounds. They get one of the radicals in the corner and fire questions at him.'

'How do the radicals stand up?'

'Oh, moderately well. Burne's a damn good talker, and so obviously sincere that you can't get anywhere with him. It's so evident that resigning from his club means so much more to him than preventing it does to us that I felt futile when I argued; finally took a position that was brilliantly neutral. In fact, I believe Burne thought for a while that he'd converted me.'

'And you say almost a third of the junior class are going to resign?'

'Call it a fourth and be safe.'

'Lord – who'd have thought it possible!'

There was a brisk knock at the door, and Burne himself came in.

'Hello, Amory – hello, Tom.'

Amory rose.

'Evening, Burne. Don't mind if I seem to rush; I'm going to Renwick's.'

Burne turned to him quickly.

'You probably know what I want to talk to Tom about, and it isn't a bit private. I wish you'd stay.'

'I'd be glad to.' Amory sat down again, and as Burne perched on a table and launched into argument with Tom, he looked at this revolutionary more carefully than he ever had before. Broad-browed and strong-chinned, with a fineness in the honest grey eyes that were like Kerry's, Burne was a man who gave an immediate impression of bigness and security – stubborn, that was evident, but his stubbornness wore no stolidity, and when he had talked for five minutes Amory knew that this keen enthusiasm had in it no quality of dilettantism.

The intense power Amory felt later in Burne Holiday differed from the admiration he had had for Humbird. This time it began as purely a mental interest. With other men of whom he had thought as primarily first-class, he had been attracted first by their personalities, and in Burne he missed that immediate magnetism to which he usually swore allegiance. But that night Amory was struck by Burne's intense earnestness, a quality he was accustomed to associate only with the dread stupidity, and by the great enthusiasm that struck dead chords in his heart. Burne stood vaguely for a land Amory hoped he was drifting toward – and it was almost time that land was in sight. Tom and Amory and Alec had reached an impasse; never did they seem to have new experiences in common, for Tom and Alec had been as blindly busy with their committees and boards as Amory had been blindly idling, and the things they had for dissection – college, contemporary personality and the like – they had hashed and rehashed for many a frugal conversational meal.

That night they discussed the clubs until twelve, and, in the main, they agreed with Burne. To the room-mates it did not seem such a vital subject as it had in the two years before, but the logic of Burne's objections to the social system dovetailed so completely with everything they had thought, that they questioned rather than argued, and envied the sanity that enabled this man to stand out so against all traditions.

Then Amory branched off and found that Burne was deep

in other things as well. Economics had interested him and he was turning socialist. Pacifism played in the back of his mind, and he read the *Masses* and Lyoff Tolstoi faithfully.

'How about religion ?' Amory asked him.

'Don't know. I'm in a muddle about a lot of things – I've just discovered that I've a mind, and I'm starting to read.'

'Read what ?'

'Everything. I have to pick and choose, of course, but mostly things to make me think. I'm reading the four gospels now, and the "Varieties of Religious Experience".'

'What chiefly started you ?'

'Wells, I guess, and Tolstoi, and a man named Edward Carpenter. I've been reading for over a year now – on a few lines, on what I consider the essential lines.'

'Poetry ?'

'Well, frankly, not what you call poetry, or for your reasons – you two write, of course, and look at things differently. Whitman is the man that attracts me.'

'Whitman ?'

'Yes; he's a definite ethical force.'

'Well, I'm ashamed to say that I'm a blank on the subject of Whitman. How about you, Tom ?'

Tom nodded sheepishly.

'Well,' continued Burne, 'you may strike a few poems that are tiresome, but I mean the mass of his work. He's tremendous – like Tolstoi. They both look things in the face, and, somehow, different as they are, stand for somewhat the same things.'

'You have me stumped, Burne,' Amory admitted. 'I've read "Anna Karénina" and the "Kreutzer Sonata" of course, but Tolstoi is mostly in the original Russian as far as I'm concerned.'

'He's the greatest man in hundreds of years,' cried Burne enthusiastically. 'Did you ever see a picture of that shaggy old head of his ?'

They talked until three, from biology to organized religion, and when Amory crept shivering into bed it was with his mind aglow with ideas and a sense of shock that some one else had discovered the path he might have followed. Burne Holiday was so evidently developing – and Amory had considered that he was doing the same. He had fallen into a deep cynicism over what had crossed his path, plotted the imperfectability of man and read Shaw and Chesterton enough to keep his mind from the edges of decadence – now suddenly all his mental processes of the last year and a half seemed stale and futile – a petty consummation of himself . . . and like a sombre background lay that incident of the spring before, that filled half his nights with a dreary terror and made him unable to pray. He was not even a Catholic, yet that was the only ghost of a code that he had, the gaudy, ritualistic, paradoxical Catholicism whose prophet was Chesterton, whose claqueurs were such reformed rakes of literature as Huysmans and Bourget, whose American sponsor was Ralph Adams Cram, with his adulation of thirteenth-century cathedrals – a Catholicism which Amory found convenient and ready-made, without priest or sacraments or sacrifice.

He could not sleep, so he turned on his reading-lamp and, taking down the 'Kreutzer Sonata,' searched it carefully for the germs of Burne's enthusiasm. Being Burne was suddenly so much realler than being clever. Yet he sighed . . . here were other possible clay feet.

He thought back through two years, of Burne as a hurried, nervous freshman, quite submerged in his brother's personality. Then he remembered an incident of sophomore year, in which Burne had been suspected of the leading rôle.

Dean Hollister had been heard by a large group arguing with a taxi-driver, who had driven him from the junction. In the course of the altercation the dean remarked that he 'might as well buy the taxicab.' He paid and walked off, but next morning he entered his private office to find the taxicab itself in the space usually occupied by his desk, bearing a sign which read 'Property of Dean Hollister. Bought and Paid for.' . . . It took two expert mechanics half a day to disassemble it into its minutest parts and remove it, which only goes to prove the rare energy of sophomore humour under efficient leadership.

Then again, that very fall, Burne had caused a sensation. A certain Phyllis Styles, an intercollegiate promtrotter, had failed to get her yearly invitation to the Harvard-Princeton game.

Jesse Ferrenby had brought her to a smaller game a few weeks before, and had pressed Burne into service – to the ruination of the latter's misogyny.

'Are you coming to the Harvard game?' Burne had asked indiscreetly, merely to make conversation.

'If you ask me,' cried Phyllis quickly.

'Of course I do,' said Burne feebly. He was unversed in the arts of Phyllis, and was sure that this was merely a vapid form of kidding. Before an hour had passed he knew that he was indeed involved. Phyllis had pinned him down and served him up, informed him the train she was arriving by, and depressed him thoroughly. Aside from loathing Phyllis, he had particularly wanted to stag that game and entertain some Harvard friends.

'She'll see,' he informed a delegation who arrived in his room to josh him. 'This will be the last game she ever persuades any young innocent to take her to!'

'But, Burne – why did you *invite* her if you didn't want her?'

'Burne, you *know* you're secretly mad about her – that's the *real* trouble.'

'What can *you* do, Burne? What can *you* do against Phyllis?'

But Burne only shook his head and muttered threats which consisted largely of the phrase: 'She'll see, she'll see!'

The blithesome Phyllis bore her twenty-five summers gaily from the train, but on the platform a ghastly sight met her eyes. There were Burne and Fred Sloane arrayed to the last dot like the lurid figures on college posters. They had bought flaring suits with huge pegtop trousers and gigantic padded shoulders. On their heads were rakish college hats, pinned up in front and sporting bright orange-and-black bands, while from their celluloid collars blossomed flaming orange ties. They wore black arm-bands with orange 'P's,' and carried canes flying Princeton pennants, the effect completed by socks and peeping handkerchiefs in the same colour motifs. On a clanking chain they led a large, angry tom-cat, painted to represent a tiger.

A good half of the station crowd was already staring at them, torn between horrified pity and riotous mirth, and as Phyllis, with her svelte jaw dropping, approached, the pair bent over and emitted a college cheer in loud, far-carrying voices, thoughtfully adding the name 'Phyllis' to the end. She was vociferously greeted and escorted enthusiastically across the campus, followed by half a hundred village urchins – to the stifled laughter of hundreds of alumni and visitors, half of whom had no idea that this was a practical joke, but thought that Burne and Fred were two varsity sports showing their girl a collegiate time.

Phyllis's feelings as she was paraded by the Harvard and Princeton stands, where sat dozens of her former devotees, can be imagined. She tried to walk a little ahead, she tried to walk a little behind – but they stayed close, that there should be no doubt whom she was with, talking in loud voices of their friends on the football team, until she could almost hear her acquaintances whispering:

'Phyllis Styles must be *awfully hard up* to have to come with *those two.*'

That had been Burne, dynamically humorous, fundamentally serious. From that root had blossomed the energy that he was now trying to orient with progress. . . .

So the weeks passed and March came and the clay feet that Amory looked for failed to appear. About a hundred juniors and seniors resigned from their clubs in a final fury of righteousness, and the clubs in helplessness turned upon Burne their finest weapon: ridicule. Every one who knew him liked him – but what he stood for (and he began to stand for more all the time) came under the lash of many tongues, until a frailer man than he would have been snowed under.

'Don't you mind losing prestige ?' asked Amory one night.

They had taken to exchanging calls several times a week.

'Of course I don't. What's prestige, at best?'

'Some people say that you're just a rather original politician.'

He roared with laughter.

'That's what Fred Sloane told me to-day. I suppose I have it coming.'

One afternoon they dipped into a subject that had interested Amory for a long time – the matter of the bearing of physical attributes on a man's make-up. Burne had gone into the biology of this, and then:

'Of course health counts – a healthy man has twice the chance of being good,' he said.

'I don't agree with you – I don't believe in "muscular Christianity".'

'I do – I believe Christ had great physical vigour.'

'Oh, no,' Amory protested. 'He worked too hard for that. I imagine that when he died he was a broken-down man – and the great saints haven't been strong.'

'Half of them have.'

'Well, even granting that, I don't think health has anything to do with goodness; of course, it's valuable to a great saint to be able to stand enormous strains, but this fad of popular preachers rising on their toes in simulated virility, bellowing that calisthenics will save the world – no, Burne, I can't go that.'

'Well, let's waive it – we won't get anywhere, and besides I haven't quite made up my mind about it myself. Now, here's something I *do* know – personal appearance has a lot to do with it.'

'Colouring?' Amory asked eagerly.

'Yes.'

'That's what Tom and I figured,' Amory agreed. 'We took the year-books for the last ten years and looked at the pictures of the senior council. I know you don't think much of that august body, but it does represent success here in a general way. Well, I suppose only about thirty-five per cent of every class here are blonds, are really light – yet *two-*

thirds of every senior council are light. We looked at pictures of ten years of them, mind you; that means that out of every *fifteen* light-haired men in the senior class *one* is on the senior council, and of the dark-haired men it's only one in *fifty*.'

'It's true,' Burne agreed. 'The light-haired man *is* a higher type, generally speaking. I worked the thing out with the Presidents of the United States once, and found that way over half of them were light-haired – yet think of the preponderant number of brunettes in the race.'

'People unconsciously admit it,' said Amory. 'You'll notice a blonde person is *expected* to talk. If a blonde girl doesn't talk we call her a "doll"; if a light-haired man is silent he's considered stupid. Yet the world is full of "dark silent men" and "languorous brunettes" who haven't a brain in their heads, but somehow are never accused of the dearth.'

'And the large mouth and broad chin and rather big nose undoubtedly make the superior face.'

'I'm not so sure.' Amory was all for classical features.

'Oh, yes – I'll show you,' and Burne pulled out of his desk a photographic collection of heavily bearded, shaggy celebrities – Tolstoi, Whitman, Carpenter, and others.

'Aren't they wonderful?'

Amory tried politely to appreciate them, and gave up laughingly.

'Burne, I think they're the ugliest-looking crowd I ever came across. They look like an old man's home.'

'Oh, Amory, look at that forehead on Emerson; look at Tolstoi's eyes.' His tone was reproachful.

Amory shook his heqd.

'No! Call them remarkable-looking or anything you want – but ugly they certainly are.'

Unabashed, Burne ran his hand lovingly across the spacious foreheads, and piling up the pictures put them back in his desk.

Walking at night was one of his favourite pursuits, and one night he persuaded Amory to accompany him.

'I hate the dark,' Amory objected. 'I didn't use to – except when I was particularly imaginative, but now, I really do – I'm a regular fool about it.'

'That's useless, you know.'

'Quite possibly.'

'We'll go east,' Burne suggested, 'and down that string of roads through the woods.'

'Doesn't sound very appealing to me,' admitted Amory reluctantly, 'but let's go.'

They set off at a good gait, and for an hour swung along in a brisk argument until the lights of Princeton were luminous white blots behind them.

'Any person with any imagination is bound to be afraid,' said Burne earnestly. 'And this very walking at night is one of the things I was afraid about. I'm going to tell you why I can walk anywhere now and not be afraid.'

'Go on,' Amory urged eagerly. They were striding toward the woods, Burne's nervous, enthusiastic voice warming to his subject.

'I used to come out here alone at night, oh, three months ago, and I always stopped at that cross-road we just passed. There were the woods looming up ahead, just as they do now, there were dogs howling and the shadows and no human sound. Of course, I peopled the woods with everything ghastly, just like you do; don't you?'

'I do,' Amory admitted.

'Well, I began analyzing it – my imagination persisted in sticking horrors into the dark – so I stuck my imagination into the dark instead, and let it look out at me – I let it play stray dog or escaped convict or ghost, and then saw myself coming along the road. That made it all right – as it always makes everything all right to project yourself completely into another's place. I knew that if I were the dog or the convict or the ghost I wouldn't be a menace to Burne Holiday any more than he was a menace to me. Then I thought of my watch. I'd better go back and leave it and then essay the woods. No; I decided, it's better on the whole that I should lose a watch than that I should turn back – and I did go into them – not only followed the road through them, but walked into them until I wasn't frightened any more – did it until one night I sat down and dozed off in there; then I knew I was through being afraid of the dark.'

'Lordy,' Amory breathed. 'I couldn't have done that. I'd have come out half-way, and the first time an automobile passed and made the dark thicker when its lamps disappeared, I'd have come in.'

'Well,' Burne said suddenly, after a few moments' silence, 'we're half-way through, let's turn back.'

On the return he launched into a discussion of will.

'It's the whole thing,' he asserted. 'It's the one dividing line between good and evil. I've never met a man who led a rotten life and didn't have a weak will.'

'How about great criminals ?'

'They're usually insane. If not, they're weak. There is no such thing as a strong, sane criminal.'

'Burne, I disagree with you altogether; how about the superman ?'

'Well ?'

'He's evil, I think, yet he's strong and sane.'

'I've never met him. I'll bet, though, that he's stupid or insane.'

'I've met him over and over and he's neither. That's why I think you're wrong.'

'I'm sure I'm not – and so I don't believe in imprisonment except for the insane.'

On this point Amory could not agree. It seemed to him that life and history were rife with the strong criminal, keen, but often self-deluding; in politics and business one found him and among the old statesmen and kings and generals; but Burne never agreed and their courses began to split on that point.

Burne was drawing farther and farther away from the world about him. He resigned the vice-presidency of the senior class and took to reading and walking as almost his only pursuits. He voluntarily attended graduate lectures in philosophy and biology, and sat in all of them with a rather

pathetically intent look in his eyes, as if waiting for something the lecturer would never quite come to. Sometimes
Amory would see him squirm in his seat; and his face would
light up; he was on fire to debate a point.

He grew more abstracted on the street and was even accused of becoming a snob, but Amory knew it was nothing
of the sort, and once when Burne passed him four feet off,
absolutely unseeingly, his mind a thousand miles away,
Amory almost choked with the romantic joy of watching
him. Burne seemed to be climbing heights where others
would be forever unable to get a foothold.

'I tell you,' Amory declared to Tom, 'he's the first contemporary I've ever met whom I'll admit is my superior in
mental capacity.'

'It's a bad time to admit it – people are beginning to think
he's odd.'

'He's way over their heads – you know you think so yourself when you talk to him – Good Lord, Tom, you *used* to
stand out against "people." Success has completely conven-
tionalized you.'

Tom grew rather annoyed.

'What's he trying to do – be excessively holy ?'

'No! not like anybody you've ever seen. Never enters the
Philadelphian Society. He has no faith in that rot. He
doesn't believe that public swimming-pools and a kind
word in time will right the wrongs of the world; moreover,
he takes a drink whenever he feels like it.'

'He certainly is getting in wrong.'

'Have you talked to him lately ?'

'No.'

'Then you haven't any conception of him.'

The argument ended nowhere, but Amory noticed more
than ever how the sentiment toward Burne had changed on
the campus.

'It's odd,' Amory said to Tom one night when they had
grown more amicable on the subject, 'that the people who
violently disapprove of Burne's radicalism are distinctly the
Pharisee class – I mean they're the best-educated men in

college – the editors of the papers, like yourself and Ferrenby, the younger professors. . . . The illiterate athletes like Langueduc think he's getting eccentric, but they just say, "Good old Burne has got some queer ideas in his head," and pass on – the Pharisee class – Gee! they ridicule him unmercifully.'

The next morning he met Burne hurrying along McCosh walk after a recitation.

'Whither bound, Tsar?'

'Over to the Prince office to see Ferrenby,' he waved a copy of the morning's *Princetonian* at Amory. 'He wrote this editorial.'

'Going to flay him alive?'

'No – but he's got me all balled up. Either I've misjudged him or he's suddenly become the world's worst radical.'

Burne hurried on, and it was several days before Amory heard an account of the ensuing conversation. Burne had come into the editor's sanctum displaying the paper cheerfully.

'Hello, Jesse.'

'Hello there, Savonarola.'

'I just read your editorial.'

'Good boy – didn't know you stooped that low.'

'Jesse, you startled me.'

'How so?'

'Aren't you afraid the faculty'll get after you if you pull this irreligious stuff?'

'What?'

'Like the morning.'

'What the devil – that editorial was on the coaching system.'

'Yes, but that quotation –'

Jesse sat up.

'What quotation?'

'You know: "He who is not with me is against me".'

'Well – what about it?'

Jesse was puzzled but not alarmed.

'Well, you say here – let me see.' Burne opened the paper

and read: '"*He who is not with me is against me*, as that gentleman said who was notoriously capable of only coarse distinctions and puerile generalities".'

'What of it?' Ferrenby began to look alarmed. 'Oliver Cromwell said it, didn't he? or was it Washington, or one of the saints? Good Lord, I've forgotten.'

Burne roared with laughter.

'Oh, Jesse, oh, good, kind Jesse.'

'Who said it, for Pete's sake?'

'Well,' said Burne, recovering his voice, 'St. Matthew attributes it to Christ.'

'My God!' cried Jesse, and collapsed backward into the waste-basket.

Amory Writes a Poem

The weeks tore by. Amory wandered occasionally to New York on the chance of finding a new shining green auto-bus, that its stick-of-candy glamour might penetrate his disposition. One day he ventured into a stock-company revival of a play whose name was faintly familiar. The curtain rose – he watched casually as a girl entered. A few phrases rang in his ear and touched a faint chord of memory. Where –? When –?

Then he seemed to hear a voice whispering beside him, a very soft, vibrant voice: 'Oh, I'm such a poor little fool; *do* tell me when I do wrong.'

The solution came in a flash and he had a quick, glad memory of Isabelle.

He found a blank space on his programme, and began to scribble rapidly:

'Here in the figured dark I watch once more,
  There, with the curtain, roll the years away;
  Two years of years – there was an idle day
Of ours, when happy endings didn't bore
Our unfermented souls; I could adore
  Your eager face beside me, wide-eyed, gay,
  Smiling a repertoire while the poor play

Reached me as a faint ripple reaches shore.
Yawning and wondering an evening through,
    I watch alone . . . and chatterings, of course,
        Spoil the one scene which, somehow, *did* have charms;
You wept a bit, and I grew sad for you
    Right here! Where Mr. X defends divorce
    And What's-Her-Name falls fainting in his arms.'

Still Calm

'Ghosts are such dumb things,' said Alec, 'they're slow-witted. I can always outguess a ghost.'

'How?' asked Tom.

'Well, it depends where. Take a bedroom, for example. If you use *any* discretion a ghost can never get you in a bedroom.'

'Go on, s'pose you think there's maybe a ghost in your bedroom – what measures do you take on getting home at night?' demanded Amory, interested.

'Take a stick,' answered Alec, with ponderous reverence, 'one about the length of a broom-handle. Now, the first thing to do is to get the room *cleared* – to do this you rush with your eyes closed into your study and turn on the lights – next, approaching the closet, carefully run the stick in the door three or four times. Then, if nothing happens, you can look in. *Always, always* run the stick in viciously first – *never* look first!'

'Of course, that's the ancient Celtic school,' said Tom gravely.

'Yes – but they usually pray first. Anyway, you use this method to clear the closets and also for behind all doors——'

'And the bed,' Amory suggested.

'Oh, Amory, no!' cried Alec in horror. 'That isn't the way – the bed requires different tactics – let the bed alone, as you value your reason – if there is a ghost in the room and that's only about a third of the time, it is *almost always* under the bed.'

'Well——' Amory began.

Alec waved him into silence.

'Of *course* you never look. You stand in the middle of the floor and before he knows what you're going to do make a sudden leap for the bed – never walk near the bed; to a ghost your ankle is your most vulnerable part – once in bed, you're safe; he may lie around under the bed all night, but you're safe as daylight. If you still have doubts pull the blanket over your head.'

'All that's very interesting,' said Tom.

'Isn't it?' Alec beamed proudly. 'All my own, too – the Sir Oliver Lodge of the new world.'

Amory was enjoying college immensely again. The sense of going forward in a direct, determined line had come back; youth was stirring and shaking out a few new feathers. He had even stored enough surplus energy to sally into a new pose.

'What's the idea of all this "distracted" stuff, Amory?' asked Alec one day, and then as Amory pretended to be cramped over his book in a daze: 'Oh, don't try to act Burne, the mystic, to me.'

Amory looked up innocently.

'What?'

'What?' mimicked Alec. 'Are you trying to read yourself into a rhapsody with – let's see the book.'

He snatched it; regarded it derisively.

'Well?' said Amory a little stiffly.

' "The Life of St. Teresa",' read Alec aloud. 'Oh, my gosh!'

'Say, Alec.'

'What?'

'Does it bother you?'

'Does what bother me?'

'My acting dazed and all that?'

'Why, no – of course it doesn't *bother* me.'

'Well, then, don't spoil it. If I enjoy going around telling people guilelessly that I think I'm a genius, let me do it.'

'You're getting a reputation for being eccentric,' said Alec, laughing, 'if that's what you mean.'

Amory finally prevailed, and Alec agreed to accept his face value in the presence of others if he was allowed rest periods when they were alone; so Amory 'ran it out' at a great rate, bringing the most eccentric characters to dinner, wild-eyed grad students, preceptors with strange theories of God and government, to the cynical amazement of the supercilious Cottage Club.

As February became slashed by sun and moved cheerfully into March, Amory went several times to spend week-ends with Monsignor; once he took Burne, with great success, for he took equal pride and delight in displaying them to each other. Monsignor took him several times to see Thornton Hancock, and once or twice to the house of a Mrs. Lawrence, a type of Rome-haunting American whom Amory liked immediately.

Then one day came a letter from Monsignor, which appended an interesting P. S.:

'Do you know,' it ran, 'that your third cousin, Clara Page, widowed six months and very poor, is living in Philadelphia? I don't think you've ever met her, but I wish, as a favour to me, you'd go to see her. To my mind, she's rather a remarkable woman, and just about your age.'

Amory sighed and decided to go, as a favour . . . .

Clara

She was immemorial. . . . Amory wasn't good enough for Clara, Clara of ripply golden hair, but then no man was. Her goodness was above the proxy morals of the husband-seeker, apart from the dull literature of female virtue.

Sorrow lay lightly around her, and when Amory found her in Philadelphia he thought her steely blue eyes held only happiness; a latent strength, a realism, was brought to its fullest development by the facts that she was compelled to face. She was alone in the world, with two small children little money, and, worst of all, a host of friends. He saw her that winter in Philadelphia entertaining a houseful of men for an evening, when he knew she had not a servant in the house except the little coloured girl guarding the babies over-head. He saw one of the greatest libertines in that city, a man who was habitually drunk and notorious at home and abroad, sitting opposite her for an evening, discussing *girls' boarding-schools* with a sort of innocent excitement. What a twist Clara had to her mind! She could make fascinating and almost brilliant conversation out of the thinnest air that ever floated through a drawing-room.

The idea that the girl was poverty-stricken had appealed to Amory's sense of situation. He arrived in Philadelphia expecting to be told that 921 Ark Street was in a miserable lane of hovels. He was even disappointed when it proved to be nothing of the sort. It was an old house that had been in her husband's family for years. An elderly aunt, who object-ed to having it sold, had put ten years' taxes with a lawyer and pranced off to Honolulu, leaving Clara to struggle with the heating-problem as best she could. So no wild-haired woman with a hungry baby at her breast and a sad Amelia-like look greeted him. Instead, Amory would have thought from his reception that she had not a care in the world.

A calm virility and a dreamy humour, marked contrasts to her level-headedness – into these moods she slipped some-times as a refuge. She could do the most prosy things (though she was wise enough never to stultify herself with such 'household arts' as *knitting* and *embroidery*), yet immed-iately afterwards pick up a book and let her imagination rove as a formless cloud with the wind. Deepest of all in her personality was the golden radiance that she diffused around her. As an open fire in a dark room throws romance and pathos into the quiet faces at its edge, so she cast her lights and shadows around the rooms that held her, until she made of her prosy old uncle a man of quaint and meditative charm, metamorphosed the stray telegraph boy into a Puck-like creature of delightful originality. At first this quality of hers somehow irritated Amory. He considered his own uniqueness sufficient, and it rather embarrassed him when she tried to read new interests into him for the benefit of what other adorers were present. He felt as if a polite but insistent stage-manager were attempting to make him give a new interpretation of a part he had conned for years.

But Clara talking, Clara telling a slender tale of a hatpin and an inebriated man and herself. . . . People tried afterward to repeat her anecdotes but for the life of them they could make them sound like nothing whatever. They gave her a sort of innocent attention and the best smiles many of them had smiled for long; there were few tears in Clara, but people smiled misty-eyed at her.

Very occasionally Amory stayed for little half-hours after the rest of the court had gone, and they would have bread and jam and tea late in the afternoon or 'maple-sugar lunches,' as she called them, at night.

'You *are* remarkable, aren't you!' Amory was becoming trite from where he perched in the centre of the dining-room table one six o'clock.

'Not a bit,' she answered. She was searching out napkins in the sideboard. 'I'm really most humdrum and commonplace. One of those people who have no interest in anything but their children.'

'Tell that to somebody else,' scoffed Amory. 'You know you're perfectly effulgent.' He asked her the one thing that he knew might embarrass her. It was the remark that the first bore made to Adam.

'Tell me about yourself.' And she gave the answer that Adam must have given.

'There's nothing to tell.'

But eventually Adam probably told the bore all the things he thought about at night when the locusts sang in the sandy grass, and he must have remarked patronizingly how *different* he was from Eve, forgetting how different she was from him . . . at any rate, Clara told Amory much about herself that evening. She had had a harried life from sixteen on, and her education had stopped sharply with her leisure. Browsing in her library, Amory found a tattered grey book out of which fell a yellow sheet that he impudently opened. It was a poem that she had written at school about a grey

convent wall on a grey day, and a girl with her cloak blown
by the wind sitting atop of it and thinking about the many-
coloured world. As a rule such sentiment bored him, but this
was done with so much simplicity and atmosphere, that it
brought a picture of Clara to his mind, of Clara on such a
cool, grey day with her keen blue eyes staring out, trying to
see her tragedies come marching over the gardens outside.
He envied that poem. How he would have loved to have
come along and seen her on the wall and talked nonsense of
romance to her, perched above him in the air. He began to
be frightfully jealous of everything about Clara: of her past,
of her babies, of the men and women who flocked to drink
deep of her cool kindness and rest their tired minds as at an
absorbing play.

'*Nobody* seems to bore you,' he objected.

'About half the world do,' she admitted, 'but I think
that's a pretty good average, don't you?' and she turned to
find something in Browning that bore on the subject. She
was the only person he ever met who could look up passages
and quotations to show him in the middle of the conversation, and yet not be irritating to distraction. She did it constantly, with such a serious enthusiasm that he grew fond of
watching her golden hair bent over a book, brow wrinkled
ever so little at hunting her sentence.

Through early March he took to going to Philadelphia for
week-ends. Almost always there was some one else there and
she seemed not anxious to see him alone, for many occasions
presented themselves when a word from her would have
given him another delicious half-hour of adoration. But he
fell gradually in love and began to speculate wildly on
marriage. Though this design flowed through his brain even
to his lips, still he knew afterwards that the desire had not
been deeply rooted. Once he dreamt that it had come true
and woke up in a cold panic, for in his dream she had been
a silly, flaxen Clara, with the gold gone out of her hair and
platitudes falling insipidly from her changeling tongue. But
she was the first fine woman he ever knew and one of the
few good people who ever interested him. She made her

goodness such an asset. Amory had decided that most good people either dragged theirs after them as a liability, or else distorted it to artificial geniality, and of course there were the ever-present prig and Pharisee – (but Amory never included *them* as being among the saved).

St. Cecilia

'Over her grey and velvet dress,
Under her molten, beaten hair,
Colour of rose in mock distress
Flushes and fades and makes her fair;
Fills the air from her to him
With light and languor and little sighs,
Just so subtly he scarcely knows . . .
Laughing lightning, colour of rose.'

'Do you like me?'

'Of course I do,' said Clara seriously.

'Why?'

'Well, we have some qualities in common. Things that are spontaneous in each of us – or were originally.'

'You're implying that I haven't used myself very well?'

Clara hesitated.

'Well, I can't judge. A man, of course, has to go through a lot more, and I've been sheltered.'

'Oh, don't stall, please, Clara,' Amory interrupted; 'but do talk about me a little, won't you?'

'Surely, I'd adore to.' She didn't smile.

'That's sweet of you. First answer some questions. Am I painfully conceited?'

'Well – no, you have tremendous vanity, but it'll amuse the people who notice its preponderance.'

'I see.'

'You're really humble at heart. You sink to the third hell of depression when you think you've been slighted. In fact, you haven't much self-respect.'

'Centre of target twice, Clara. How do you do it? You never let me say a word.'

'Of course not – I can never judge a man while he's talking. But I'm not through; the reason you have so little real self-confidence, even though you gravely announce to the occasional philistine that you think you're a genius, is that you've attributed all sorts of atrocious faults to yourself and are trying to live up to them. For instance, you're always saying that you are a slave to high-balls.'

'But I am, potentially.'

'And you say you're a weak character, that you've no will.'

'Not a bit of will – I'm a slave to my emotions, to my likes, to my hatred of boredom, to most of my desires——'

'You are not!' She brought one little fist down on to the other. 'You're a slave, a bound helpless slave to one thing in the world, your imagination.'

'You certainly interest me. If this isn't boring you, go on.'

'I notice that when you want to stay over an extra day from college you go about it in a sure way. You never decide at first while the merits of going or staying are fairly clear in your mind. You let your imagination shinny on the side of your desires for a few hours, and then you decide. Naturally your imagination, after a little freedom, thinks up a million reasons why you should stay, so your decision when it comes isn't true. It's biassed.'

'Yes,' objected Amory, 'but isn't it lack of will-power to let my imagination shinny on the wrong side?'

'My dear boy, there's your big mistake. This has nothing to do with will-power; that's a crazy, useless word, anyway; you lack judgment – the judgment to decide at once when you know your imagination will play you false, given half a chance.'

'Well, I'll be darned!' exclaimed Amory in surprise, 'that's the last thing I expected.'

Clara didn't gloat. She changed the subject immediately. But she had started him thinking and he believed she was partly right. He felt like a factory-owner who after accusing a clerk of dishonesty finds that his own son, in the office, is changing the books once a week. His poor, mistreated will that he had been holding up to the scorn of himself and his friends, stood before him innocent, and his judgment walked off to prison with the unconfinable imp, imagination, dancing in mocking glee beside him. Clara's was the only advice he ever asked without dictating the answer himself – except, perhaps, in his talks with Monsignor Darcy.

How he loved to do any sort of thing with Clara! Shopping with her was a rare, epicurean dream. In every store where she had ever traded she was whispered about as the beautiful Mrs. Page.

'I'll bet she won't stay single long.'

'Well, don't scream it out. She ain't lookin' for no advice.'

'*Ain't* she beautiful!'

(*Enter a floor-walker – silence till he moves forward, smirking.*)

'Society person, ain't she?'

'Yeah, but poor now, I guess; so they say.'

'Gee! girls, *ain't* she some kid!'

And Clara beamed on all alike. Amory believed that tradespeople gave her discounts, sometimes to her knowledge and sometimes without it. He knew she dressed very well, had always the best of everything in the house, and was inevitably waited upon by the head floor-walker at the very least.

Sometimes they would go to church together on Sunday and he would walk beside her and revel in her cheeks moist from the soft water in the new air. She was very devout, always had been, and God knows what heights she attained and what strength she drew down to herself when she knelt and bent her golden hair into the stained-glass light.

'St. Cecilia,' he cried aloud one day, quite involuntarily, and the people turned and peered, and the priest paused in his sermon and Clara and Amory turned to fiery red.

That was the last Sunday they had, for he spoiled it all that night. He couldn't help it.

They were walking through the March twilight where it was as warm as June, and the joy of youth filled his soul so that he felt he must speak.

'I think,' he said and his voice trembled, 'that if I lost faith in you I'd lose faith in God.'

She looked at him with such a startled face that he asked her the matter.

'Nothing,' she said slowly, 'only this: five men have said that to me before, and it frightens me.'

'Oh, Clara, is that your fate!'

She did not answer.

'I suppose love to you is –' he began.

She turned like a flash.

'I have never been in love.'

They walked along, and he realized slowly how much she had told him . . . never in love. . . . She seemed suddenly a daughter of light alone. His entity dropped out of her plane and he longed only to touch her dress with almost the realization that Joseph must have had of Mary's eternal significance. But quite mechanically he heard himself saying:

'And I love you – any latent greatness that I've got is . . . oh, I can't talk, but Clara, if I come back in two years in a position to marry you——'

She shook her head.

'No,' she said; 'I'd never marry again. I've got my two children and I want myself for them. I like you – I like all clever men, you more than any – but you know me well enough to know that I'd never marry a clever man –' She broke off suddenly.

'Amory.'

'What?'

'You're not in love with me. You never wanted to marry me, did you?'

'It was the twilight,' he said wonderingly. 'I didn't feel as though I were speaking aloud. But I love you – or adore you – or worship you——'

'There you go – running through your catalogue of emotions in five seconds.'

He smiled unwillingly.

'Don't make me out such a light-weight, Clara; you *are* depressing sometimes.'

'You're not a light-weight, of all things,' she said intently, taking his arm and opening wide her eyes – he could see

their kindliness in the fading dusk. 'A light-weight is an
eternal nay.'

'There's so much spring in the air – there's so much lazy
sweetness in your heart.'

She dropped his arm.

'You're all fine now, and I feel glorious. Give me a cigarette. You've never seen me smoke, have you ? Well, I do,
about once a month.'

And then that wonderful girl and Amory raced to the
corner like two mad children gone wild with pale-blue
twilight.

'I'm going to the country for to-morrow,' she announced,
as she stood panting, safe beyond the flare of the corner
lamp-post. 'These days are too magnificent to miss, though
perhaps I feel them more in the city.'

'Oh, Clara!' Amory said; 'what a devil you could have
been if the Lord had just bent your soul a little the other
way!'

'Maybe,' she answered; 'but I think not. I'm never really
wild and never have been. That little outburst was pure
spring.'

'And you are, too,' said he.

They were walking along now.

'No – you're wrong again, how can a person of your own
self-reputed brains be so constantly wrong about me ? I'm
the opposite of everything spring ever stood for. It's unfortunate, if I happen to look like what pleased some soppy
old Greek sculptor, but I assure you that if it weren't for my
face I'd be a quiet nun in the convent without' – then she
broke into a run and her raised voice floated back to him as
he followed – 'my precious babies, which I must go back
and see.'

She was the only girl he ever knew with whom he could
understand how another man might be preferred. Often
Amory met wives whom he had known as débutantes, and
looking intently at them imagined that he found something
in their faces which said:

'Oh, if I could only have gotten *you !*' Oh, the enormous conceit of the man!

But that night seemed a night of stars and singing and Clara's bright soul still gleamed on the ways they had trod.

'*Golden, golden is the air –*' he chanted to the little pools of water. . . . '*Golden is the air, golden notes from golden mandolins, golden frets of golden violins, fair, oh, wearily fair . . . Skeins from braided basket, mortals may not hold; oh, what young extravagant God, who would know or ask it ? . . . who could give such gold . . .*'

Amory is Resentful

Slowly and inevitably, yet with a sudden surge at the last, while Amory talked and dreamed, war rolled swiftly up the beach and washed the sands where Princeton played. Every night the gymnasium echoed as platoon after platoon swept over the floor and shuffled out the basket-ball markings. When Amory went to Washington the next week-end he caught some of the spirit of crisis which changed to repulsion in the Pullman car coming back, for the berths across from him were occupied by stinking aliens – Greeks, he guessed, or Russians. He thought how much easier patriotism had been to a homogeneous race, how much easier it would have been to fight as the Colonies fought, or as the Confederacy fought. And he did no sleeping that night, but listened to the aliens guffaw and snore while they filled the car with the heavy scent of latest America.

In Princeton every one bantered in public and told themselves privately that their deaths at least would be heroic. The literary students read Rupert Brooke passionately; the lounge-lizards worried over whether the government would permit the English-cut uniform for officers; a few of the hopelessly lazy wrote to the obscure branches of the War Department, seeking an easy commission and a soft berth.

Then, after a week, Amory saw Burne and knew at once that argument would be futile – Burne had come out as a pacifist. The socialist magazines, a great smattering of

Tolstoi, and his own intense longing for a cause that would bring out whatever strength lay in him, had finally decided him to preach peace as a subjective ideal.

'When the German army entered Belgium,' he began, 'if the inhabitants had gone peaceably about their business, the German army would have been disorganized in——'

'I know,' Amory interrupted, 'I've heard it all. But I'm not going to talk propaganda with you. There's a chance that you're right – but even so we're hundreds of years before the time when non-resistance can touch us as a reality.'

'But, Amory, listen——'

'Burne, we'd just argue——'

'Very well.'

'Just one thing – I don't ask you to think of your family or friends, because I know they don't count a picayune with you beside your sense of duty – but, Burne, how do you know that the magazines you read and the societies you join and these idealists you meet aren't just plain *German?*'

'Some of them are, of course.'

'How do you know they aren't *all* pro-German – just a lot of weak ones – with German-Jewish names.'

'That's the chance, of course,' he said slowly. 'How much or how little I'm taking this stand because of propaganda I've heard, I don't know; naturally I think that it's my most innermost conviction – it seems a path spread before me just now.'

Amory's heart sank.

'But think of the cheapness of it – no one's really going to martyr you for being a pacifist – it's just going to throw you in with the worst——'

'I doubt it,' he interrupted.

'Well, it all smells of Bohemian New York to me.'

'I know what you mean, and that's why I'm not sure I'll agitate.'

'You're one man, Burne – going to talk to people who won't listen – with all God's given you.'

'That's what Stephen must have thought many years ago. But he preached his sermon and they killed him. He probably thought as he was dying what a waste it all was. But you see, I've always felt that Stephen's death was the thing that occurred to Paul on the road to Damascus, and sent him to preach the word of Christ all over the world.'

'Go on.'

'That's all – this is my particular duty. Even if right now I'm just a pawn – just sacrificed. God! Amory – you don't think *I* like the Germans!'

'Well, I can't say anything else – I get to the end of all the logic about non-resistance, and there, like an excluded middle, stands the huge spectre of man as he is and always will be. And this spectre stands right beside the one logical necessity of Tolstoi's, and the other logical necessity of Nietzsche's—' Amory broke off suddenly. 'When are you going?'

'I'm going next week.'

'I'll see you, of course.'

As he walked away it seemed to Amory that the look in his face bore a great resemblance to that in Kerry's when he had said good-bye under Blair Arch two years before. Amory wondered unhappily why he could never go into anything with the primal honesty of those two.

'Burne's a fanatic,' he said to Tom, 'and he's dead wrong and, I'm inclined to think, just an unconscious pawn in the hands of anarchistic publishers and German-paid rag weavers – but he haunts me – just leaving everything worth while——'

Burne left in a quietly dramatic manner a week later. He sold all his possessions and came down to the room to say goodbye, with a battered old bicycle, on which he intended to ride to his home in Pennsylvania.

'Peter the Hermit bidding farewell to Cardinal Richelieu,' suggested Alec, who was lounging in the window-seat as Burne and Amory shook hands.

But Amory was not in a mood for that, and as he saw Burne's long legs propel his ridiculous bicycle out of sight beyond Alexander Hall, he knew he was going to have a bad week. Not that he doubted the war – Germany stood for everything repugnant to him; for materialism and the direction of tremendous licentious force; it was just that Burne's face stayed in his memory and he was sick of the hysteria he was beginning to hear.

'What on earth is the use of suddenly running down Goethe,' he declared to Alex and Tom. 'Why write books to prove he started the war – or that that stupid, overestimated Schiller is a demon in disguise?'

'Have you ever read anything of theirs?' asked Tom shrewdly.

'No,' Amory admitted.

'Neither have I,' he said laughing.

'People will shout,' said Alec quietly, 'but Goethe's on his same old shelf in the library – to bore any one that wants to read him!'

Amory subsided, and the subject dropped.

'What are you going to do, Amory?'

'Infantry or aviation, I can't make up my mind – I hate mechanics, but then of course aviation's the thing for me——'

'I feel as Amory does,' said Tom. 'Infantry or aviation – aviation sounds like the romantic side of the war, of course – like cavalry used to be, you know; but like Amory I don't know a horse-power from a piston-rod.'

Somehow Amory's dissatisfaction with his lack of enthusiasm culminated in an attempt to put the blame for the whole war on the ancestors of his generation . . . all the people who cheered for Germany in 1870. . . . All the materialists rampant, all the idolizers of German science and efficiency. So he sat one day in an English lecture and heard 'Locksley Hall' quoted and fell into a brown study with contempt for Tennyson and all he stood for – for he took him as a representative of the Victorians.

'*Victorians, Victorians, who never learned to weep*
Who sowed the bitter harvest that your children go to reap——'

scribbled Amory in his note-book. The lecturer was saying something about Tennyson's solidity and fifty heads were bent to take notes. Amory turned over to a fresh page and began scrawling again.

'They shuddered when they found what Mr. Darwin was about,
They shuddered when the waltz came in and Newman hurried
out——'

But the waltz came in much earlier; he crossed that out.

'And entitled *A Song in the Time of Order*,' came the professor's voice, droning far away. 'Time of Order' – Good Lord! Everything crammed in the box and the Victorians sitting on the lid smiling serenely. . . . With Browning in his Italian villa crying bravely: 'All's for the best.' Amory scribbled again.

'You knelt up in the temple and he bent to hear you pray,
You thanked him for your "glorious gains" – reproached him
for "Cathay." '

Why could he never get more than a couplet at a time?
Now he needed something to rhyme with:

'You would keep Him straight with science, tho He had gone
wrong before . . .'

Well, anyway. . . .

'You met your children in your home – "I've fixed it up!" you
cried,
Took your fifty years of Europe, and then virtuously – died.'

'That was to a great extent Tennyson's idea,' came the lecturer's voice. 'Swinburne's *Song in the Time of Order* might well have been Tennyson's title. He idealized order against chaos, against waste.'

At last Amory had it. He turned over another page and scrawled vigorously for the twenty minutes that was left of the hour. Then he walked up to the desk and deposited a page torn out of his note-book.

'Here's a poem to the Victorians, sir,' he said coldly.

The professor picked it up curiously while Amory backed rapidly through the door:

Here is what he had written:

> '*Songs in the time of order*
> *You left for us to sing,*
> *Proofs with excluded middles,*
> *Answers to life in rhyme,*
>
> *Keys of the prison warder*
> *And ancient bells to ring,*
> *Time was the end of riddles,*
> *We were the end of time . . .*
>
> *Here were domestic oceans*
> *And a sky that we might reach,*
> *Guns and a guarded border,*
> *Gantlets – but not to fling,*
>
> *Thousands of old emotions*
> *And a platitude for each,*
> *Songs in the time of order—*
> *And tongues, that we might sing.*'

The End of Many Things

Early April slipped by in a haze – a haze of long evenings on the club veranda with the graphophone playing 'Poor Butterfly' inside . . . for 'Poor Butterfly' had been the song of that last year. The war seemed scarcely to touch them and it might have been one of the senior springs of the past, except for the drilling every other afternoon, yet Amory realized poignantly that this was the last spring under the old régime.

'This is the great protest against the superman,' said Amory.

'I suppose so,' Alec agreed.

'He's absolutely irreconcilable with any Utopia. As long as he occurs, there's trouble and all the latent evil that makes a crowd list and sway when he talks.'

'And of course all that he is is a gifted man without a moral sense.'

'That's all. I think the worst thing to contemplate is this – it's all happened before, how soon will it happen again? Fifty years after Waterloo Napoleon was as much a hero to English school children as Wellington. How do we know our grandchildren won't idolize Von Hindenburg the same way?'

'What brings it about?'

'Time, damn it, and the historian. If we could only learn to look on evil *as* evil, whether it's clothed in filth or monotony or magnificence.'

'God! Haven't we raked the universe over the coals for four years?'

Then the night came that was to be the last. Tom and Amory, bound in the morning for different training-camps, paced the shadowy walks as usual and seemed still to see around them the faces of the men they knew.

'The grass is full of ghosts to-night.'

'The whole campus is alive with them.'

They paused by Little and watched the moon rise, to make silver of the slate roof of Dodd and blue the rustling trees.

'You know,' whispered Tom, 'what we feel now is the sense of all the gorgeous youth that has rioted through here in two hundred years.'

A last burst of singing flooded up from Blair Arch – broken voices for some long parting.

'And what we leave here is more than this class; it's the whole heritage of youth. We're just one generation – we're breaking all the links that seemed to bind us here to top-booted and high-stocked generations. We've walked arm and arm with Burr and Light-Horse Harry Lee through half these deep-blue nights.'

'That's what they are,' Tom tangented off, 'deep blue – a bit of colour would spoil them, make them exotic. Spires, against a sky that's a promise of dawn, and blue light on the slate roofs – it hurts . . . rather——'

'Good-bye, Aaron Burr,' Amory called toward deserted Nassau Hall, 'you and I knew strange corners of life.'

His voice echoed in the stillness.

'The torches are out,' whispered Tom. 'Ah, Messalina, the long shadows are building minarets on the stadium——'

For an instant the voices of freshmen year surged around them and then they looked at each other with faint tears in their eyes.

'Damn!'

'Damn!'

The last light fades and drifts across the land – the low, long land, the sunny land of spires; the ghosts of evening tune again their lyres and wander singing in a plaintive band down the long corridors of trees; pale fires echo the night from tower top to tower: Oh, sleep that dreams, and dream that never tires, press from the petals of the lotus flower something of this to keep, the essence of an hour.

No more to wait the twilight of the moon in this sequestered vale of star and spire, for one eternal morning of desire passes to time and earthy afternoon. Here, Heraclitus, did you find in fire and shifting things the prophecy you hurled down the dead years; this midnight my desire will see, shadowed among the embers, furled in flame, the splendour and the sadness of the world.

INTERLUDE

May, 1917 – February, 1919

A letter dated January, 1918, written by Monsignor Darcy to Amory, who is a second lieutenant in the 171st Infantry, Port of Embarkation, Camp Mills, Long Island.

MY DEAR BOY:

All you need tell me of yourself is that you still are; for the rest I merely search back in a restive memory, a thermometer that records only fevers, and match you with what I was at your age. But men will chatter and you and I will still shout our futilities to each other across the stage until the last silly curtain falls *plump!* upon our bobbing heads. But you are starting the spluttering magic-lantern show of life with much the same array of slides as I had, so I need to write you if only to shriek the colossal stupidity of *people*. . . .

This is the end of one thing: for better or worse you will never again be quite the Amory Blaine that I knew, never again will we meet as we have met, because your generation is growing hard, much harder than mine ever grew, nourished as they were on the stuff of the nineties.

Amory, lately I reread Æschylus and there in the divine irony of the 'Agamemnon' I find the only answer to this bitter age – all the world tumbled about our ears, and the closest parallel ages back in that hopeless resignation. There are times when I think of the men out there as Roman legionaries, miles from their corrupt city, stemming back the hordes . . . hordes a little more menacing, after all, than the corrupt city . . . another blind blow at the race, furies that we passed with ovations years ago, over whose corpses we bleated triumphantly all through the Victorian era. . . .

And afterwards an out-and-out materialistic world – and the Catholic Church. I wonder where you'll fit in. Of one thing I'm sure – Celtic you'll live and Celtic you'll die; so if you don't use heaven as a continual referendum for your ideas you'll find earth a continual recall to your ambitions.

Amory, I've discovered suddenly that I'm an old man. Like all old men, I've had dreams sometimes and I'm going to tell you of them. I've enjoyed imagining that you were my son, that perhaps when I was young I went into a state of coma and begat you, and when I came to, had no recollection of it . . . it's the paternal instinct, Amory – celibacy goes deeper than the flesh. . . .

Sometimes I think that the explanation of our deep resemblance is some common ancestor, and I find that the only blood that the Darcy's and the O'Haras have in common is that of the O'Donahues . . . Stephen was his name, I think. . . .

When the lightning strikes one of us it strikes both: you had hardly arrived at the port of embarkation when I got my papers to start for Rome, and I am waiting every moment to be told where to take ship. Even before you get this letter I shall be on the ocean; then will come your turn. You went to war as a gentleman should, just as you went to school and college, because it was the thing to do. It's better to leave the blustering and tremulo-heroism to the middle classes; they do it so much better.

Do you remember that week-end last March when you brought Burne Holiday from Princeton to see me? What a magnificent boy he is! It gave me a frightful shock afterwards when you wrote that he thought me splendid; how could he be so deceived? Splendid is the one thing that neither you nor I are. We are many other things – we're extraordinary, we're clever, we could be said, I suppose, to be brilliant. We can attract people, we can make atmosphere, we can almost lose our Celtic souls in Celtic subtleties, we can almost always have our own way; but splendid – rather not!

I am going to Rome with a wonderful dossier and letters of introduction that cover every capital in Europe, and there will be 'no small stir' when I get there. How I wish you were with me! This sounds like a rather cynical paragraph, not at all the sort of thing that a middle-aged clergyman should write to a youth about to depart for the war; the only excuse is that the middle-aged clergyman is talking to himself. There are deep things in us and you know what they are as well as I do. We have great faith, though yours at present is uncrystallized; we have a terrible honesty that all our sophistry cannot destroy and, above all, a childlike simplicity that keeps us from ever being really malicious.

I have written a keen for you which follows. I am sorry your cheeks are not up to the description I have written of them, but you *will* smoke and read all night——

At any rate here it is:

A Lament for a Foster Son, and He going to the War Against the King of Foreign.

'Ochone
He is gone from me the son of my mind
   And he in his golden youth like Angus Oge
Angus of the bright birds
   And his mind strong and subtle like the mind of Cuchulin
     on Muirtheme.

Awirra sthrue
His brow is as white as the milk of the cows of Maeve
   And his cheeks like the cherries of the tree
And it bending down to Mary and she feeding the Son of
   God.

Aveelia Vrone
His hair is like the golden collar of the Kings at Tara
   And his eyes like the four grey seas of Erin.
And they swept with the mists of rain.

Mavrone go Gudyo
He to be in the joyful and red battle
   Amongst the chieftans and they doing great deeds of valour
His life to go from him
   It is the chords of my own soul would be loosed.

A Vich Deelish
My heart is in the heart of my son
   And my life is in his life surely
A man can be twice young
   In the life of his sons only.

Jia du Vaha Alanav
May the Son of God be above him and beneath him, before
   him and behind him
   May the King of the elements cast a mist over the eyes of
     the King of Foreign,
May the Queen of the Graces lead him by the hand the way
   he can go through the midst of his enemies and they not
   seeing him
   May Patrick of the Gael and Collumb of the Churches
     and the five thousand Saints of Erin be better than a
     shield to him

And he go into the fight.
   Och Ochone.'

Amory – Amory – I feel, somehow, that this is all; one or both of us is not going to last out this war. . . . I've been trying to tell you how much this reincarnation of myself in you has meant in the last few years . . . curiously alike we are . . . curiously unlike.

Good-bye, dear boy, and God be with you.

THAYER DARCY.

Embarking at Night

Amory moved forward on the deck until he found a stool under an electric light. He searched in his pocket for note-book and pencil and then began to write, slowly, laboriously:

> 'We leave to-night . . .
>   Silent, we filled the still, deserted street,
>   A column of dim grey,
>   And ghosts rose startled at the muffled beat
>   Along the moonless way;
>   The shadowy shipyards echoed to the feet
>   That turned from night and day.
>
>   And so we linger on the windless decks,
>   See on the spectre shore
>   Shades of a thousand days, poor grey-ribbed wrecks . . .
>   Oh, shall we then deplore
>   Those futile years !
>   See how the sea is white !
>   The clouds have broken and the heavens burn
>   To hollow highways, paved with gravelled light
>   The churning of the waves about the stern
>   Rises to one voluminous nocturne,
>   . . . We leave to-night.'

A letter from Amory, headed 'Brest, March 11th, 1919,' to Lieutenant T. P. D'Invilliers, Camp Gordon, Ga.

DEAR BAUDELAIRE:
   We meet in Manhattan on the 30th of this very mo.; we

then proceed to take a very sporty apartment, you and I and Alec, who is at me elbow as I write. I don't know what I'm going to do but I have a vague dream of going into politics. Why is it that the pick of the young Englishmen from Oxford and Cambridge go into politics and in the U.S.A. we leave it to the muckers ? – raised in the ward, educated in the assembly and sent to Congress, fat-paunched bundles of corruption, devoid of 'both ideas and ideals' as the debaters used to say. Even forty years ago we had good men in politics, but *we*, we are brought up to pile up a million and 'show what we are made of.' Sometimes I wish I'd been an Englishman; American life is so damned dumb and stupid and healthy.

Since poor Beatrice died I'll probably have a little money, but very darn little. I can forgive mother almost everything except the fact that in a sudden burst of religiosity toward the end, she left half of what remained to be spent in stained-glass windows and seminary endowments. Mr. Barton, my lawyer, writes me that my thousands are mostly in street railways and that the said Street R.R.s are losing money because of the five-cent fares. Imagine a salary list that gives $350 a month to a man that can't read and write! – yet I believe in it, even though I've seen what was once a sizeable fortune melt away between speculation, extravagance, the democratic administration, and the income tax – modern, that's me all over, Mabel.

At any rate we'll have really knock-out rooms – you can get a job on some fashion magazine, and Alec can go into the Zinc Company or whatever it is that his people own – he's looking over my shoulder and he says it's a brass company, but I don't think it matters much, do you ? There's probably as much corruption in zinc-made money as brass-made money. As for the well-known Amory, he would write immortal literature if he were sure enough about anything to risk telling any one else about it. There is no more dangerous gift to posterity than a few cleverly turned platitudes.

Tom, why don't you become a Catholic ? Of course to be

a good one you'd have to give up those violent intrigues you used to tell me about, but you'd write better poetry if you were linked up to tall golden candlesticks and long, even chants, and even if the American priests are rather bourgeois, as Beatrice used to say, still you need only go to the sporty churches, and I'll introduce you to Monsignor Darcy who really is a wonder.

Kerry's death was a blow, so was Jesse's to a certain extent. And I have a great curiosity to know what queer corner of the world has swallowed Burne. Do you suppose he's in prison under some false name? I confess that the war instead of making me orthodox, which is the correct reaction, has made me a passionate agnostic. The Catholic Church has had its wings clipped so often lately that its part was timidly negligible, and they haven't any good writers any more. I'm sick of Chesterton.

I've only discovered one soldier who passed through the much-advertised spiritual crisis, like this fellow, Donald Hankey, and the one I knew was already studying for the ministry, so he was ripe for it. I honestly think that's all pretty much rot, though it seemed to give sentimental comfort to those at home; and may make fathers and mothers appreciate their children. This crisis-inspired religion is rather valueless and fleeting at best. I think four men have discovered Paris to one that discovered God.

But *us* – you and me and Alec – oh, we'll get a Jap butler and dress for dinner and have wine on the table and lead a contemplative, emotionless life until we decide to use machine-guns with the property owners – or throw bombs with the Bolshevik. God! Tom, I hope something happens. I'm restless as the devil and have a horror of getting fat or falling in love and growing domestic.

The place at Lake Geneva is now for rent but when I land I'm going West to see Mr. Barton and get some details. Write me care of the Blackstone, Chicago.

S'ever, dear Boswell,

SAMUEL JOHNSON.

BOOK TWO

THE EDUCATION OF A PERSONAGE

I. THE DÉBUTANTE

The time is February. The place is a large, dainty bedroom in the Connage house on Sixty-eighth Street, New York. A girl's room: pink walls and curtains and a pink bedspread on a cream-coloured bed. Pink and cream are the motifs of the room, but the only article of furniture in full view is a luxurious dressing-table with a glass top and a three-sided mirror. On the walls there is an expensive print of 'Cherry Ripe,' a few polite dogs by Landseer, and the 'King of the Black Isles,' by Max-field Parrish.

Great disorder consisting of the following items: (1) seven or eight empty cardboard boxes, with tissue-paper tongues hanging panting from their mouths; (2) an assortment of street dresses mingled with their sisters of the evening, all upon the table, all evidently new; (3) a roll of tulle, which has lost its dignity and wound itself tortuously around everything in sight, and (4) upon the two small chairs, a collection of lingerie that beggars description. One would enjoy seeing the bill called forth by the finery displayed and one is possessed by a desire to see the princess for whose benefit – Look! There's some one! Disappointment! This is only a maid hunting for something – she lifts a heap from a chair – Not there; another heap, the dressing-table, the chiffonier drawers. She brings to light several beautiful chemises and amazing pyjamas but this does not satisfy her – she goes out.

An indistinguishable mumble from the next room.

163

Now, we are getting warm. This is Alec's mother, Mrs. Connage, ample, dignified, rouged to the dowager point and quite worn out. Her lips move significantly as she looks for IT. Her search is less thorough than the maid's but there is a touch of fury in it, that quite makes up for its sketchiness. She stumbles on the tulle and her 'damn' is quite audible. She retires, empty-handed.

More chatter outside and a girl's voice, a very spoiled voice, says: 'Of all the stupid people——'

After a pause a third seeker enters, not she of the spoiled voice, but a younger edition. This is Cecelia Connage, sixteen, pretty, shrewd, and constitutionally good-humoured. She is dressed for the evening in a gown the obvious simplicity of which probably bores her. She goes to the nearest pile, selects a small pink garment and holds it up appraisingly.

CECELIA: Pink?

ROSALIND: (*Outside*) Yes!

CECELIA: *Very* snappy?

ROSALIND: Yes!

CECELIA: I've got it!

(*She sees herself in the mirror of the dressing-table and commences to shimmy enthusiastically.*)

ROSALIND: (*Outside*) What are you doing – trying it on?

(CECELIA *ceases and goes out carrying the garment at the right shoulder.*

From the other door, enters ALEC CONNAGE. *He looks around quickly and in a huge voice shouts:* Mama! *There is a chorus of protest from next door and encouraged he starts toward it, but is repelled by another chorus.*)

ALEC: So *that's* where you all are! Amory Blaine is here.

CECELIA: (*Quickly*) Take him downstairs.

ALEC: Oh, he *is* downstairs.

MRS. CONNAGE: Well, you can show him where his room is. Tell him I'm sorry that I can't meet him now.

ALEC: He's heard a lot about you all. I wish you'd hurry. Father's telling him all about the war and he's restless. He's sort of temperamental.

(This last suffices to draw CECELIA *into the room.)*

CECELIA: *(Seating herself high upon lingerie)* How do you mean – temperamental? You used to say that about him in letters.

ALEC: Oh, he writes stuff.

CECELIA: Does he play the piano?

ALEC: Don't think so.

CECELIA: *(Speculatively)* Drink?

ALEC: Yes – nothing queer about him.

CECELIA: Money?

ALEC: Good Lord – ask him, he used to have a lot, and he's got some income now.

*(*MRS. CONNAGE *appears.)*

MRS. CONNAGE: Alec, of course we're glad to have any friend of yours——

ALEC: You certainly ought to meet Amory.

MRS. CONNAGE: Of course, I want to. But I think it's so childish of you to leave a perfectly good home to go and live with two other boys in some impossible apartment. I hope it isn't in order that you can all drink as much as you want. *(She pauses.)* He'll be a little neglected to-night. This is Rosalind's week, you see. When a girl comes out, she needs *all* the attention.

ROSALIND: *(Outside)* Well, then, prove it by coming here and hooking me.

*(*MRS. CONNAGE *goes.)*

ALEC: Rosalind hasn't changed a bit.

CECELIA: *(In a lower tone)* She's awfully spoiled.

ALEC: She'll meet her match to-night.

CECELIA: Who – Mr. Amory Blaine?

*(*ALEC *nods.)*

CECELIA: Well, Rosalind has still to meet the man she can't outdistance. Honestly, Alec, she treats men terribly. She abuses them and cuts them and breaks dates with them and yawns in their faces – and they come back for more.

ALEC: They love it.

CECELIA: They hate it. She's a – she's a sort of vampire, I

think – and she can make girls do what she wants usually –
only she hates girls.

ALEC: Personality runs in our family.

CECELIA: (*Resignedly*) I guess it ran out before it got to me.

ALEC: Does Rosalind behave herself?

CECELIA: Not particularly well. Oh, she's average – smokes
sometimes, drinks punch, frequently kissed – Oh, yes –
common knowledge – one of the effects of the war, you know.

(*Emerges* MRS. CONNAGE.)

MRS. CONNAGE: Rosalind's almost finished so I can go down
and meet your friend.

(ALEC *and his mother go out.*)

ROSALIND: (*Outside*) Oh, mother——

CECELIA: Mother's gone down.

(*And now* ROSALIND *enters.* ROSALIND *is – utterly* ROSALIND.
*She is one of those girls who need never make the slightest
effort to have men fall in love with them. Two types of men
seldom do: dul men are usually afraid of her cleverness and
intellectual menlare usually afraid of her beauty. All others are
hers by natural prerogative.*

If ROSALIND *could be spoiled the process would have been
complete by this time, and as a matter of fact, her disposition is
not all it should be; she wants what she wants when she wants
it and she is prone to make every one around her pretty miserable when she doesn't get it – but in the true sense she is not
spoiled. Her fresh enthusiasm, her will to grow and learn,
her endless faith in the inexhaustibility of romance, her courage
and fundamental honesty – these things are not spoiled.*

*There are long periods when she cordially loathes her whole
family. She is quite unprincipled; her philosophy is carpe diem
for herself and laissez faire for others. She loves shocking
stories: she has that coarse streak that usually goes with
natures that are both fine and big. She wants people to like her,
but if they do not it never worries her or changes her.*

She is by no means a model character.

*The education of all beautiful women is the knowledge of
men.* ROSALIND *had been disappointed in man after man as
individuals, but she had great faith in man as a sex. Women*

she detested. *They represented qualities that she felt and despised in herself – incipient meanness, conceit, cowardice, and petty dishonesty. She once told a roomful of her mother's friends that the only excuse for women was the necessity for a disturbing element among men. She danced exceptionally well, drew cleverly but hastily, and had a startling facility with words, which she used only in love letters.*

But all criticism of ROSALIND *ends in her beauty. There was that shade of glorious yellow hair, the desire to imitate which supports the dye industry. There was the eternal kissable mouth, small, slightly sensual, and utterly disturbing. There were grey eyes and an unimpeachable skin with two spots of vanishing colour. She was slender and athletic, without underdevelopment, and it was a delight to watch her move about a room, walk along a street, swing a golf club, or turn a 'cartwheel.'*

A last qualification – her vivid, instant personality escaped that conscious, theatrical quality that AMORY *had found in* ISABELLE. MONSIGNOR DARCY *would have been quite up a tree whether to call her a personality or a personage. She was perhaps the delicious inexpressible, once-in-a-century blend.*

On the night of her debut she is, for all her strange, stray wisdom, quite like a happy little girl. Her mother's maid has just done her hair, but she has decided impatiently that she can do a better job herself. She is too nervous just now to stay in one place. To that we owe her presence in this littered room. She is going to speak. ISABELLE'S *alto tones had been like a violin, but if you could hear* ROSALIND, *you would say her voice was musical as a waterfall.*

ROSALIND: Honestly, there are only two costumes in the world that I really enjoy being in— (*Combing her hair at the dressing-table.*) One's a hoop skirt with pantaloons; the other's a one-piece bathing-suit. I'm quite charming in both of them.

CECELIA: Glad you're coming out?

ROSALIND: Yes; aren't you?

CECELIA: (*Cynically*) You're glad so you can get married and live on Lond Island with the *fast younger married set.* You want life to be a chain of flirtation with a man for every link.

ROSALIND: *Want* it to be one! You mean I've *found* it one.

CECELIA: Ha!

ROSALIND: Cecelia, darling, you don't know what a trial it is to be – like me. I've got to keep my face like steel in the street to keep men from winking at me. If I laugh hard from a front row in the theatre, the comedian plays to me for the rest of the evening. If I drop my voice, my eyes, my hand-kerchief at a dance, my partner calls me up on the 'phone every day for a week.

CECELIA: It must be an awful strain.

ROSALIND: The unfortunate part is that the only men who interest me at all are the totally ineligible ones. Now – if I were poor I'd go on the stage.

CECELIA: Yes, you might as well get paid for the amount of acting you do.

ROSALIND: Sometimes when I've felt particularly radiant I've thought, why should this be wasted on one man?

CECELIA: Often when you're particularly sulky, I've wondered why it should all be wasted on just one family. (*Getting up*.) I think I'll go down and meet Mr. Amory Blaine. I like temperamental men.

ROSALIND: There aren't any. Men don't know how to be really angry or really happy – and the ones that do, go to pieces.

CECELIA: Well, I'm glad I don't have all your worries. I'm engaged.

ROSALIND: (*With a scornful smile*) Engaged? Why, you little lunatic! If mother heard you talking like that she'd send you off to boarding-school, where you belong.

CECELIA: You won't tell her, though, because I know things I could tell – and you're too selfish!

ROSALIND: (*A little annoyed*) Run along, little girl! Who are you engaged to, the iceman? the man that keeps the candy-store?

CECELIA: Cheap wit – good-bye, darling, I'll see you later.

ROSALIND: Oh, be *sure* and do that – you're *such* a help.

(Exit CECELIA. ROSALIND *finishes her hair and rises, humming. She goes up to the mirror and starts to dance in front of it on the soft carpet. She watches not her feet, but her eyes – never casually but always intently, even when she smiles. The door suddenly opens and then slams behind* AMORY, *very cool and handsome as usual. He melts into instant confusion.)*

HE: Oh, I'm sorry. I thought——

SHE: *(Smiling radiantly)* Oh, you're Amory Blaine, aren't you?

HE: *(Regarding her closely)* And you're Rosalind?

SHE: I'm going to call you Amory – oh, come in – it's all right – mother'll be right in – *(under her breath)* unfortunately.

HE: *(Gazing around)* This is sort of a new wrinkle for me.

SHE: This is No Man's Land.

HE: This is where you – you – *(pause)*

SHE: Yes – all those things. *(She crosses to the bureau.)* See, here's my rouge – eye pencils.

HE: I didn't know you were that way.

SHE: What did you expect?

HE: I thought you'd be sort of – sort of – sexless, you know, swim and play golf.

SHE: Oh, I do – but not in business hours.

HE: Business?

SHE: Six to two – strictly.

HE: I'd like to have some stock in the corporation.

SHE: Oh, it's not a corporation – it's just 'Rosalind, Un-limited.' Fifty-one shares, name, good-will, and everything goes at $25,000 a year.

HE: *(Disapprovingly)* Sort of a chilly proposition.

SHE: Well, Amory, you don't mind – do you? When I meet a man that doesn't bore me to death after two weeks, per-haps it'll be different.

HE: Odd, you have the same point of view on men that I have on women.

SHE: I'm not really feminine, you know – in my mind.

HE: *(Interested)* Go on.

SHE: No, you – you go on – you've made me talk about myself. That's against the rules.

HE: Rules?

SHE: My own rules – but you— Oh, Amory, I hear you're brilliant. The family expects *so* much of you.

HE: How encouraging!

SHE: Alec said you'd taught him to think. Did you? I didn't believe any one could.

HE: No. I'm really quite dull.

(*He evidently doesn't intend this to be taken seriously.*)

SHE: Liar.

HE: I'm – I'm religious – I'm literary. I've – I've even written poems.

SHE: Vers libre – splendid! (*She declaims.*)

> 'The trees are green,
>   The birds are singing in the trees,
>   The girl sips her poison
>   The bird flies away the girl dies.'

HE: (*Laughing*) No, not that kind.

SHE: (*Suddenly*) I like you.

HE: Don't.

SHE: Modest too——

HE: I'm afraid of you. I'm always afraid of a girl – until I've kissed her.

SHE: (*Emphatically*) My dear boy, the war is over.

HE: So I'll always be afraid of you.

SHE: (*Rather sadly*) I suppose you will

(*A slight hesitation on both their parts.*)

HE: (*After due consideration*) Listen. This is a frightful thing to ask.

SHE: (*Knowing what's coming*) After five minutes.

HE: But will you – kiss me? Or are you afraid?

SHE: I'm never afraid – but your reasons are so poor.

HE: Rosalind, I really *want* to kiss you.

SHE: So do I.

(*They kiss – definitely and thoroughly.*)

HE: (*After a breathless second*) Well, is your curiosity satisfied?

SHE: Is yours?

HE: No, it's only aroused.
    (*He looks it.*)
SHE: (*Dreamily*) I've kissed dozens of men. I suppose I'll kiss dozens more.
HE: (*Abstractedly*) Yes, I suppose you could – like that.
SHE: Most people like the way I kiss.
HE: (*Remembering himself*) Good Lord, yes. Kiss me once more, Rosalind.
SHE: No – my curiosity is generally satisfied at one.
HE (*Discouraged*) Is that a rule?
SHE: I make rules to fit the cases.
HE: You and I are somewhat alike – except that I'm years older in experience.
SHE: How old are you?
HE: Almost twenty-three. You?
SHE: Nineteen – just.
HE: I suppose you're the product of a fashionable school.
SHE: No – I'm fairly raw material. I was expelled from Spence – I've forgotten why.
HE: What's your general trend?
SHE: Oh, I'm bright, quite selfish, emotional when aroused, fond of admiration——
HE: (*Suddenly*) I don't want to fall in love with you——
SHE: (*Raising her eyebrows*) Nobody asked you to.
HE: (*Continuing coldly*) But I probably will. I love your mouth.
SHE: Hush! Please don't fall in love with my mouth – hair, eyes, shoulders, slippers – but *not* my mouth. Everybody falls in love with my mouth.
HE: It's quite beautiful.
SHE: It's too small.
HE: No it isn't – let's see.
    (*He kisses her again with the same thoroughness.*)
SHE: (*Rather moved*) Say something sweet.
HE: (*Frightened*) Lord help me.
SHE: (*Drawing away*) Well, don't – if it's so hard.
HE: Shall we pretend? So soon?
SHE: We haven't the same standards of time as other people.

HE: Already it's – other people.

SHE: Let's pretend.

HE: No – I can't – it's sentiment.

SHE: You're not sentimental?

HE: No, I'm romantic – a sentimental person thinks things will last – a romantic person hopes against hope that they won't. Sentiment is emotional.

SHE: And you're not. (*With her eyes half-closed.*) You probably flatter yourself that that's a superior attitude.

HE: Well – Rosalind, Rosalind, don't argue – kiss me again.

SHE: (*Quite chilly now*) No – I have no desire to kiss you.

HE: (*Openly taken aback*) You wanted to kiss me a minute ago.

SHE: This is now.

HE: I'd better go.

SHE: I suppose so.

(*He goes toward the door.*)

SHE: Oh!

(*He turns.*)

SHE: (*Laughing*) Score – Home Team: One hundred – Opponents: Zero.

(*He starts back.*)

SHE: (*Quickly*) Rain – no game.

(*He goes out.*)

(*She goes quietly to the chiffonier, takes out a cigarette-case and hides it in the side drawer of a desk. Her mother enters, note-book in hand.*)

MRS. CONNAGE: Good – I've been wanting to speak to you alone before we go downstairs.

ROSALIND: Heavens! you frighten me!

MRS. CONNAGE: Rosalind, you've been a very expensive proposition.

ROSALIND: (*Resignedly*) Yes.

MRS. CONNAGE: And you know your father hasn't what he once had.

ROSALIND: (*Making a wry face*) Oh, please don't talk about money.

MRS. CONNAGE: You can't do anything without it. This is our

last year in this house – and unless things change Cecelia
won't have the advantages you've had.

ROSALIND: (*Impatiently*) Well – what is it?

MRS. CONNAGE: So I ask you to please mind me in several
things I've put down in my note-book. The first one is:
don't disappear with young men. There may be a time when
it's valuable, but at present I want you on the dance-floor
where I can find you. There are certain men I want to have
you meet and I don't like finding you in some corner of the
conservatory exchanging silliness with any one – or listening to it.

ROSALIND: (*Sarcastically*) Yes, listening to it *is* better.

MRS. CONNAGE: And don't waste a lot of time with the college set – little boys nineteen and twenty years old. I don't
mind a prom or a football game, but staying away from
advantageous parties to eat in little cafés down-town with
Tom, Dick, and Harry——

ROSALIND: (*Offering her code, which is, in its way, quite as
high as her mother's*) Mother, it's done – you can't run
everything now the way you did in the early nineties.

MRS. CONNAGE: (*Paying no attention*) There are several
bachelor friends of your father's that I want you to meet
to-night – youngish men.

ROSALIND: (*Nodding wisely*) About forty-five?

MRS. CONNAGE: (*Sharply*) Why not?

ROSALIND: Oh, *quite* all right – they know life and are so
adorably tired looking (*shakes her head*) – but they *will* dance.

MRS. CONNAGE: I haven't met Mr. Blaine – but I don't think
you'll care for him. He doesn't sound like a money-maker.

ROSALIND: Mother, I never *think* about money.

MRS. CONNAGE: You never keep it long enough to think
about it.

ROSALIND: (*Sighs*) Yes, I suppose some day I'll marry a ton
of it – out of sheer boredom.

MRS. CONNAGE: (*Referring to note-book*) I had a wire from
Hartford. Dawson Ryder is coming up. Now there's a
young man I like, and he's floating in money. It seems to me
that since you seem tired of Howard Gillespie you might give

Mr. Ryder some encouragement. This is the third time he's been up in a month.

ROSALIND: How did you know I was tired of Howard Gillespie?

MRS. CONNAGE: The poor boy looks so miserable every time he comes.

ROSALIND: That was one of those romantic, pre-battle affairs. They're all wrong.

MRS. CONNAGE: (*Her say said*) At any rate, make us proud of you to-night.

ROSALIND: Don't you think I'm beautiful?

MRS. CONNAGE: You know you are.

(*From downstairs is heard the moan of a violin being tuned, the roll of a drum.* MRS. CONNAGE *turns quickly to her daughter.*)

MRS. CONNAGE: Come!

ROSALIND: One minute!

(*Her mother leaves.* ROSALIND *goes to the glass where she gazes at herself with great satisfaction. She kisses her hand and touches her mirrored mouth with it. Then she turns out the lights and leaves the room. Silence for a moment. A few chords from the piano, the discreet patter of faint drums, the rustle of new silk, all blend on the staircase outside and drift in through the partly opened door. Bundled figures pass in the lighted hall. The laughter heard below becomes doubled and multiplied. Then some one comes in, closes the door, and switches on the lights. It is* CECELIA. *She goes to the chiffonier, looks in the drawers, hesitates – then to the desk whence she takes the cigarette-case and extracts one. She lights it and then, puffing and blowing, walks toward the mirror.*)

CECELIA: (*In tremendously sophisticated accents*) Oh, yes, coming out is *such* a farce nowadays, you know. One really plays around so much before one is seventeen, that it's positively anticlimax. (*Shaking hands with a visionary middle-aged nobleman.*) Yes, your grace – I b'lieve I've heard my sister speak of you. Have a puff – they're very good. They're – they're Coronas. You don't smoke? What a pity! The king doesn't allow it, I suppose. Yes, I'll dance.

(*So she dances around the room to a tune from downstairs,*

*her arms outstretched to an imaginary partner, the cigarette
waving in her hand.*)

Several Hours Later

*The corner of a den downstairs, filled by a very comfortable
leather lounge. A small light is on each side above, and in the
middle, over the couch hangs a painting of a very old, very
dignified gentleman, period 1860. Outside the music is heard in
a fox-trot.*

ROSALIND *is seated on the lounge and on her left is* HOWARD
GILLESPIE, *a vapid youth of about twenty-four. He is obviously
very unhappy, and she is quite bored.*

GILLESPIE: (*Feebly*) What do you mean I've changed. I feel
the same toward you.

ROSALIND: But you don't look the same to me.

GILLESPIE: Three weeks ago you used to say that you liked
me because I was so blasé, so indifferent – I still am.

ROSALIND: But not about me. I used to like you because you
had brown eyes and thin legs.

GILLESPIE: (*Helplessly*) They're still thin and brown. You're
a vampire, that's all.

ROSALIND: The only thing I know about vamping is what's
on the piano score. What confuses men is that I'm perfectly
natural. I used to think you were never jealous. Now you
follow me with your eyes wherever I go.

GILLESPIE: I love you.

ROSALIND: (*Coldly*) I know it.

GILLESPIE: And you haven't kissed me for two weeks. I had
an idea that after a girl was kissed she was – was – won.

ROSALIND: Those days are over. I have to be won all over
again every time you see me.

GILLESPIE: Are you serious?

ROSALIND: About as usual. There used to be two kinds of
kisses: first when girls were kissed and deserted; second,
when they were engaged. Now there's a third kind, where
the man is kissed and deserted. If Mr. Jones of the nineties
bragged he'd kissed a girl, every one knew he was through

with her. If Mr. Jones of 1919 brags the same every one
knows it's because he can't kiss her any more. Given a decent
start any girl can beat a man nowadays.

GILLESPIE: Then why do you play with men?

ROSALIND: (*Leaning forward confidentially*) For that first
moment, when he's interested. There is a moment – Oh,
just before the first kiss, a whispered word – something that
makes it worth while.

GILLESPIE: And then?

ROSALIND: Then after that you make him talk about himself.
Pretty soon he thinks of nothing but being alone with you –
he sulks, he won't fight, he doesn't want to play – Victory!

(*Enter* DAWSON RYDER, *twenty-six, handsome, wealthy,
faithful to his own, a bore perhaps, but steady and sure of
success.*)

RYDER: I believe this is my dance, Rosalind.

ROSALIND: Well, Dawson, so you recognize me. Now I know
I haven't got too much paint on. Mr. Ryder, this is Mr.
Gillespie.

(*They shake hands and* GILLESPIE *leaves, tremendously
downcast.*)

RYDER: Your party is certainly a success.

ROSALIND: Is it – I haven't seen it lately. I'm weary – Do you
mind sitting out a minute?

RYDER: Mind – I'm delighted. You know I loathe this 'rushing' idea. See a girl yesterday, to-day, to-morrow.

ROSALIND: Dawson!

RYDER: What?

ROSALIND: I wonder if you know you love me.

RYDER: (*Startled*) What – Oh – you know you're remarkable!

ROSALIND: Because you know I'm an awful proposition. Any
one who marries me will have his hands full. I'm mean –
mighty mean.

RYDER: Oh, I wouldn't say that.

ROSALIND: Oh, yes, I am – especially to the people nearest to
me. (*She rises.*) Come, let's go. I've changed my mind and I
want to dance. Mother is probably having a fit.

(*Exeunt. Enter* ALEC *and* CECELIA.)

CECELIA: Just my luck to get my own brother for an inter-mission.

ALEC: (*Gloomily*) I'll go if you want me to.

CECELIA: Good heavens, no – with whom would I begin the next dance? (*Sighs.*) There's no colour in a dance since the French officers went back.

ALEC: (*Thoughtfully*) I don't want Amory to fall in love with Rosalind.

CECELIA: Why, I had an idea that that was just what you did want.

ALEC: I did, but since seeing these girls – I don't know. I'm awfully attached to Amory. He's sensitive and I don't want him to break his heart over somebody who doesn't care about him.

CECELIA: He's very good looking.

ALEC: (*Still thoughtfully*) She won't marry him, but a girl doesn't have to marry a man to break his heart.

CECELIA: What does it? I wish I knew the secret.

ALEC: Why, you cold-blooded little kitty. It's lucky for some that the Lord gave you a pug nose.

(*Enter* MRS. CONNAGE.)

MRS. CONNAGE: Where on earth is Rosalind?

ALEC: (*Brilliantly*) Of course you've come to the best people to find out. She'd naturally be with us.

MRS. CONNAGE: Her father has marshalled eight bachelor millionaires to meet her.

ALEC: You might form a squad and march through the halls.

MRS. CONNAGE: I'm perfectly serious – for all I know she may be at the Cocoanut Grove with some football player on the night of her début. You look left and I'll——

ALEC: (*Flippantly*) Hadn't you better send the butler through the cellar?

MRS. CONNAGE: (*Perfectly serious*) Oh, you don't think she'd be there?

CECELIA: He's only joking, mother.

ALEC: Mother had a picture of her tapping a keg of beer with some high hurdler.

MRS. CONNAGE: Let's look right away.

(*They go out.* ROSALIND *comes in with* GILLESPIE.)

GILLESPIE: Rosalind – Once more I ask you. Don't you care a blessed thing about me?

(AMORY *walks in briskly.*)

AMORY: My dance.

ROSALIND: Mr. Gillespie, this is Mr. Blaine.

GILLESPIE: I've met Mr. Blaine. From Lake Geneva, aren't you?

AMORY: Yes.

GILLESPIE: (*Desperately*) I've been there. It's in the – the Middle West, isn't it?

AMORY: (*Spicily*) Approximately. But I always felt that I'd rather be provincial hot-tamale than soup without seasoning.

GILLESPIE: What!

AMORY: Oh, no offence.

(GILLESPIE *bows and leaves.*)

ROSALIND: He's too much *people.*

AMORY: I was in love with a *people* once.

ROSALIND: So?

AMORY: Oh, yes – her name was Isabelle – nothing at all to her except what I read into her.

ROSALIND: What happened?

AMORY: Finally I convinced her that she was smarter than I was – then she threw me over. Said I was critical and impractical, you know.

ROSALIND: What do you mean impractical?

AMORY: Oh – drive a car, but can't change a tyre.

ROSALIND: What are you going to do?

AMORY: Can't say – run for President, write——

ROSALIND: Greenwich Village?

AMORY: Good heavens, no – I said write – not drink.

ROSALIND: I like business men. Clever men are usually so homely.

AMORY: I feel as if I'd known you for ages.

ROSALIND: Oh, are you going to commence the 'pyramid' story?

AMORY: No – I was going to make it French. I was Louis

XIV and you were one of my – my – (*Changing his tone.*) Suppose – we fell in love.

ROSALIND: I've suggested pretending.

AMORY: If we did it would be very big.

ROSALIND: Why?

AMORY: Because selfish people are in a way terribly capable of great loves.

ROSALIND: (*Turning her lips up*) Pretend.

(*Very deliberately they kiss.*)

AMORY: I can't say sweet things. But you *are* beautiful.

ROSALIND: Not that.

AMORY: What then?

ROSALIND: (*Sadly*) Oh, nothing – only I want sentiment, real sentiment – and I never find it.

AMORY: I never find anything else in the world – and I loathe it.

ROSALIND: It's so hard to find a male to gratify one's artistic taste.

(*Some one has opened a door and the music of a waltz surges into the room.* ROSALIND *rises.*)

ROSALIND: Listen! they're playing 'Kiss Me Again.'

(*He looks at her.*)

AMORY: Well?

ROSALIND: Well?

AMORY: (*Softly – the battle lost*) I love you.

ROSALIND: I love you – now.

(*They kiss.*)

AMORY: Oh, God, what have I done?

ROSALIND: Nothing. Oh, don't talk. Kiss me again.

AMORY: I don't know why or how, but I love you – from the moment I saw you.

ROSALIND: Me too – I – I – oh, to-night's to-night.

(*Her brother strolls in, starts and then in a loud voice says:* 'Oh, excuse me,' *and goes.*)

ROSALIND: (*Her lips scarcely stirring*) Don't let me go – I don't care who knows what I do.

AMORY: Say it!

ROSALIND: I love you – now. (*They part.*) Oh – I am very

youthful, thank God – and rather beautiful, thank God –
and happy, thank God, thank God – (*She pauses and then,
in an odd burst of prophecy, adds*) Poor Amory!
(*He kisses her again.*)

Kismet

Within two weeks Amory and Rosalind were deeply and
passionately in love. The critical qualities which had spoiled
for each of them a dozen romances were dulled by the great
wave of emotion that washed over them.

'It may be an insane love-affair,' she told her anxious
mother, 'but it's not inane.'

The wave swept Amory into an advertising agency early
in March, where he alternated between astonishing bursts of
rather exceptional work and wild dreams of becoming
suddenly rich and touring Italy with Rosalind.

They were together constantly, for lunch, for dinner, and
nearly every evening – always in a sort of breathless hush, as
if they feared that any minute the spell would break and
drop them out of this paradise of rose and flame. But the
spell became a trance, seemed to increase from day to day;
they began to talk of marrying in July – in June. All life was
transmitted into terms of their love, all experience, all desires, all ambitions, were nullified – their senses of humour
crawled into corners to sleep; their former love-affairs
seemed faintly laughable and scarcely regretted juvenalia.

For the second time in his life Amory had had a complete
bouleversement and was hurrying into line with his generation.

A Little Interlude

Amory wandered slowly up the avenue and thought of the
night as inevitably his – the pageantry and carnival of rich
dusk and dim streets . . . it seemed that he had closed the
book of fading harmonies at last and stepped into the sensuous vibrant walks of life. Everywhere these countless lights,
this promise of a night of streets and singing – he moved in

a half-dream through the crowd as if expecting to meet Rosalind hurrying toward him with eager feet from every corner. . . . How the unforgettable faces of dusk would blend to her, the myriad footsteps, a thousand overtures, would blend to her footsteps; and there would be more drunkenness than wine in the softness of her eyes on his. Even his dreams now were faint violins drifting like summer sounds upon the summer air.

The room was in darkness except for the faint glow of Tom's cigarette where he lounged by the open window. As the door shut behind him, Amory stood a moment with his back against it.

'Hello, Benvenuto Blaine. How went the advertising business to-day?'

Amory sprawled on a couch.

'I loathed it as usual!' The momentary vision of the bustling agency was displaced quickly by another picture.

'My God! She's wonderful!'

Tom sighed.

'I can't tell you,' repeated Amory, 'just how wonderful she is. I don't want you to know. I don't want any one to know.'

Another sigh came from the window – quite a resigned sigh.

'She's life and hope and happiness, my whole world now.'

He felt the quiver of a tear on his eyelid.

'Oh, *Golly*, Tom!'

Bitter Sweet

'Sit like we do,' she whispered.

He sat in the big chair and held out his arms so that she could nestle inside them.

'I knew you'd come to-night,' she said softly, 'like summer, just when I needed you most . . . darling . . . darling . . .'

His lips moved lazily over her face.

'You *taste* so good,' he sighed.

'How do you mean, lover?'

'Oh, just sweet, just sweet . . .' he held her closer.

'Amory,' she whispered, 'when you're ready for me I'll marry you.'

'We won't have much at first.'

'Don't!' she cried. 'It hurts when you reproach yourself for what you can't give me. I've got your precious self – and that's enough for me.'

'Tell me . . .'

'You know, don't you? Oh, you know.'

'Yes, but I want to hear you say it.'

'I love you, Amory, with all my heart.'

'Always, will you?'

'All my life— Oh, Amory——'

'What?'

'I want to belong to you. I want your people to be my people. I want to have your babies.'

'But I haven't any people.'

'Don't laugh at me, Amory. Just kiss me.'

'I'll do what you want,' he said.

'No, I'll do what *you* want. We're *you* – not me. Oh, you're so much a part, so much all of me . . .'

He closed his eyes.

'I'm so happy that I'm frightened. Wouldn't it be awful if this was – was the high point? . . .'

She looked at him dreamily.

'Beauty and love pass, I know. . . . Oh, there's sadness, too. I suppose all great happiness is a little sad. Beauty means the scent of roses and then the death of roses——'

'Beauty means the agony of sacrifice and the end of agony . . . .'

'And, Amory, we're beautiful, I know. I'm sure God loves us——'

'He loves you. You're his most precious possession.'

'I'm not his, I'm yours. Amory, I belong to you. For the first time I regret all the other kisses; now I know how much a kiss can mean.'

Then they would smoke and he would tell her about his day at the office – and where they might live. Sometimes, when he was particularly loquacious, she went to sleep in his arms, but he loved that Rosalind – all Rosalinds as he had never in the world loved any one else. Intangibly fleeting, unrememberable hours.

Aquatic Incident

One day Amory and Howard Gillespie meeting by accident down-town took lunch together, and Amory heard a story that delighted him. Gillespie after several cocktails was in a talkative mood; he began by telling Amory that he was sure Rosalind was slightly eccentric.

He had gone with her on a swimming party up in West-chester Country, and some one mentioned that Annette Kellerman had been there one day on a visit and had dived from the top of a rickety, thirty-foot summer-house. Immediately Rosalind insisted that Howard should climb up with her to see what it looked like.

A minute later, as he sat and dangled his feet on the edge, a form shot by him; Rosalind, her arms spread in a beautiful swan dive, had sailed through the air into the clear water.

'Of course *I* had to go, after that – and I nearly killed myself. I thought I was pretty good to even try it. Nobody else in the party tried it. Well, afterwards Rosalind had the nerve to ask me why I stooped over when I dove. "It didn't make it any easier," she said, "it just took all the courage out of it." I ask you, what can a man do with a girl like that ? Unnecessary, I call it.'

Gillespie failed to understand why Amory was smiling delightedly all through lunch. He thought perhaps he was one of these hollow optimists.

Five Weeks Later

Again the library of the Connage house. ROSALIND *is alone, sitting on the lounge staring very moodily and unhappily at nothing. She has changed perceptibly – she is a trifle thinner for one thing; the light in her eyes is not so bright; she looks easily a year older.*

Her mother comes in, muffled in an opera-cloak. She takes in ROSALIND *with a nervous glance.*

MRS. CONNAGE: Who is coming to-night?

(ROSALIND *fails to hear her, at least takes no notice.*)

MRS. CONNAGE: Alec is coming up to take me to this Barrie play, 'Et tu, Brutus.' (*She perceives that she is talking to herself.*) Rosalind! I asked you who is coming to-night?

ROSALIND: (*Starting*) Oh – what – oh – Amory——

MRS. CONNAGE: (*Sarcastically*) You have so *many* admirers lately that I couldn't imagine *which* one. (ROSALIND *doesn't answer.*) Dawson Ryder is more patient than I thought he'd be. You haven't given him an evening this week.

ROSALIND: (*With a very weary expression that is quite new to her face.*) Mother – please——

MRS. CONNAGE: Oh, *I* won't interfere. You've already wasted over two months on a theoretical genius who hasn't a penny to his name, but *go* ahead, waste your life on him. *I* won't interfere.

ROSALIND: (*As if repeating a tiresome lesson*) You know he has a little income – and you know he's earning thirty-five dollars a week in advertising——

MRS. CONNAGE: And it wouldn't buy your clothes. (*She pauses but* ROSALIND *makes no reply.*) I have your best interests at heart when I tell you not to take a step you'll spend your days regretting. It's not as if your father could help you. Things have been hard for him lately and he's an old man. You'd be dependent absolutely on a dreamer, a nice, well-born boy, but a dreamer – merely *clever*. (*She implies that this quality in itself is rather vicious.*)

ROSALIND: For heaven's sake, mother——

(*A maid appears, announces Mr. Blaine who follows immediately.* AMORY'S *friends have been telling him for ten days that he 'looks like the wrath of God,' and he does. As a matter of fact he has not been able to eat a mouthful in the last thirty-six hours.*)

AMORY: Good evening, Mrs. Connage.

MRS. CONNAGE: (*Not unkindly*) Good evening, Amory. (AMORY *and* ROSALIND *exchange glances – and* ALEC *comes in.*

ALEC'S *attitude throughout has been neutral. He believes in his heart that the marriage would make* AMORY *mediocre and* ROSALIND *miserable, but he feels a great sympathy for both of them.*)

ALEC: Hi, Amory!

AMORY: Hi, Alec! Tom said he'd meet you at the theatre.

ALEC: Yeah, just saw him. How's the advertising to-day? Write some brilliant copy?

AMORY: Oh, it's about the same. I got a raise – (*Every one looks at him rather eagerly*) – of two dollars a week. (*General collapse.*)

MRS. CONNAGE: Come, Alec, I hear the car.

(*A good night, rather chilly in sections. After* MRS. CONNAGE *and* ALEC *go out there is a pause.* ROSALIND *still stares moodily at the fireplace.* AMORY *goes to her and puts his arm around her.*)

AMORY: Darling girl.

(*They kiss. Another pause and then she seizes his hand, covers it with kisses and holds it to her breast.*)

ROSALIND: (*Sadly*) I love your hands, more than anything. I see them often when you're away from me – so tired; I know every line of them. Dear hands!

(*Their eyes meet for a second and then she begins to cry – a tearless sobbing.*)

AMORY: Rosalind!

ROSALIND: Oh, we're so darned pitiful!

AMORY: Rosalind!

ROSALIND: Oh, I want to die!

AMORY: Rosalind, another night of this and I'll go to pieces. You've been this way four days now. You've got to be more encouraging or I can't work or eat or sleep. (*He looks around helplessly as if searching for new words to clothe an old, shop-worn phrase.*) We'll have to make a start. I *like* having to make a start together. (*His forced hopefulness fades as he sees her unresponsive.*) What's the matter? (*He gets up suddenly and starts to pace the floor.*) It's Dawson Ryder, that's what it is. He's been working on your nerves. You've been with him every afternoon for a week. People come and tell me they've seen you together, and I have to smile and nod and pretend it hasn't the slightest significance for me. And you won't tell me anything as it develops.

ROSALIND: Amory, if you don't sit down I'll scream.

AMORY: (*Sitting down suddenly beside her*) Oh, Lord.

ROSALIND: (*Taking his hand gently*) You know I love you, don't you?

AMORY: Yes.

ROSALIND: You know I'll always love you——

AMORY: Don't talk that way; you frighten me. It sounds as if we weren't going to have each other. (*She cries a little and rising from the couch goes to the armchair.*) I've felt all afternoon that things were worse. I nearly went wild down at the office – couldn't write a line. Tell me everything.

ROSALIND: There's nothing to tell, I say. I'm just nervous.

AMORY: Rosalind, you're playing with the idea of marrying Dawson Ryder.

ROSALIND: (*After a pause*) He's been asking me to all day.

AMORY: Well, he's got his nerve!

ROSALIND: (*After another pause*) I like him.

AMORY: Don't say that. It hurts me.

ROSALIND: Don't be a silly idiot. You know you're the only man I've ever loved, ever will love.

AMORY: (*Quickly*) Rosalind, let's get married – next week.

ROSALIND: We can't.

AMORY: Why not?

ROSALIND: Oh, we can't. I'd be your squaw – in some horrible place.

AMORY: We'll have two hundred and seventy-five dollars a month all told.

ROSALIND: Darling, I don't even do my own hair, usually.

AMORY: I'll do it for you.

ROSALIND: (*Between a laugh and a sob*) Thanks.

AMORY: Rosalind, you *can't* be thinking of marrying some one else. Tell me! You leave me in the dark. I can help you fight it out if you'll only tell me.

ROSALIND: It's just – us. We're pitiful, that's all. The very qualities I love you for are the ones that will always make you a failure.

AMORY: (*Grimly*) Go on.

ROSALIND: Oh – it *is* Dawson Ryder. He's so reliable, I almost feel that he'd be a – a background.

AMORY: You don't love him.

ROSALIND: I know, but I respect him, and he's a good man and a strong one.

AMORY: (*Grudgingly*) Yes – he's that.

ROSALIND: Well – here's one little thing. There was a little poor boy we met in Rye Tuesday afternoon – and, oh, Dawson took him on his lap and talked to him and promised him an Indian suit – and next day he remembered and bought it – and, oh, it was so sweet and I couldn't help thinking he'd be so nice to – to our children – take care of them – and I wouldn't have to worry.

AMORY: (*In despair*) Rosalind! Rosalind!

ROSALIND: (*With a faint roguishness*) Don't look so consciously suffering.

AMORY: What power we have of hurting each other!

ROSALIND: (*Commencing to sob again*) It's been so perfect – you and I. So like a dream that I'd longed for and never thought I'd find. The first real unselfishness I've ever felt in my life. And I can't see it fade out in a colourless atmosphere!

AMORY: It won't – it won't!

ROSALIND: I'd rather keep it as a beautiful memory – tucked away in my heart.

AMORY: Yes, women can do that – but not men. I'd remember always, not the beauty of it while it lasted, but just the bitterness, the long bitterness.

ROSALIND: Don't!

AMORY: All the years never to see you, never to kiss you, just a gate shut and barred – you don't dare be my wife.

ROSALIND: No – no – I'm taking the hardest course, the strongest course. Marrying you would be a failure and I never fail – if you don't stop walking up and down I'll scream!

(*Again he sinks despairingly on to the lounge.*)

AMORY: Come over here and kiss me.

ROSALIND: No.

AMORY: Don't you *want* to kiss me?

ROSALIND: To-night I want you to love me calmly and coolly.

AMORY: The beginning of the end.

ROSALIND: (*With a burst of insight*) Amory, you're young. I'm young. People excuse us now for our poses and vanities, for treating people like Sancho and yet getting away with it. They excuse us now. But you've got a lot of knocks coming to you——

AMORY: And you're afraid to take them with me.

ROSALIND: No, not that. There was a poem I read some-where – you'll say Ella Wheeler Wilcox and laugh – but listen:

> 'For this is wisdom – to love and live,
> To take what fate or the gods may give,
> To ask no question, to make no prayer,
> To kiss the lips and caress the hair,
> Speed passion's ebb as we greet its flow,
> To have and to hold, and, in time – let go.'

AMORY: But we haven't had.

ROSALIND: Amory, I'm yours – you know it. There have been times in the last month I'd have been completely yours if you'd said so. But I can't marry you and ruin both our lives.

AMORY: We've got to take our chance for happiness.

ROSALIND: Dawson says I'd learn to love him.

(AMORY *with his head sunk in his hands does not move. The life seems suddenly gone out of him.*) ..

ROSALIND: Lover! Lover! I can't do with you, and I can't imagine life without you.

AMORY: Rosalind, we're on each other's nerves. It's just that we're both high-strung, and this week——

(*His voice is curiously old. She crosses to him and taking his face in her hands, kisses him.*)

ROSALIND: I can't, Amory. I can't be shut away from the

trees and flowers, cooped up in a little flat, waiting for you.
You'd hate me in a narrow atmosphere. I'd make you hate
me.

(*Again she is blinded by sudden uncontrolled tears.*)

AMORY: Rosalind——

ROSALIND: Oh, darling, go – Don't make it harder! I can't
stand it——

AMORY (*His face drawn, his voice strained*) Do you know what
you're saying? Do you mean forever?

(*There is a difference somehow in the quality of their suffering.*)

ROSALIND: Can't you see——

AMORY: I'm afraid I can't if you love me. You're afraid of
taking two years' knocks with me.

ROSALIND: I wouldn't be the Rosalind you love.

AMORY: (*A little hysterically*) I can't give you up! I can't,
that's all! I've got to have you!

ROSALIND: (*A hard note in her voice*) You're being a baby
now.

AMORY: (*Wildly*) I don't care! You're spoiling our lives!

ROSALIND: I'm doing the wise thing, the only thing.

AMORY: Are you going to marry Dawson Ryder?

ROSALIND: Oh, don't ask me. You know I'm old in some
ways – in others – well, I'm just a little girl. I like sunshine
and pretty things and cheerfulness – and I dread responsibility. I don't want to think about pots and kitchens and
brooms. I want to worry whether my legs will get slick and
brown when I swim in the summer.

AMORY: And you love me.

ROSALIND: That's just why it has to end. Drifting hurts too
much. We can't have any more scenes like this.

(*She draws his ring from her finger and hands it to him.
Their eyes blind again with tears.*)

AMORY: (*His lips against her wet cheek*) Don't! Keep it,
please – oh, don't break my heart!

(*She presses the ring softly into his hand.*)

ROSALIND (*Brokenly*) You'd better go.

AMORY: Good-bye——

(*She looks at him once more, with infinite longing, infinite sadness.*)

ROSALIND: Don't ever forget me, Amory——

AMORY: Good-bye——

(*He goes to the door, fumbles for the knob, finds it – she sees him throw back his head – and he is gone. Gone – she half starts from the lounge and then sinks forward on her face into the pillows.*)

ROSALIND: Oh, God, I want to die! (*After a moment she rises and with her eyes closed feels her way to the door. Then she turns and looks once more at the room. Here they had sat and dreamed: that tray she had so often filled with matches for him; that shade that they had discreetly lowered one long Sunday afternoon. Misty-eyed she stands and remembers; she speaks aloud.*) Oh, Amory, what have I done to you?

(*And deep under the aching sadness that will pass in time, Rosalind feels that she has lost something, she knows not what, she knows not why.*)

II. EXPERIMENTS IN CONVALESCENCE

THE Knickerbocker Bar, beamed upon by Maxfield Parrish's jovial, colourful 'Old King Cole,' was well crowded. Amory stopped in the entrance and looked at his wrist-watch; he wanted particularly to know the time, for something in his mind that catalogued and classified liked to chip things off cleanly. Later it would satisfy him in a vague way to be able to think 'that thing ended at exactly twenty minutes after eight on Thursday, June 10, 1919.' This was allowing for the walk from her house – a walk concerning which he had afterwards not the faintest recollection.

He was in rather grotesque condition: two days of worry and nervousness, of sleepless nights, of untouched meals, culminating in the emotional crisis and Rosalind's abrupt decision – the strain of it had drugged the foreground of his mind into a merciful coma. As he fumbled clumsily with the olives at the free-lunch table, a man approached and spoke to him, and the olives dropped from his nervous hands.

'Well, Amory . . .'

It was some one he had known at Princeton; he had no idea of the name.

'Hello, old boy—' he heard himself saying.

'Name's Jim Wilson – you've forgotten.'

'Sure, you bet, Jim. I remember.'

'Going to reunion?'

'You know!' Simultaneously he realized that he was not going to reunion.

'Get overseas?'

Amory nodded, his eyes staring oddly. Stepping back to let some one pass, he knocked the dish of olives to a crash on the floor.

'Too bad,' he muttered. 'Have a drink?'

Wilson, ponderously diplomatic, reached over and slapped him on the back.

'You've had plenty, old boy.'

Amory eyed him dumbly until Wilson grew embarrassed under the scrutiny.

'Plenty, hell!' said Amory finally. 'I haven't had a drink to-day.'

Wilson looked incredulous.

'Have a drink or not?' cried Amory rudely.

Together they sought the bar.

'Rye high.'

'I'll just take a Bronx.'

Wilson had another; Amory had several more. They decided to sit down. At ten o'clock Wilson was displaced by Carling, class of '15. Amory, his head spinning gorgeously, layer upon layer of soft satisfaction setting over the bruised spots of his spirit, was discoursing volubly on the war.

"S a mental was'e,' he insisted with owl-like wisdom. 'Two years my life spent inalleshual vacuity. Los' idealism, got be physcal anmal,' he shook his fist expressively at Old King Cole, 'got be Prussian 'bout ev'thing, women 'specially.

Use' be straight 'bout women college. Now don'givadam.' He expressed his lack of principle by sweeping a seltzer bottle with a broad gesture to noisy extinction on the floor, but this did not interrupt his speech. 'Seek pleasure where find it for to-morrow die. 'At's philos'phy for me now on.'

Carling yawned, but Amory, waxing brilliant, continued:

'Use' wonder 'bout things – people satisfied compromise, fif'y-fif'y att'tude on life. Now don' wonder, don' wonder—

He became so emphatic in impressing on Carling the fact that he didn't wonder that he lost the thread of his discourse and concluded by announcing to the bar at large that he was a 'physcal anmal.'

'What are you celebrating, Amory ?'

Amory leaned forward confidentially.

'Cel'brating blowmylife. Great moment blow my life. Can't tell you 'bout it——'

He heard Carling addressing a remark to the bartender:

'Give him a bromo-seltzer.'

Amory shook his head indignantly.

'None that stuff!'

'But listen, Amory, you're making yourself sick. You're white as a ghost.'

Amory considered the question. He tried to look at himself in the mirror but even by squinting up one eye could only see as far as the row of bottles behind the bar.

'Like som'n solid. We go get some – some salad.'

He settled his coat with an attempt at nonchalance, but letting go of the bar was too much for him, and he slumped against a chair.

'We'll go over to Shanley's,' suggested Carling, offering an elbow.

With this assistance Amory managed to get his legs in motion enough to propel him across Forty-second Street.

Shanley's was very dim. He was conscious that he was talking in a loud voice, very succinctly and convincingly, he thought, about a desire to crush people under his heel. He consumed three club sandwiches, devouring each as though it were no larger than a chocolate-drop. Then Rosalind began popping into his mind again, and he found his lips forming her name over and over. Next he was sleepy, and he had a hazy, listless sense of people in dress suits, probably waiters, gathering around the table. . . .

. . . He was in a room and Carling was saying something about a knot in his shoe-lace.

'Nemmine,' he managed to articulate drowsily. 'Sleep in 'em. . . .'

Still Alcoholic

He awoke laughing and his eyes lazily roamed his surroundings, evidently a bedroom and bath in a good hotel. His head was whirring and picture after picture was forming and blurring and melting before his eyes, but beyond the desire to laugh he had no entirely conscious reaction. He reached for the 'phone beside his bed.

'Hello – what hotel is this—?'

'Knickerbocker? All right, send up two rye high-balls——'

He lay for a moment and wondered idly whether they'd send up a bottle or just two of those little glass containers. Then, with an effort, he struggled out of bed and ambled into the bathroom.

When he emerged, rubbing himself lazily with a towel, he found the bar boy with the drinks and had a sudden desire to kid him. On reflection he decided that this would be undignified, so he waved him away.

As the new alcohol tumbled into his stomach and warmed him, the isolated pictures began slowly to form a cinema reel of the day before. Again he saw Rosalind curled weeping among the pillows, again he felt her tears against his cheek. Her words began ringing in his ears: 'Don't ever forget me, Amory – don't ever forget me——'

'Hell!' he faltered aloud, and then he choked and collapsed on the bed in a shaken spasm of grief. After a minute he opened his eyes and regarded the ceiling.

'Damned fool!' he exclaimed in disgust, and with a voluminous sigh rose and approached the bottle. After another glass he gave way loosely to the luxury of tears. Purposely he called up into his mind little incidents of the vanished spring, phrased to himself emotions that would make him react even more strongly to sorrow.

'We were so happy,' he intoned dramatically, 'so very happy.' Then he gave way again and knelt beside the bed, his head half-buried in the pillow.

'My own girl – my own— Oh——'

He clenched his teeth so that the tears streamed in a flood from his eyes.

'Oh . . . my baby girl, all I had, all I wanted! . . . Oh, my girl, come back, come back! I need you . . . need you . . . we're so pitiful . . . just misery we brought each other. . . . She'll be shut away from me. . . . I can't see her; I can't be her friend. It's got to be that way – it's got to be——'

And then again:

'We've been so happy, so very happy. . . .'

He rose to his feet and threw himself on the bed in an ecstasy of sentiment, and then lay exhausted while he realized slowly that he had been very drunk the night before, and that his head was spinning again wildly. He laughed, rose, and crossed again to Lethe. . . .

At noon he ran into a crowd in the Biltmore bar, and the riot began again. He had a vague recollection afterwards of discussing French poetry with a British officer who was introduced to him as 'Captain Corn, of his Majesty's Foot,' and he remembered attempting to recite 'Clair de Lune' at luncheon; then he slept in a big, soft chair until almost five o'clock when another crowd found and woke him; there followed an alcoholic dressing of several temperaments for the ordeal of dinner. They selected theatre tickets at Tyson's for a play that had a four-drink programme – a play with two monotonous voices, with turbid, gloomy scenes, and lighting effects that were hard to follow when his eyes behaved so amazingly. He imagined afterwards that it must have been 'The Jest.' . . .

. . . Then the Cocoanut Grove, where Amory slept again on a little balcony outside. Out in Shanley's, Yonkers, he became almost logical, and by a careful control of the number of high-balls he drank, grew quite lucid and garrulous. He found that the party consisted of five men, two of whom he knew slightly; he became righteous about paying his share of the expense and insisted in a loud voice on arranging everything then and there to the amusement of the tables around him. . . .

Some one mentioned that a famous cabaret star was at the next table, so Amory rose and, approaching gallantly, introduced himself . . . this involved him in an argument, first with her escort and then with the head-waiter – Amory's attitude being a lofty and exaggerated courtesy . . . he consented, after being confronted with irrefutable logic, to being led back to his own table.

'Decided to commit suicide,' he announced suddenly.

'When? Next year?'

'Now. To-morrow morning. Going to take a room at the Commodore, get into a hot bath and open a vein.'

'He's getting morbid!'

'You need another rye, old boy!'

'We'll all talk it over to-morrow.'

But Amory was not to be dissuaded, from argument at least.

'Did you ever get that way?' he demanded confidentially fortaccio.

'Sure!'

'Often?'

'My chronic state.'

This provoked discussion. One man said that he got so depressed sometimes that he seriously considered it. Another agreed that there was nothing to live for. 'Captain Corn,' who had somehow rejoined the party, said that in his opinion it was when one's health was bad that one felt that way most. Amory's suggestion was that they should each order a Bronx, mix broken glass in it, and drink it off. To his relief no one applauded the idea, so having finished his high-ball, he balanced his chin in his hand and his elbow on the table – a most delicate, scarcely noticeable sleeping position, he assured himself – and went into a deep stupor. . . .

He was awakened by a woman clinging to him, a pretty woman, with brown, disarranged hair and dark blue eyes.

'Take me home!' she cried.

'Hello!' said Amory, blinking.

'I like you,' she announced tenderly.

'I like you too.'

He noticed that there was a noisy man in the background and that one of his party was arguing with him.

'Fella I was with's a damn fool,' confided the blue-eyed woman. 'I hate him. I want to go home with you.'

'You drunk?' queried Amory with intense wisdom.

She nodded coyly.

'Go home with him,' he advised gravely. 'He brought you.'

At this point the noisy man in the background broke away from his detainers and approached.

'Say!' he said fiercely. 'I brought this girl out here and you're butting in!'

Amory regarded him coldly, while the girl clung to him closer.

'You let go that girl!' cried the noisy man.

Amory tried to make his eyes threatening.

'You go to hell!' he directed finally, and turned his attention to the girl.

'Love first sight,' he suggested.

'I love you,' she breathed and nestled close to him. She *did* have beautiful eyes.

Some one leaned over and spoke in Amory's ear.

'That's just Margaret Diamond. She's drunk and this fellow here brought her. Better let her go.'

'Let him take care of her, then!' shouted Amory furiously. 'I'm no W.Y.C.A. worker, am I? – am I?'

'Let her go!'

'It's *her* hanging on, damn it! Let her hang!'

The crowd around the table thickened. For an instant a brawl threatened, but a sleek waiter bent back Margaret

Diamond's fingers until she released her hold on Amory, whereupon she slapped the waiter furiously in the face and flung her arms about her raging original escort.

'Oh, Lord!' cried Amory.

'Let's go!'

'Come on, the taxis are getting scarce!'

'Check, waiter.'

'C'mon, Amory. Your romance is over.'

Amory laughed.

'You don't know how true you spoke. No idea. 'At's the whole trouble.'

Amory on the Labour Question

Two mornings later he knocked at the president's door at Bascome and Barlow's advertising agency.

'Come in!'

Amory entered unsteadily.

' 'Morning, Mr. Barlow.'

Mr. Barlow brought his glasses to the inspection and set his mouth slightly ajar that he might better listen.

'Well, Mr. Blaine. We haven't seen you for several days.'

'No,' said Amory. 'I'm quitting.'

'Well – well – this is——'

'I don't like it here.'

'I'm sorry. I thought our relations had been quite – ah – pleasant. You seemed to be a hard worker – a little inclined perhaps to write fancy copy——'

'I just got tired of it,' interrupted Amory rudely. 'It didn't matter a damn to me whether Harebell's flour was any better than any one else's. In fact, I never ate any of it. So I got tired of telling people about it – oh, I know I've been drinking——'

Mr. Barlow's face steeled by several ingots of expression.

'You asked for a position——'

Amory waved him to silence.

'And I think I was rottenly underpaid. Thirty-five dollars a week – less than a good carpenter.'

'You had just started. You'd never worked before,' said Mr. Barlow coolly.

'But it took about ten thousand dollars to educate me where I could write your darned stuff for you. Anyway, as far as length of service goes, you've got stenographers here you've paid fifteen a week for five years.'

'I'm not going to argue with you, sir,' said Mr. Barlow rising.

'Neither am I. I just wanted to tell you I'm quitting.'

They stood for a moment looking at each other impassively and then Amory turned and left the office.

A Little Lull

Four days after that he returned at last to the apartment. Tom was engaged on a book review for *The New Democracy* on the staff of which he was employed. They regarded each other for a moment in silence.

'Well?'

'Well?'

'Good Lord, Amory, where'd you get the black eye – and the jaw?'

Amory laughed.

'That's a mere nothing.'

He peeled off his coat and bared his shoulders.

'Look here!'

Tom emitted a low whistle.

'What hit you?'

Amory laughed again.

'Oh, a lot of people. I got beaten up. Fact.' He slowly replaced his shirt. 'It was bound to come sooner or later and I wouldn't have missed it for anything.'

'Who was it?'

'Well, there were some waiters and a couple of sailors and a few stray pedestrians, I guess. It's the strangest feeling. You ought to get beaten up just for the experience of it. You fall down after a while and everybody sort of slashes in at you before you hit the ground – then they kick you.'

Tom lighted a cigarette.

'I spent a day chasing you all over town, Amory. But you always kept a little ahead of me. I'd say you've been on some party.'

Amory tumbled into a chair and asked for a cigarette.

'You sober now?' asked Tom quizzically.

'Pretty sober. Why?'

'Well, Alec has left. His family had been after him to go home and live, so he——'

A spasm of pain shook Amory.

'Too bad.'

'Yes, it is too bad. We'll have to get some one else if we're going to stay here. The rent's going up.'

'Sure. Get anybody. I'll leave it to you, Tom.'

Amory walked into his bedroom. The first thing that met his glance was a photograph of Rosalind that he had intended to have framed, propped up against a mirror on his dresser. He looked at it unmoved. After the vivid mental pictures of her that were his portion at present, the portrait was curiously unreal. He went back into the study.

'Got a cardboard box?'

'No,' answered Tom, puzzled. 'Why should I have? Oh, yes – there may be one in Alec's room.'

Eventually Amory found what he was looking for and, returning to his dresser, opened a drawer full of letters, notes, part of a chain, two little handkerchiefs, and some snapshots. As he transferred them carefully to the box his mind wandered to some place in a book where the hero, after preserving for a year a cake of his lost love's soap, finally washed his hands with it. He laughed and began to hum 'After you've gone' . . . ceased abruptly. . . .

The string broke twice, and then he managed to secure it, dropped the package into the bottom of his trunk, and having slammed the lid returned to the study.

'Going out?' Tom's voice held an undertone of anxiety.

'Uh-huh.'

'Where?'

'Couldn't say, old keed.'

'Let's have dinner together.'

'Sorry. I told Sukey Brett I'd eat with him.'

'Oh.'

'Bye-bye.'

Amory crossed the street and had a high-ball; then he walked to Washington Square and found a top seat on a bus. He disembarked at Forty-third Street and strolled to the Biltmore bar.

'Hi, Amory!'

'What'll you have?'

'Yoho! Waiter!'

Temperature Normal

The advent of Prohibition with the 'thirsty-first' put a sudden stop to the submerging of Amory's sorrows, and when he awoke one morning to find that the old bar-to-bar days were over, he had neither remorse for the past three weeks nor regret that their repetition was impossible. He had taken the most violent, if the weakest, method to shield himself from the stabs of memory, and while it was not a course he would have prescribed for others, he found in the end that it had done its business: he was over the first flush of pain.

Don't misunderstand! Amory had loved Rosalind as he would never love another living person. She had taken the first flush of his youth and brought from his unplumbed depths tenderness that had surprised him, gentleness and unselfishness that he had never given to another creature. He had later love-affairs, but of a different sort: in those he went back to that, perhaps, more typical frame of mind, in which the girl became the mirror of a mood in him. Rosalind had drawn out what was more than passionate admiration; he had a deep, undying affection for Rosalind.

But there had been, near the end, so much dramatic tragedy, culminating in the arabesque nightmare of his three weeks' spree, that he was emotionally worn out. The people and surroundings that he remembered as being cool

or delicately artificial, seemed to promise him a refuge. He
wrote a cynical story which featured his father's funeral and
despatched it to a magazine, receiving in return a cheque for
sixty dollars and a request for more of the same tone. This
tickled his vanity, but inspired him to no further effort.

He read enormously. He was puzzled and depressed by
'A Portrait of the Artist as a Young Man'; intensely interested by 'Joan and Peter' and 'The Undying Fire,' and rather
surprised by his discovery through a critic named Mencken
of several excellent American novels: 'Vandover and the
Brute,' 'The Damnation of Theron Ware,' and 'Jennie
Gerhardt.' Mackenzie, Chesterton, Galsworthy, Bennet,
had sunk in his appreciation from sagacious, life-saturated
geniuses to merely diverting contemporaries. Shaw's aloof
clarity and brilliant consistency and the gloriously intoxi-
cated efforts of H. G. Wells to fit the key of romantic symmetry into the elusive lock of truth, alone won his rapt attention.

He wanted to see Monsignor Darcy, to whom he had
written when he landed, but he had not heard from him;
besides he knew that a visit to Monsignor would entail the
story of Rosalind, and the thought of repeating it turned
him cold with horror.

In his search for cool people he remembered Mrs. Lawrence, a very intelligent, very dignified lady, a convert to the
church, and a great devotee of Monsignor's.

He called her on the 'phone one day. Yes, she remembered him perfectly; no, Monsignor wasn't in town, was in
Boston she thought; he'd promised to come to dinner when
he returned. Couldn't Amory take luncheon with her?

'I thought I'd better catch up, Mrs. Lawrence,' he said
rather ambiguously when he arrived.

'Monsignor was here just last week,' said Mrs. Lawrence
regretfully. 'He was very anxious to see you, but he'd left
your address at home.'

'Did he think I'd plunged into Bolshevism?' asked
Amory, interested.

'Oh, he's having a frightful time.'

'Why?'

'About the Irish Republic. He thinks it lacks dignity.'

'So?'

'He went to Boston when the Irish President arrived and he was greatly distressed because the receiving committee, when they rode in an automobile, *would* put their arms around the President.'

'I don't blame him.'

'Well, what impressed you more than anything while you were in the army? You look a great deal older.'

'That's from another, more disastrous battle,' he answered, smiling in spite of himself. 'But the army – let me see – well, I discovered that physical courage depends to a great extent on the physical shape a man is in. I found that I was as brave as the next man – it used to worry me before.'

'What else?'

'Well, the idea that men can stand anything if they get used to it, and the fact that I got a high mark in the psychological examination.'

Mrs. Lawrence laughed. Amory was finding it a great relief to be in this cool house on Riverside Drive, away from more condensed New York and the sense of people expelling great quantities of breath into a little space. Mrs. Lawrence reminded him vaguely of Beatrice, not in temperament, but in her perfect grace and dignity. The house, its furnishings, the manner in which dinner was served, were in immense contrast to what he had met in the great places on Long Island, where the servants were so obtrusive that they had positively to be bumped out of the way, or even in the houses of more conservative 'Union Club' families. He wondered if this air of symmetrical restraint, this grace, which he felt was continental, was distilled through Mrs. Lawrence's New England ancestry or acquired in long residence in Italy and Spain.

Two glasses of sauterne at luncheon loosened his tongue, and he talked, with what he felt was something of his old charm, of religion and literature and the menacing phenomena of the social order. Mrs. Lawrence was ostensibly pleased with him, and her interest was especially in his mind; he wanted people to like his mind again – after a while it might be such a nice place in which to live.

'Monsignor Darcy still thinks that you're his reincarnation, that your faith will eventually clarify.'

'Perhaps,' he assented. 'I'm rather pagan at present. It's just that religion doesn't seem to have the slightest bearing on life at my age.'

When he left her house he walked down Riverside Drive with a feeling of satisfaction. It was amusing to discuss again such subjects as this young poet, Stephen Vincent Benét, or the Irish Republic. Between the rancid accusations of Edward Carson and Justice Cohalan he had completely tired of the Irish question; yet there had been a time when his own Celtic traits were pillars of his personal philosophy.

There seemed suddenly to be much left in life, if only this revival of old interests did not mean that he was backing away from it again – backing away from life itself.

Restlessness

'I'm tres old and tres bored, Tom,' said Amory one day, stretching himself at ease in the comfortable window-seat. He always felt most natural in a recumbent position.

'You used to be entertaining before you started to write,' he continued. 'Now you save any idea that you think would do to print.'

Existence had settled back to an ambitionless normality. They had decided that with economy they could still afford the apartment, which Tom, with the domesticity of an elderly cat, had grown fond of. The old English hunting prints on the wall were Tom's, and the large tapestry by courtesy, a relic of decadent days in college, and the great profusion of orphaned candlesticks and the carved Louis XV chair in which no one could sit more than a minute without acute spinal disorders – Tom claimed that this was because one was sitting in the lap of Montespan's wraith – at any rate, it was Tom's furniture that decided them to stay.

They went out very little: to an occasional play, or to dinner at the Ritz or the Princeton Club. With Prohibition the great rendezvous had received their death wounds; no longer could one wander to the Biltmore bar at twelve or five and find congenial spirits, and both Tom and Amory had outgrown the passion for dancing with mid-Western or New Jersey debbies at the Club-de-Vingt (surnamed the 'Club de Gink') or the Plaza Rose Room – besides even that required several cocktails 'to come down to the intellectual level of the women present,' as Amory had once put it to a horrified matron.

Amory had lately received several alarming letters from Mr. Barton – the Lake Geneva house was too large to be easily rented; the best rent obtainable at present would serve this year to little more than pay for the taxes and necessary improvements; in fact, the lawyer suggested that the whole property was simply a white elephant on Amory's hands. Nevertheless, even though it might not yield a cent for the next three years, Amory decided with a vague sentimentality that for the present, at any rate, he would not sell the house.

This particular day on which he announced his ennui to Tom had been quite typical. He had risen at noon, lunched with Mrs. Lawrence, and then ridden abstractedly homeward atop one of his beloved buses.

'Why shouldn't you be bored,' yawned Tom. 'Isn't that the conventional frame of mind for the young man of your age and condition?'

'Yes,' said Amory speculatively, 'but I'm more than bored; I am restless.'

'Love and war did for you.'

'Well,' Amory considered, 'I'm not sure that the war itself had any great effect on either you or me – but it certainly ruined the old backgrounds, sort of killed individualism out of our generation.'

Tom looked up in surprise.

'Yes it did,' insisted Amory. 'I'm not sure it didn't kill it out of the whole world. Oh, Lord, what a pleasure it used to be to dream I might be a really great dictator or writer or religious or political leader – and now even a Leonardo da Vinci or Lorenzo de Medici couldn't be a real old-fashioned bolt in the world. Life is too huge and complex. The world is so overgrown that it can't lift its own fingers, and I was planning to be such an important finger——'

'I don't agree with you,' Tom interrupted. 'There never were men placed in such egotistic positions since – oh, since the French Revolution.'

Amory disagreed violently.

'You're mistaking this period when every nut is an individualist for a period of individualism. Wilson has only been powerful when he has represented; he's had to compromise over and over again. Just as soon as Trotsky and Lenin take a definite, consistent stand they'll become merely two-minute figures like Kerensky. Even Foch hasn't half the significance of Stonewall Jackson. War used to be the most individualistic pursuit of man, and yet the popular heroes of the war had neither authority nor responsibility: Guynemer and Sergeant York. How could a schoolboy make a hero of Pershing? A big man has no time really to do anything but just sit and be big.'

'Then you don't think there will be any more permanent world heroes?'

'Yes – in history – not in life. Carlyle would have difficulty getting material for a new chapter on "The Hero as a Big Man".'

'Go on. I'm a good listener to-day.'

'People try so hard to believe in leaders now, pitifully hard. But we no sooner get a popular reformer or politician or soldier or writer or philosopher – a Roosevelt, a Tolstoi, a Wood, a Shaw, a Nietzsche, than the cross-currents of criticism wash him away. My Lord, no man can stand prominence these days. It's the surest path to obscurity. People get sick of hearing the same name over and over.'

'Then you blame it on the press?'

'Absolutely. Look at you; you're on *The New Democracy*, considered the most brilliant weekly in the country, read by the men who do things and all that. What's your business? Why, to be as clever, as interesting, and as brilliantly cynical as possible about every man, doctrine, book, or policy that is assigned you to deal with. The more strong lights, the more spiritual scandal you can throw on the matter, the more money they pay you, the more the people buy the issue. You, Tom d'Invilliers, a blighted Shelley, changing, shifting, clever, unscrupulous, represent the critical consciousness of the race— Oh, don't protest, I know the stuff. I used to write book reviews in college; I considered it rare sport to refer to the latest honest, conscientious effort to propound a theory or a remedy as a "welcome addition to our light summer reading." Come on now, admit it.'

Tom laughed, and Amory continued trimphantly.

'We *want* to believe. Young students try to believe in older authors, constituents try to believe in their Congressmen, countries try to believe in their statesmen, but they *can't*. Too many voices, too much scattered, illogical, ill-considered criticism. It's worse in the case of newspapers. Any rich, unprogressive old party with that particularly grasping, acquisitive form of mentality known as financial genius can own a paper that is the intellectual meat and drink of thousands of tired, hurried men, men too involved in the business of modern living to swallow anything but predigested food. For two cents the voter buys his politics, prejudices, and philosophy. A year later there is a new political ring or a change in the paper's ownership, consequence: more confusion, more contradiction, a sudden inrush of new ideas, their tempering, their distillation, the reaction against them——'

He paused only to get his breath.

'And that is why I have sworn not to put pen to paper until my ideas either clarify or depart entirely; I have quite enough sins on my soul without putting dangerous, shallow epigrams into people's heads; I might cause a poor, inoffensive capitalist to have a vulgar liaison with a bomb, or get some innocent little Bolshevik tangled up with a machine-gun bullet——'

Tom was growing restless under this lampooning of his connection with *The New Democracy*.

'What's all this got to do with your being bored?'

Amory considered that it had much to do with it.

'How'll I fit in?' he demanded. 'What am I for? To propagate the race? According to the American novels we are led to believe that the "healthy American boy" from nineteen to twenty-five is an entirely sexless animal. As a matter of fact, the healthier he is the less that's true. The only alternative to letting it get you is some violent interest. Well, the war is over; I believe too much in the responsibilities of authorship to write just now; and business, well, business speaks for itself. It has no connection with anything in the world that I've ever been interested in, except a slim, utilitarian connection with economics. What I'd see of it, lost in a clerkship, for the next and best ten years of my life would have the intellectual content of an industrial movie.'

'Try fiction,' suggested Tom.

'Trouble is I get distracted when I start to write stories – get afraid I'm doing it instead of living – get thinking maybe life is waiting for me in the Japanese gardens at the Ritz or at Atlantic City or on the lower East Side.'

'Anyway,' he continued, 'I haven't the vital urge. I wanted to be a regular human being but the girl couldn't see it that way.'

'You'll find another.'

'God! Banish the thought. Why don't you tell me that "if the girl had been worth having she'd have waited for you"? No, sir, the girl really worth having won't wait for anybody. If I thought there'd be another I'd lose my remaining faith in human nature. Maybe I'll play – but Rosalind was the only girl in the wide world that could have held me.'

'Well,' yawned Tom, 'I've played confidant a good hour

by the clock. Still, I'm glad to see you're beginning to have violent views again on something.'

'I am,' agreed Amory reluctantly. 'Yet when I see a happy family it makes me sick at my stomach——'

'Happy families try to make people feel that way,' said Tom cynically.

Tom the Censor

There were days when Amory listened. These were when Tom, wreathed in smoke, indulged in the slaughter of American literature. Words failed him.

'Fifty thousand dollars a year,' he would cry. 'My God! Look at them, look at them – Edna Ferber, Gouverneur Morris, Fanny Hurst, Mary Roberts Rinehart – not producing among 'em one story or novel that will last ten years. This man Cobb – I don't think he's either clever or amusing – and what's more, I don't think very many people do, except the editors. He's just groggy with advertising. And – oh Harold Bell Wright oh Zane Grey——'

'They try.'

'No, they don't even try. Some of them *can* write, but they won't sit down and do one honest novel. Most of them *can't* write, I'll admit. I believe Rupert Hughes tries to give a real, comprehensive picture of American life, but his style and perspective are barbarous. Ernest Poole and Dorothy Canfield try but they're hindered by their absolute lack of any sense of humour; but at least they crowd their work instead of spreading it thin. Every author ought to write every book as if he were going to be beheaded the day he finished it.'

'Is that double entente?'

'Don't slow me up! Now there's a few of 'em that seem to have some cultural background, some intelligence and a good deal of literary felicity but they just simply won't write honestly; they'd all claim there was no public for good stuff. Then why the devil is it that Wells, Conrad, Galsworthy, Shaw, Bennett, and the rest depend on America for over half their sales?'

'How does little Tommy like the poets?'

Tom was overcome. He dropped his arms until they swung loosely beside the chair and emitted faint grunts.

'I'm writing a satire on 'em now, calling it "Boston Bards and Hearst Reviewers".'

'Let's hear it,' said Amory eagerly.

'I've only got the last few lines done.'

'That's very modern. Let's hear 'em, if they're funny.'

Tom produced a folded paper from his pocket and read aloud, pausing at intervals so that Amory could see that it was free verse:

> 'So
> Walter Arensberg,
> Alfred Kreymborg,
> Carl Sandburg,
> Louis Untermeyer,
> Eunice Tietjens,
> Clara Shanafelt,
> James Oppenheim,
> Maxwell Bodenheim,
> Richard Glaenzer,
> Scharmel Iris,
> Conrad Aiken,
> I place your names here
> So that you may live
> If only as names,
> Sinuous, mauve-coloured names,
> In the Juvenalia
> Of my collected editions.'

Amory roared.

'You win the iron pansy. I'll buy you a meal on the arrogance of the last two lines.'

Amory did not entirely agree with Tom's sweeping damnation of American novelists and poets. He enjoyed both Vachel Lindsay and Booth Tarkington, and admired the conscientious, if slender, artistry of Edgar Lee Masters.

'What I hate is this idiotic drivel about "I am God – I am man – I ride the winds – I look through the smoke – I am the life sense".'

'It's ghastly!'

'And I wish American novelists would give up trying to make business romantically interesting. Nobody wants to read about it, unless it's crooked business. If it was an entertaining subject, they'd buy the life of James J. Hill and not one of these long office tragedies that harp along on the significance of smoke——'

'And gloom,' said Tom. 'That's another favourite, though I'll admit the Russians have the monopoly. Our specialty is stories about little girls who break their spines and get adopted by grouchy old men because they smile so much. You'd think we were a race of cheerful cripples and that the common end of the Russian peasant was suicide——'

'Six o'clock,' said Amory, glancing at his wrist-watch. 'I'll buy you a grea' big dinner on the strength of the Juvenalia of your collected editions.'

Looking Backward

July sweltered out with a last hot week, and Amory in another surge of unrest realized that it was just five months since he and Rosalind had met. Yet it was already hard for him to visualize the heart-whole boy who had stepped off the transport, passionately desiring the adventure of life. One night while the heat, over-powering and enervating, poured into the windows of his room he struggled for several hours in a vague effort to immortalize the poignancy of that time.

The February streets, wind-washed by night, blow full of strange half-intermittent damps, bearing on wasted walks in shining sight wet snow plashed into gleams under the lamps, like golden oil from some divine machine, in an hour of thaw and stars.

Strange damps – full of the eyes of many men, crowded with life borne in upon a lull . . . . Oh, I was young, for I could turn again to you, most finite and most beautiful, and taste the stuff of half-remembered dreams, sweet and new on your mouth.

. . . There was a tanging in the midnight air – silence was dead and sound not yet awoken – Life cracked like ice! – one brilliant note and there, radiant and pale, you stood . . . and spring had broken. (The icicles were short upon the roofs and the changeling city swooned.)

Our thoughts were frosty mist along the eaves; our two ghosts kissed, high on the long, mazed wires – eerie half-laughter echoes here and leaves only a fatuous sigh for young desires; regret has followed after things she loved, leaving the great husk.

Another Ending

In mid-August came a letter from Monsignor Darcy, who had evidently just stumbled on his address:

MY DEAR BOY:

Your last letter was quite enough to make me worry about you. It was not a bit like yourself. Reading between the lines I should imagine that your engagement to this girl is making you rather unhappy, and I see you have lost all the feeling of romance that you had before the war. You make a great mistake if you think you can be romantic without re-ligion. Sometimes I think that with both of us the secret of success, when we find it, is the mystical element in us: something flows into us that enlarges our personalities, and when it ebbs out our personalities shrink; I should call your last two letters rather shrivelled. Beware of losing your-self in the personality of another being, man or woman.

His Eminence Cardinal O'Neill and the Bishop of Boston are staying with me at present, so it is hard for me to get a moment to write, but I wish you would come up here later if only for a week-end. I go to Washington this week.

What I shall do in the future is hanging in the balance. Absolutely between ourselves I should not be surprised to see the red hat of a cardinal descend upon my unworthy head within the next eight months. In any event, I should like to have a house in New York or Washington where you could drop in for week-ends.

Amory, I'm very glad we're both alive; this war could easily have been the end of a brilliant family. But in regard to matrimony, you are now at the most dangerous period of your life. You might marry in haste and repent at leisure, but I think you won't. From what you write me about the present calamitous state of your finances, what you want is naturally impossible. However, if I judge you by the means I usually choose, I should say that there will be something of an emotional crisis within the next year.

Do write me. I feel annoyingly out of date on you.

> With great affection,
> THAYER DARCY.

Within a week after the receipt of this letter their little household fell precipitously to pieces. The immediate cause was the serious and probably chronic illness of Tom's mother. So they stored the furniture, gave instructions to sublet and shook hands gloomily in the Pennsylvania Station. Amory and Tom seemed always to be saying good-bye.

Feeling very much alone, Amory yielded to an impulse and set off southward, intending to join Monsignor in Washington. They missed connections by two hours, and, deciding to spend a few days with an ancient, remembered uncle, Amory journeyed up through the luxuriant fields of Maryland into Ramilly County. But instead of two days his stay lasted from mid-August nearly through September, for in Maryland he met Eleanor.

III. YOUNG IRONY

For years afterwards when Amory thought of Eleanor he

seemed still to hear the wind sobbing around him and sending little chills into the places beside his heart. The night
when they rode up the slope and watched the cold moon
float through the clouds, he lost a further part of him that
nothing could restore; and when he lost it he lost also the
power of regretting it. Eleanor was, say, the last time that
evil crept close to Amory under the mask of beauty, the last
weird mystery that held him with wild fascination and
pounded his soul to flakes.

With her his imagination ran riot and that is why they
rode to the highest hill and watched an evil moon ride high,
for they knew then that they could see the devil in each
other. But Eleanor – did Amory dream her? Afterwards
their ghosts played, yet both of them hoped from their
souls never to meet. Was it the infinite sadness of her eyes
that drew him or the mirror of himself that he found in the
gorgeous clarity of her mind? She will have no other adventure like Amory, and if she reads this she will say:

'And Amory will have no other adventure like me.'

Nor will she sigh, any more than he would sigh.

Eleanor tried to put it on paper once:

> 'The fading things we only know
> We'll have forgotten . . .
> Put away . . .
> Desires that melted with the snow,
> And dreams begotten
> This to-day:
> The sudden dawns we laughed to greet,
> That all could see, that none could share,
> Will be but dawns . . . and if we meet
> We shall not care.
>
> Dear . . . not one tear will rise for this . . .
> A little while hence
> No regret
> Will stir for a remembered kiss—
> Not even silence,
> When we've met,

> Will give old ghosts a waste to roam,
> Or stir the surface of the sea . . .
> If grey shapes drift beneath the foam
> We shall not see.'

They quarrelled dangerously because Amory maintained that *sea* and *see* couldn't possibly be used as a rhyme. And then Eleanor had part of another verse that she couldn't find a beginning for:

> '. . . But wisdom passes . . . still the years
> Will feed us wisdom. . . . Age will go
> Back to the old— For all our tears
> We shall not know.'

Eleanor hated Maryland passionately. She belonged to the oldest of the old families of Ramilly County and lived in a big, gloomy house with her grandfather. She had been born and brought up in France. . . . I see I am starting wrong. Let me begin again.

Amory was bored, as he usually was in the country. He used to go for far walks by himself – and wander along reciting 'Ulalume' to the corn-fields, and congratulating Poe for drinking himself to death in that atmosphere of smiling complacency. One afternoon he had strolled for several miles along a road that was new to him, and then through a wood on bad advice from a coloured woman . . . losing himself entirely. A passing storm decided to break out, and to his great impatience the sky grew black as pitch and the rain began to splatter down through the trees, become suddenly furtive and ghostly. Thunder rolled with menacing crashes up the valley and scattered through the woods in intermittent batteries. He stumbled blindly on, hunting for a way out, and finally, through webs of twisted branches caught sight of a rift in the trees where the unbroken lightning showed open country. He rushed to the edge of the woods and then hesitated whether or not to cross the fields and try to reach the shelter of the little house marked by a light far down the valley. It was only half past five, but he could see scarcely ten steps before him, except when the lightning made everything vivid and grotesque for great sweeps around.

Suddenly a strange sound fell on his ears. It was a song in a low husky voice, a girl's voice, and whoever was singing was very close to him. A year before he might have laughed, or trembled; but in his restless mood he only stood and listened while the words sank into his consciousness:

> *'Les sanglots longs*
> *Des violons*
> *De l'automne*
> *Blessent mon coeur*
> *D'une langueur*
> *Monotone.'*

The lightning split the sky, but the song went on without a quaver. The girl was evidently in the field and the voice seemed to come vaguely from a haystack about twenty feet in front of him.

Then it ceased; ceased and began again in a weird chant that soared and hung and fell and blended with the rain:

> *'Tout suffocant*
> *Et blême quand*
> *Sonne l'heure*
> *Je me souviens*
> *Des jours anciens*
> *Et je pleure. . . .'*

'Who the devil is there in Ramilly County,' muttered Amory aloud, 'who would deliver Verlaine in an extemporaneous tune to a soaking haystack?'

'Somebody's there!' cried the voice unalarmed. 'Who are you ? – Manfred, St. Christopher, or Queen Victoria ?'

'I'm Don Juan!' Amory shouted on impulse, raising his voice above the noise of the rain and the wind.

A delighted shriek came from the haystack.

'I know who you are – you're the blond boy that likes "Ulalume" – I recognize your voice.'

'How do I get up?' he cried from the foot of the haystack, whither he had arrived, dripping wet. A head appeared over the edge – it was so dark that Amory could just make out a patch of damp hair and two eyes that gleamed like a cat's.

'Run back!' came the voice, 'and jump and I'll catch your hand – no, not there – on the other side.'

He followed directions and as he sprawled up the side, knee-deep in hay, a small, white hand reached out, gripped his, and helped him on to the top.

'Here you are, Juan,' cried she of the damp hair. 'Do you mind if I drop the Don?'

'You've got a thumb like mine!' he exclaimed.

'And you're holding my hand, which is dangerous without seeing my face.' He dropped it quickly.

As if in answer to his prayers came a flash of lightning and he looked eagerly at her who stood beside him on the soggy haystack, ten feet above the ground. But she had covered her face and he saw nothing but a slender figure, dark, damp, bobbed hair, and the small white hands with the thumbs that bent back like his.

'Sit down,' she suggested politely, as the dark closed in on them. 'If you'll sit opposite me in this hollow you can have half of the raincoat, which I was using as a water-proof tent until you so rudely interrupted me.'

'I was asked,' Amory said joyfully; 'you asked me – you know you did.'

'Don Juan always manages that,' she said, laughing, 'but I shan't call you that any more, because you've got reddish hair. Instead you can recite "Ulalume" and I'll be Psyche, your soul.'

Amory flushed, happily invisible under the curtain of wind and rain. They were sitting opposite each other in a slight hollow in the hay with the raincoat spread over most of them, and the rain doing for the rest. Amory was trying desperately to see Psyche, but the lightning refused to flash again, and he waited impatiently. Good Lord! supposing she wasn't beautiful – supposing she was forty and pedantic – heavens! Suppose, only suppose, she was mad. But he knew the last was unworthy. Here had Providence sent a girl to amuse him just as it sent Benvenuto Cellini men to murder, and he was wondering if she was mad, just because she exactly filled his mood.

'I'm not,' she said.

'Not what?'

'Not mad. I didn't think you were mad when I first saw you, so it isn't fair that you should think so of me.'

'How on earth——'

As long as they knew each other Eleanor and Amory could be 'on a subject' and stop talking with the definite thought of it in their heads, yet ten minutes later speak aloud and find that their minds had followed the same channels and led them each to a parallel idea, an idea that others would have found absolutely unconnected with the first.

'Tell me,' he demanded, leaning forward eagerly, 'how do you know about "Ulalume" – how did you know the colour of my hair? What's your name? What were you doing here? Tell me all at once!'

Suddenly the lightning flashed in with a leap of overreaching light and he saw Eleanor, and looked for the first time into those eyes of hers. Oh, she was magnificent – pale skin, the colour of marble in starlight, slender brows, and eyes that glittered green as emeralds in the blinding glare. She was a witch, of perhaps nineteen, he judged, alert and dreamy and with the tell-tale white line over her upper lip that was a weakness and a delight. He sank back with a gasp against the wall of hay.

'Now you've seen me,' she said calmly, 'and I suppose you're about to say that my green eyes are burning into your brain.'

'What colour is your hair?' he asked intently. 'It's bobbed, isn't it?'

'Yes, it's bobbed. I don't know what colour it is,' she answered, musing, 'so many men have asked me. It's medium, I suppose— No one ever looks long at my hair. I've got beautiful eyes, though, haven't I. I don't care what you say, I have beautiful eyes.'

'Answer my question, Madeline.'

'Don't remember them all – besides my name isn't Madeline, it's Eleanor.'

'I might have guessed it. You *look* like Eleanor – you have that Eleanor look. You know what I mean.'

There was a silence as they listened to the rain.

'It's going down my neck, fellow lunatic,' she offered finally.

'Answer my questions.'

'Well – name of Savage, Eleanor; live in big old house mile down road; nearest living relation to be notified, grandfather – Ramilly Savage; height, five feet four inches; number on watch-case, 3077 W; nose, delicate aquiline; temperament, uncanny——'

'And me,' Amory interrupted, 'where did you see me?'

'Oh, you're one of *those* men,' she answered haughtily, 'must lug old self into conversation. Well, my boy, I was behind a hedge sunning myself one day last week, and along comes a man saying in a pleasant, conceited way of talking:

> "And now when the night was senescent"
> > (says he)
> "And the star dials pointed to morn
> At the end of the path a liquescent"
> > (says he)
> "And nebulous lustre was born."

So I poked my eyes up over the hedge, but you had started to run, for some unknown reason, and so I saw but the back of your beautiful head. "Oh!" says I, "there's a man for whom many of us might sigh," and I continued in my best Irish——'

'All right,' Amory interrupted. 'Now go back to yourself.'

'Well, I will. I'm one of those people who go through the world giving other people thrills, but getting few myself except those I read into men on such nights as these. I have the social courage to go on the stage, but not the energy; I haven't the patience to write books; and I never met a man I'd marry. However, I'm only eighteen.'

The storm was dying down softly and only the wind kept up its ghostly surge and made the stack lean and gravely settle from side to side. Amory was in a trance. He felt that every moment was precious. He had never met a girl like this before – she would never seem quite the same again. He didn't at all feel like a character in a play, the appropriate feeling in an unconventional situation – instead, he had a sense of coming home.

'I have just made a great decision,' said Eleanor after another pause, 'and that is why I'm here, to answer another of your questions. I have just decided that I don't believe in immortality.'

'Really! how banal!'

'Frightfully so,' she answered, 'but depressing with a stale, sickly depression, nevertheless. I came out here to get wet – like a wet hen; wet hens always have great clarity of mind,' she concluded.

'Go on,' Amory said politely.

'Well – I'm not afraid of the dark, so I put on my slicker and rubber boots and came out. You see I was always afraid, before, to say I didn't believe in God – because the lightning might strike me – but here I am and it hasn't, of course, but the main point is that this time I wasn't any more afraid of it than I had been when I was a Christian Scientist, like I was last year. So now I know I'm a materialist and I was fraternizing with the hay when you came out and stood by the woods, scared to death.'

'Why, you little wretch—' cried Amory indignantly. 'Scared of what?'

'*Yourself!*' she shouted, and he jumped. She clapped her hands and laughed. 'See – see! Conscience – kill it like me! Eleanor Savage, materiologist – no jumping, no starting, come early——'

'But I *have* to have a soul,' he objected. 'I can't be rational – and I won't be molecular.'

She leaned toward him, her burning eyes never leaving his own and whispered with a sort of romantic finality:

'I thought so, Juan, I feared so – you're sentimental. You're not like me. I'm a romantic little materialist.'

'I'm not sentimental – I'm as romantic as you are. The idea, you know, is that the sentimental person thinks things will last – the romantic person has a desperate confidence that they won't.' (This was an ancient distinction of Amory's.)

'Epigrams. I'm going home,' she said sadly. 'Let's get off the haystack and walk to the cross-roads.'

They slowly descended from their perch. She would not let him help her down and motioning him away arrived in a graceful lump in the soft mud where she sat for an instant, laughing at herself. Then she jumped to her feet and slipped her hand into his, and they tip-toed across the fields, jumping and swinging from dry spot to dry spot. A transcendent delight seemed to sparkle in every pool of water, for the moon had risen and the storm had scurried away into western Maryland. When Eleanor's arm touched his he felt his hands grow cold with deadly fear lest he should lose the shadow brush with which his imagination was painting wonders of her. He watched her from the corners of his eyes as ever he did when he walked with her – she was a feast and a folly and he wished it had been his destiny to sit forever on a haystack and see life through her green eyes. His paganism soared that night and when she faded out like a grey ghost down the road, a deep singing came out of the fields and filled his way homeward. All night the summer moths flitted in and out of Amory's window; all night large looming sounds swayed in mystic revery through the silver grain – and he lay awake in the clear darkness.

September

Amory selected a blade of grass and nibbled at it scientifically.

'I never fall in love in August or September,' he proffered.

'When then?'

'Christmas or Easter. I'm a liturgist.'

'Easter!' She turned up her nose. 'Huh! Spring in corsets!'

'Easter *would* bore spring, wouldn't she? Easter has her hair braided, wears a tailored suit.'

'Bind on thy sandals, oh, thou most fleet.
Over the splendour and speed of thy feet——'

quoted Eleanor softly, and then added: 'I suppose Hallowe'en is a better day for autumn than Thanksgiving.'

'Much better – and Christmas eve does very well for winter, but summer . . .'

'Summer has no day,' she said. 'We can't possibly have a summer love. So many people have tried that the name's become proverbial. Summer is only the unfulfilled promise of spring, a charlatan in place of the warm balmy nights I dream of in April. It's a sad season of life without growth.... It has no day.'

'Fourth of July,' Amory suggested facetiously.

'Don't be funny!' she said, raking him with her eyes.

'Well, what could fulfil the promise of spring?'

She thought a moment.

'Oh, I suppose heaven would, if there was one,' she said finally, 'a sort of pagan heaven – you ought to be a materialist,' she continued irrelevantly.

'Why?'

'Because you look a good deal like the pictures of Rupert Brooke.'

To some extent Amory tried to play Rupert Brooke as long as he knew Eleanor. What he said, his attitude toward life, toward her, toward himself, were all reflexes of the dead Englishman's literary moods. Often she sat in the grass, a lazy wind playing with her short hair, her voice husky as she ran up and down the scale from Grantchester to Waikiki. There was something most passionate in Eleanor's reading aloud. They seemed nearer, not only mentally, but physically, when they read, than when she was in his arms, and this was often, for they fell half into love almost from the first. Yet was Amory capable of love now? He could, as always, run through the emotions in a half hour, but even while they revelled in their imaginations, he knew that neither of them could care as he had cared once before – I suppose that was why they turned to Brooke, and Swinburne, and Shelley. Their chance was to make everything fine and finished and rich and imaginative; they must bend tiny golden tentacles from his imagination to hers, that would take the place of the great, deep love that was never so near, yet never so much of a dream.

One poem they read over and over; Swinburne's 'Triumph of Time,' and four lines of it rang in his memory afterwards on warm nights when he saw the fireflies among dusky tree trunks and heard the low drone of many frogs. Then Eleanor seemed to come out of the night and stand by him, and he heard her throaty voice, with its tone of a fleecy-headed drum, repeating:

> '*Is it worth a tear, is it worth an hour,*
> *To think of things that are well outworn;*
> *Of fruitless husk and fugitive flower,*
> *The dream foregone and the deed foreborne ?*'

They were formally introduced two days later, and his aunt told him her history. The Ramillys were two: old Mr. Ramilly and his granddaughter, Eleanor. She had lived in France with a restless mother whom Amory imagined to have been very like his own, on whose death she had come to America, to live in Maryland. She had gone to Baltimore first to stay with a bachelor uncle, and there she insisted on being a débutante at the age of seventeen. She had a wild winter and arrived in the country in March, having quarrelled frantically with all her Baltimore relatives, and shocked them into fiery protest. A rather fast crowd had come out, who drank cocktails in limousines and were promiscuously condescending and patronizing toward older people, and Eleanor with an esprit that hinted strongly of the boulevards, led many innocents still redolent of St. Timothy's and Farmington, into paths of Bohemian naughtiness. When the story came to her uncle, a forgetful cavalier of a more hypocritical era, there was a scene, from which Eleanor emerged, subdued but rebellious and indignant, to seek haven with her grandfather who hovered in the country on the near side of senility. That's as far as her story went; she told him the rest herself, but that was later.

Often they swam and as Amory floated lazily in the water he shut his mind to all thoughts except those of hazy soap-bubble lands where the sun splattered through wind-drunk trees. How could any one possibly think or worry, or do anything except splash and dive and loll there on the edge of time while the flower months failed. Let the days move over – sadness and memory and pain recurred outside, and here, once more, before he went on to meet them he wanted to drift and be young.

There were days when Amory resented that life had changed from an even progress along a road stretching ever in sight, with the scenery merging and blending, into a succession of quick, unrelated scenes – two years of sweat and blood, that sudden absurd instinct for paternity that Rosalind had stirred; the half-sensual, half-neurotic quality of this autumn with Eleanor. He felt that it would take all time, more than he could ever spare, to glue these strange cumbersome pictures into the scrap-book of his life. It was all like a banquet where he sat for this half-hour of his youth and tried to enjoy brilliant epicurean courses.

Dimly he promised himself a time where all should be welded together. For months it seemed that he had alternated between being borne along a stream of love or fascination, or left in an eddy, and in the eddies he had not desired to think, rather to be picked up on a wave's top and swept along again.

'The despairing, dying autumn and our love – how well they harmonize!' said Eleanor sadly one day as they lay dripping by the water.

'The Indian summer of our hearts—' he ceased.

'Tell me,' she said finally, 'was she light or dark?'

'Light.'

'Was she more beautiful than I am?'

'I don't know,' said Amory shortly.

One night they walked while the moon rose and poured a great burden of glory over the garden until it seemed fairyland with Amory and Eleanor, dim phantasmal shapes, expressing eternal beauty in curious elfin love moods. Then they turned out of the moonlight into the trellised darkness of a vine-hung pagoda, where there were scents so plaintive as to be nearly musical.

'Light a match,' she whispered. 'I want to see you.'

Scratch! Flare!

The night and the scarred trees were like scenery in a play, and to be there with Eleanor, shadowy and unreal, seemed somehow oddly familiar. Amory thought how it was only the past that ever seemed strange and unbelievable. The match went out.

'It's black as pitch.'

'We're just voices now,' murmured Eleanor, 'little lonesome voices. Light another.'

'That was my last match.'

Suddenly he caught her in his arms.

'You *are* mine – you know you're mine!' he cried wildly . . . the moonlight twisted in through the vines and listened . . . the fireflies hung upon their whispers as if to win his glance from the glory of their eyes.

The End of Summer

'No wind is stirring in the grass; not one wind stirs . . . the water in the hidden pools, as glass, fronts the full moon and so inters the golden token in its icy mass,' chanted Eleanor to the trees that skeletoned the body of the night. 'Isn't it ghostly here? If you can hold your horse's feet up, let's cut through the woods and find the hidden pools.'

'It's after one, and you'll get the devil,' he objected, 'and I don't know enough about horses to put one away in the pitch dark.'

'Shut up, you old fool,' she whispered irrelevantly, and,

leaning over, she patted him lazily with her riding-crop. 'You can leave your old plug in our stable and I'll send him over to-morrow.'

'But my uncle has got to drive me to the station with this old plug at seven o'clock.'

'Don't be a spoil-sport – remember, you have a tendency toward wavering that prevents you from being the entire light of my life.'

Amory drew his horse up close beside, and, leaning toward her, grasped her hand.

'Say I am – *quick*, or I'll pull you over and make you ride behind me.'

She looked up and smiled and shook her head excitedly.

'Oh, do! – or rather, don't! Why are all the exciting things so uncomfortable, like fighting and exploring and skiing in Canada? By the way, we're going to ride up Harper's Hill. I think that comes in our programme about five o'clock.'

'You little devil,' Amory growled. 'You're going to make me stay up all night and sleep in the train like an immigrant all day to-morrow, going back to New York.'

'Hush! some one's coming along the road – let's go! *Whoo-ee-oop!*' And with a shout that probably gave the belated traveller a series of shivers, she turned her horse into the woods and Amory followed slowly, as he had followed her all day for three weeks.

The summer was over, but he had spent the days in watching Eleanor, a graceful, facile Manfred, build herself intellectual and imaginative pyramids while she revelled in the artificialities of the temperamental teens and they wrote poetry at the dinner-table.

When Vanity kissed Vanity, a hundred happy Junes ago, he pondered o'er her breathlessly, and, that all men might ever know, he rhymed her eyes with life and death:
'Thru Time I'll save my love!' he said . . . yet Beauty vanished with his breath, and, with her lovers, she was dead . . .

8

—Ever his wit and not her eyes, ever his art and not her hair:

'Who'd learn a trick in rhyme, be wise and pause before his sonnet there' . . . So all my words, however true, might sing you to a thousandth June, and no one ever *know* that you were Beauty for an afternoon.

So he wrote one day, when he pondered how coldly we thought of the 'Dark Lady of the Sonnets,' and how little we remembered her as the great man wanted her remembered. For what Shakespeare *must* have desired, to have been able to write with such divine despair, was that the lady should live . . . and now we have no real interest in her . . . The irony of it is that if he had cared *more* for the poem than for the lady the sonnet would be only obvious, imitative rhetoric and no one would ever have read it after twenty years. . . .

This was the last night Amory ever saw Eleanor. He was leaving in the morning and they had agreed to take a long farewell trot by the cold moonlight. She wanted to talk, she said – perhaps the last time in her life that she could be rational (she meant pose with comfort). So they had turned into the woods and rode for half an hour with scarcely a word, except when she whispered 'Damn!' at a bothersome branch – whispered it as no other girl was ever able to whisper it. Then they started up Harper's Hill, walking their tired horses.

'Good Lord! It's quiet here!' whispered Eleanor; 'much more lonesome than the woods.'

'I hate woods,' Amory said, shuddering. 'Any kind of foliage or underbrush at night. Out here it's so broad and easy on the spirit.'

'The long slope of a long hill.'

'And the cold moon rolling moonlight down it.'

'And thee and me, last and most important.'

It was quiet that night – the straight road they followed up to the edge of the cliff knew few footsteps at any time. Only an occasional negro cabin, silver-grey in the rock-ribbed moonlight, broke the long line of bare ground; behind lay the black edge of the woods like a dark frosting on white cake, and ahead the sharp, high horizon. It was much colder – so cold that it settled on them and drove all the warm nights from their minds.

'The end of summer,' said Eleanor softly. 'Listen to the beat of our horses' hoofs – "tump-tump-tump-a-tump."' Have you ever been feverish and had all noises divide into "tump-tump-tump" until you could swear eternity was divisible into so many tumps? That's the way I feel – old horses go tump-tump. . . . I guess that's the only thing that separates horses and clocks from us. Human beings can't go "tump-tump-tump" without going crazy.'

The breeze freshened and Eleanor pulled her cape around her and shivered.

'Are you very cold?' asked Amory.

'No, I'm thinking about myself – my black old inside self, the real one, with the fundamental honesty that keeps me from being absolutely wicked by making me realize my own sins.'

They were riding up close by the cliff and Amory gazed over. Where the fall met the ground a hundred feet below, a black stream made a sharp line, broken by tiny glints in the swift water.

'Rotten, rotten old world,' broke out Eleanor suddenly, 'and the wretchedest thing of all is me – oh, *why* am I a girl? Why am I not a stupid—? Look at you; you're stupider than I am, not much, but some, and you can lope about and get bored and then lope somewhere else, and you can play around with girls without being involved in meshes of senti-ment, and you can do anything and be justified – and here am I with the brains to do everything, yet tied to the sinking ship of future matrimony. If I were born a hundred years from now, well and good, but now what's in store for me – I have to marry, that goes without saying. Who? I'm too bright for most men, and yet I have to descend to their level and let them patronize my intellect in order to get their atten-tion. Every year that I don't marry I've got less chance for a first-class man. At the best I can have my choice from one or two cities and, of course, I have to marry into a dinner-coat.'

'Listen,' she leaned close again, 'I like clever men and good-looking men, and, of course, no one cares more for personality than I do. Oh, just one person in fifty has any glimmer of what sex is. I'm hipped on Freud and all that, but it's rotten that every bit of *real* love in the world is ninety-nine per cent passion and one little soupçon of jealousy.' She finished as suddenly as she began.

'Of course, you're right,' Amory agreed. 'It's a rather un-pleasant overpowering force that's part of the machinery under everything. It's like an actor that lets you see his mechanics! Wait a minute till I think this out. . . .'

He paused and tried to get a metaphor. They had turned the cliff and were riding along the road about fifty feet to the left.

'You see every one's got to have some cloak to throw around it. The mediocre intellects, Plato's second class, use the remnants of romantic chivalry diluted with Victorian sentiment – and we who consider ourselves the intellectuals cover it up by pretending that it's another side of us, has nothing to do with our shining brains; we pretend that the fact that we realize it is really absolving us from being a prey to it. But the truth is that sex is right in the middle of our purest abstractions, so close that it obscures vision. . . . I can kiss you now and will. . . .' He leaned toward her in his saddle, but she drew away.

'I can't – I can't kiss you now – I'm more sensitive.'

'You're more stupid then,' he declared rather impatiently. 'Intellect is no protection from sex any more than convention is . . .'

'What is?' she fired up. 'The Catholic Church or the maxims of Confucius?'

Amory looked up, rather taken aback.

'That's your panacea, isn't it?' she cried. 'Oh, you're just an old hypocrite, too. Thousands of scowling priests keeping the degenerate Italians and illiterate Irish repentant with gabble-gabble about the sixth and ninth commandments.

It's just all cloaks, sentiment and spiritual rouge and pana-
ceas. I'll tell you there *is* no God, not even a definite abstract
goodness; so it's all got to be worked out for the individual
by the individual here in high white foreheads like mine, and
you're too much the prig to admit it.' She let go her reins
and shook her little fists at the stars.

'If there's a God let him strike me – strike me!'

'Talking about God again after the manner of atheists,'
Amory said sharply. His materialism, always a thin cloak,
was torn to shreds by Eleanor's blasphemy. . . . She knew
it and it angered him that she knew it.

'And like most intellectuals who don't find faith convenient,' he continued coldly, 'like Napoleon and Oscar Wilde
and the rest of your type, you'll yell loudly for a priest on
your death-bed.'

Eleanor drew her horse up sharply and he reined in beside
her.

'Will I?' she said in a queer voice that scared him. 'Will
I? Watch! *I'm going over the cliff!*' And before he could
interfere she had turned and was riding breakneck for the
end of the plateau.

He wheeled and started after her, his body like ice, his
nerves in a vast clangour. There was no chance of stopping
her. The moon was under a cloud and her horse would step
blindly over. Then some ten feet from the edge of the cliff
she gave a sudden shriek and flung herself sideways –
plunged from her horse and, rolling over twice, landed in a
pile of brush five feet from the edge. The horse went over
with a frantic whinny. In a minute he was by Eleanor's side
and saw that her eyes were open.

'Eleanor!' he cried.

She did not answer, but her lips moved and her eyes filled
with sudden tears.

'Eleanor, are you hurt?'

'No; I don't think so,' she said faintly, and then began
weeping.

'My horse dead?'

'Good God— Yes!'

'Oh!' she wailed. 'I thought I was going over. I didn't know——'

He helped her gently to her feet and boosted her on to his saddle. So they started homeward; Amory walking and she bent forward on the pommel, sobbing bitterly.

'I've got a crazy streak,' she faltered, 'twice before I've done things like that. When I was eleven mother went – went mad – stark raving crazy. We were in Vienna——'

All the way back she talked haltingly about herself, and Amory's love waned slowly with the moon. At her door they started from habit to kiss good-night, but she could not run into his arms, nor were they stretched to meet her as in the week before. For a minute they stood there, hating each other with a bitter sadness. But as Amory had loved himself in Eleanor, so now what he hated was only a mirror. Their poses were strewn about the pale dawn like broken glass. The stars were long gone and there were left only the little sighing gusts of wind and the silences between . . . but naked souls are poor things ever, and soon he turned homeward and let new lights come in with the sun.

A Poem that Eleanor Sent Amory
Several Years Later

'Here, Earth-born, over the lilt of the water,
   Lisping its music and bearing a burden of light,
Bosoming day as a laughing and radiant daughter . . .
   Here we may whisper unheard, unafraid of the night.
Walking alone . . . was it splendour, or what, we were bound
      with,
   Deep in the time when summer lets down her hair?
Shadows we loved and the patterns they covered the ground
      with
   Tapestries, mystical, faint in the breathless air.

That was the day . . . and the night for another story,
   Pale as a dream and shadowed with pencilled trees –
Ghosts of the stars came by who had sought for glory,
   Whispered to us of peace in the plaintive breeze,

Whispered of old dead faiths that the day had shattered,
  Youth the penny that bought delight of the moon;
That was the urge that we knew and the language that mat-
    tered
  That was the debt that we paid to the usurer June.

Here, deepest of dreams, by the waters that bring not
  Anything back of the past that we need not know,
What if the light is but sun and the little streams sing not,
  We are together, it seems . . . I have loved you so . . .
What did the last night hold, with the summer over,
  Drawing us back to the home in the changing glade?
What leered out of the dark in the ghostly clover?

  God! . . . till you stirred in your sleep . . . and were wild
    afraid . . .
Well . . . we have passed . . . we are chronicle now to the
    eerie.
  Curious metal from meteors that failed in the sky;
Earth-born the tireless is stretched by the water, quite
    weary,
  Close to this ununderstandable changeling that's I . . .
Fear is an echo we traced to Security's daughter;
  Now we are faces and voices . . . and less, too soon,
Whispering half-love over the lilt of the water . . .
  Youth the penny that bought delight of the moon.'

A Poem Amory Sent to Eleanor and Which
He Called 'Summer Storm'

  'Faint winds, and a song fading and leaves falling,
  Faint winds, and far away a fading laughter . . .
  And the rain and over the fields a voice calling . . .

  Our grey blown cloud scurries and lifts above,
  Slides on the sun and flutters there to waft her
  Sisters on. The shadow of a dove
  Falls on the cote, the trees are filled with wings;
  And down the valley through the crying trees
  The body of the darker storm flies; brings

With its new air the breath of sunken seas
And slender tenuous thunder . . .
                    But I wait . . .
Wait for the mists and for the blacker rain –
Heavier winds that stir the veil of fate,
Happier winds that pile her hair;
                    Again
They tear me, teach me, strew the heavy air
Upon me, winds that I know, and storm.

There was a summer every rain was rare;
There was a season every wind was warm. . . .
And now *you* pass me in the mist . . . your hair
Rain-blown about you, damp lips curved once more
In that wild irony, that gay despair
That made you old when we have met before;
Wraith-like you drift on out before the rain,
Across the fields, blown with the stemless flowers,
With your old hopes, dead leaves and loves again –
Dim as a dream and wan with all old hours
(Whispers will creep into the growing dark . . .
Tumult will die over the trees)
                    Now night
Tears from her wetted breast the splattered blouse
Of day, glides down the dreaming hills, tear-bright,
To cover with her hair the eerie green . . .
Love for the dusk . . . Love for the glistening after;
Quiet the trees to their last tops . . . serene . . .

Faint winds, and far away a fading laughter . . .'

IV. THE SUPERCILIOUS SACRIFICE

Atlantic City. Amory paced the board walk at day's end,
lulled by the everlasting surge of changing waves, smelling
the half-mournful odour of the salt breeze. The sea, he

thought, had treasured its memories deeper than the faith-less land. It seemed still to whisper of Norse galleys plough-ing the water world under raven-figured flags, of the British dreadnoughts, grey bulwarks of civilization steaming up through the fog of one dark July into the North Sea.

'Well – Amory Blaine!'

Amory looked down into the street below. A low racing car had drawn to a stop and a familiar cheerful face pro-truded from the driver's seat.

'Come on down, goopher!' cried Alec.

Amory called a greeting and descending a flight of wooden steps approached the car. He and Alec had been meeting intermittently, but the barrier of Rosalind lay always be-tween them. He was sorry for this; he hated to lose Alec.

'Mr. Blaine, this is Miss Waterson, Miss Wayne, and Mr. Tully.'

'How d'y do?'

'Amory,' said Alec exuberantly, 'if you'll jump in we'll take you to some secluded nook and give you a wee jolt of Bourbon.'

Amory considered.

'That's an idea.'

'Step in – move over, Jill, and Amory will smile very handsomely at you.'

Amory squeezed into the back seat beside a gaudy, vermilion-lipped blonde.

'Hello, Doug Fairbanks,' she said flippantly. 'Walking for exercise or hunting for company?'

'I was counting the waves,' replied Amory gravely. 'I'm going in for statistics.'

'Don't kid me, Doug.'

When they reached an unfrequented side street Alec stopped the car among deep shadows.

'What you doing down here these cold days, Amory?' he demanded, as he produced a quart of Bourbon from under the fur rug.

Amory avoided the question. Indeed, he had had no defi-nite reason for coming to the coast.

'Do you remember that party of ours, sophomore year?' he asked instead.

'Do I? When we slept in the pavilions up in Asbury Park——'

'Lord, Alec! It's hard to think that Jesse and Dick and Kerry are all three dead.'

Alec shivered.

'Don't talk about it. These dreary fall days depress me enough.'

Jill seemed to agree.

'Doug here is sorta gloomy anyways,' she commented. 'Tell him to drink deep – it's good and scarce these days.'

'What I really want to ask you, Amory, is where you are——'

'Why, New York, I suppose——'

'I mean to-night, because if you haven't got a room yet you'd better help me out.'

'Glad to.'

'You see, Tully and I have two rooms with bath between at the Ranier, and he's got to go back to New York. I don't want to have to move. Question is, will you occupy one of the rooms?'

Amory was willing, if he could get in right away.

'You'll find the key in the office; the rooms are in my name.'

Declining further locomotion or further stimulation, Amory left the car and sauntered back along the board walk to the hotel.

He was in an eddy again, a deep, lethargic gulf, without desire to work or write, love or dissipate. For the first time in his life he rather longed for death to roll over his generation, obliterating their petty fevers and struggles and exultations. His youth seemed never so vanished as now in the contrast between the utter loneliness of this visit and that riotous, joyful party of four years before. Things that had been the merest commonplaces of his life then, deep sleep, the sense of beauty around him, all desire, had flown away and the gaps they left were filled only with the great listlessness of his disillusion.

'To hold a man a woman has to appeal to the worst in him.' This sentence was the thesis of most of his bad nights, of which he felt this was to be one. His mind had already started to play variations on the subject. Tireless passion, fierce jealousy, longing to possess and crush – these alone were left of all his love for Rosalind; these remained to him as payment for the loss of his youth – bitter calomel under the thin sugar of love's exaltation.

In his room he undressed and wrapping himself in blankets to keep out the chill October air drowsed in an armchair by the open window.

He remembered a poem he had read months before:

'Oh staunch old heart who toiled so long for me,
  I waste my years sailing along the sea——'

Yet he had no sense of waste, no sense of the present hope that waste implied. He felt that life had rejected him.

'Rosalind! Rosalind!' He poured the words softly into the half-darkness until she seemed to permeate the room; the wet salt breeze filled his hair with moisture, the rim of a moon seared the sky and made the curtains dim and ghostly. He fell asleep.

When he awoke it was very late and quiet. The blanket had slipped partly off his shoulders and he touched his skin to find it damp and cold.

Then he became aware of a tense whispering not ten feet away.

He became rigid.

'*Don't make a sound!*' It was Alec's voice. '*Jill – do you hear me?*'

'*Yes –*' breathed very low, very frightened. They were in the bathroom.

Then his ears caught a louder sound from somewhere along the corridor outside. It was a mumbling of men's voices and a repeated muffled rapping. Amory threw off the blankets and moved close to the bathroom door.

'My God!' came the girl's voice again. 'You'll have to let
them in.'

'*Sh!*'

Suddenly a steady, insistent knocking began at Amory's
hall door and simultaneously out of the bathroom came
Alec, followed by the vermilion-lipped girl. They were both
clad in pyjamas.

'Amory!' an anxious whisper.

'What's the trouble?'

'It's house detectives. My God, Amory – they're just
looking for a test-case——'

'Well, better let them in.'

'You don't understand. They can get me under the Mann
Act.'

The girl followed him slowly, a rather miserable, pathetic
figure in the darkness.

Amory tried to plan quickly.

'You make a racket and let them in your room', he suggested anxiously, 'and I'll get her out by this door.'

'They're here too, though. They'll watch this door.'

'Can't you give a wrong name?'

'No chance. I registered under my own name; besides,
they'd trail the auto licence number.'

'Say you're married.'

'Jill says one of the house detectives knows her.'

The girl had stolen to the bed and tumbled upon it; lay
there listening wretchedly to the knocking which had grown
gradually to a pounding. Then came a man's voice, angry
and imperative:

'Open up or we'll break the door in!'

In the silence when this voice ceased Amory realized that
there were other things in the room besides people . . . over
and around the figure crouched on the bed there hung an
aura, gossamer as a moonbeam, tainted as stale, weak wine,
yet a horror, diffusively brooding already over the three of
them . . . and over by the window among the stirring curtains stood something else, featureless and indistinguishable,
yet strangely familiar. . . . Simultaneously two great cases

presented themselves side by side to Amory; all that took place in his mind, then, occupied in actual time less than ten seconds.

The first fact that flashed radiantly on his comprehension was the great impersonality of sacrifice – perceived that what we call love and hate, reward and punishment, had no more to do with it than the date of the month. He quickly recapitulated the story of a sacrifice he had heard of in college: a man had cheated in an examination; his roommate in a gust of sentiment had taken the entire blame – due to the shame of it the innocent one's entire future seemed shrouded in regret and failure, capped by the ingratitude of the real culprit. He had finally taken his own life – years afterward the facts had come out. At the time the story had both puzzled and worried Amory. Now he realized the truth; that sacrifice was no purchase of freedom. It was like a great elective office, it was like an inheritance of power – to certain people at certain times an essential luxury, carrying with it not a guarantee but a responsibility, not a security but an infinite risk. Its very momentum might drag him down to ruin – the passing of the emotional wave that made it possible might leave the one who made it high and dry forever on an island of despair.

. . . Amory knew that afterwards Alec would secretly hate him for having done so much for him. . . .

. . . All this was flung before Amory like an opened scroll, while ulterior to him and speculating upon him were those two breathless, listening forces: the gossamer aura that hung over and about the girl and that familiar thing by the window.

Sacrifice by its very nature was arrogant and impersonal; sacrifice should be eternally supercilious.

Weep not for me but for thy children.

That – thought Amory – would be somehow the way God would talk to me.

Amory felt a sudden surge of joy and then like a face in a motion-picture the aura over the bed faded out; the dynamic shadow by the window, that was as near as he could name it, remained for the fraction of a moment and then the breeze seemed to lift it swiftly out of the room. He clenched his hands in quick ecstatic excitement . . . the ten seconds were up. . . .

'Do what I say, Alec – do what I say. Do you under-stand ?'

Alec looked at him dumbly – his face a tableau of anguish.

'You have a family,' continued Amory slowly. 'You have a family and it's important that you should get out of this. Do you hear me ?' He repeated clearly what he had said. 'Do you hear me ?'

'I hear you.' The voice was curiously strained, the eyes never for a second left Amory's.

'Alec, you're going to lie down here. If any one comes in you act drunk. You do what I say – if you don't I'll probably kill you.'

There was another moment while they stared at each other. Then Amory went briskly to the bureau and, taking his pocket-book, beckoned peremptorily to the girl. He heard one word from Alec that sounded like 'penitentiary,' then he and Jill were in the bathroom with the door bolted behind them.

'You're here with me,' he said sternly. 'You've been with me all evening.'

She nodded, gave a little half-cry.

In a second he had the door of the other room open and three men entered. There was an immediate flood of electric light and he stood there blinking.

'You've been playing a little too dangerous a game, young man!'

Amory laughed.

'Well ?'

The leader of the trio nodded authoritatively at a burly man in a check suit.

'All right, Olson.'

'I got you, Mr. O'May,' said Olson, nodding. The other two took a curious glance at their quarry and then withdrew, closing the door angrily behind them.

The burly man regarded Amory contemptuously.

'Didn't you ever hear of the Mann Act? Coming down here with her,' he indicated the girl with his thumb, 'with a New York licence on your car – to a hotel like *this*.' He shook his head implying that he had struggled over Amory but now gave him up.

'Well,' said Amory rather impatiently, 'what do you want us to do?'

'Get dressed, quick – and tell your friend not to make such a racket.' Jill was sobbing noisily on the bed, but at these words she subsided sulkily and, gathering up her clothes, retired to the bathroom. As Amory slipped into Alec's B. V. D.'s he found that his attitude toward the situation was agreeably humorous. The aggrieved virtue of the burly man made him want to laugh.

'Anybody else here?' demanded Olson, trying to look keen and ferret-like.

'Fellow who had the rooms,' said Amory carelessly. 'He's drunk as an owl, though. Been in there asleep since six o'clock.'

'I'll take a look at him presently.'

'How did you find out?' asked Amory curiously.

'Night clerk saw you go upstairs with this woman.'

Amory nodded; Jill reappeared from the bathroom, completely if rather untidily arrayed.

'Now then,' began Olson, producing a note-book, 'I want your real names – no damn John Smith or Mary Brown.'

'Wait a minute,' said Amory quietly. 'Just drop that big-bully stuff. We merely got caught, that's all.'

Olson glared at him.

'Name?' he snapped.

Amory gave his name and New York address.

'And the lady?'

'Miss Jill——'

'Say,' cried Olson indignantly, 'just ease up on the nursery rhymes. What's your name? Sarah Murphy? Minnie Jackson?'

'Oh, my God!' cried the girl cupping her tear-stained face

in her hands. 'I don't want my mother to know. I don't want my mother to know.'

'Come on now!'

'Shut up!' cried Amory at Olson.

An instant's pause.

'Stella Robbins,' she faltered finally. 'General Delivery, Rugway, New Hampshire.'

Olson snapped his note-book shut and looked at them very ponderously.

'By rights the hotel could turn the evidence over to the police and you'd go to penitentiary, you would, for bringin' a girl from one State to 'nother f'r immoral purp'ses' – he paused to let the majesty of his words sink in. 'But – the hotel is going to let you off.'

'It doesn't want to get in the papers,' cried Jill fiercely. 'Let us off! Huh!'

A great lightness surrounded Amory. He realized that he was safe and only then did he appreciate the full enormity of what he might have incurred.

'However,' continued Olson, 'there's a protective association among the hotels. There's been too much of this stuff, and we got a 'rangement with the newspapers so that you get a little free publicity. Not the name of the hotel, but just a line sayin' that you had a little trouble in 'lantic City. See?'

'I see.'

'You're gettin' off light – damn light – but——'

'Come on,' said Amory briskly. 'Let's get out of here. We don't need a valedictory.'

Olson walked through the bathroom and took a cursory glance at Alec's still form. Then he extinguished the lights and motioned them to follow him. As they walked into the elevator Amory considered a piece of bravado – yielded finally. He reached out and tapped Olson on the arm.

'Would you mind taking off your hat? There's a lady in the elevator.'

Olson's hat came off slowly. There was a rather embarrassing two minutes under the lights of the lobby while the night clerk and a few belated guests stared at them curiously; the loudly dressed girl with bent head, the handsome young man with his chin several points aloft; the inference was quite obvious. Then the chill outdoors – where the salt air was fresher and keener still with the first hints of morning.

'You can get one of those taxis and beat it,' said Olson, pointing to the blurred outline of two machines whose drivers were presumably asleep inside.

'Good-bye,' said Olson. He reached in his pocket suggestively, but Amory snorted, and, taking the girl's arm, turned away.

'Where did you tell the driver to go ?' she asked as they whirled along the dim street.

'The station.'

'If that guy writes my mother——'

'He won't. Nobody'll ever know about this – except our friends and enemies.'

Dawn was breaking over the sea.

'It's getting blue,' she said.

'It does very well,' agreed Amory critically, and then as an after-thought: 'It's almost breakfast-time – do you want something to eat ?'

'Food——' she said with a cheerful laugh. 'Food is what queered the party. We ordered a big supper to be sent up to the room about two o'clock. Alec didn't give the waiter a tip, so I guess the little bastard snitched.'

Jill's low spirits seemed to have gone faster than the scattering night. 'Let me tell you,' she said emphatically, 'when you want to stage that sorta party stay away from liquor, and when you want to get tight stay away from bed-rooms.'

'I'll remember.'

He tapped suddenly at the glass and they drew up at the door of an all-night restaurant.

'Is Alec a great friend of yours ?' asked Jill as they perched themselves on high stools inside, and set their elbows on the dingy counter.

'He used to be. He probably won't want to be any more – and never understand why.'

'It was sorta crazy you takin' all that blame. Is he pretty important? Kinda more important than you are?'

Amory laughed.

'That remains to be seen,' he answered. 'That's the question.'

The Collapse of Several Pillars

Two days later back in New York Amory found in a news-paper what he had been searching for – a dozen lines which announced to whom it might concern that Mr. Amory Blaine, who 'gave his address' as, etc., had been requested to leave his hotel in Atlantic City because of entertaining in his room a lady *not* his wife.

Then he started, and his fingers trembled, for directly above was a longer paragraph of which the first words were:

'Mr. and Mrs. Leland R. Connage are announcing the engagement of their daughter, Rosalind, to Mr. J. Dawson Ryder, of Hartford, Connecticut——'

He dropped the paper and lay down on his bed with a frightened, sinking sensation in the pit of his stomach. She was gone, definitely, finally gone. Until now he had half un-consciously cherished the hope deep in his heart that some day she would need him and send for him, cry that it had been a mistake, that her heart ached only for the pain she had caused him. Never again could he find even the sombre luxury of wanting her – not this Rosalind, harder, older – nor any beaten, broken woman that his imagination brought to the door of his forties – Amory had wanted her youth, the fresh radiance of her mind and body, the stuff that she was selling now once and for all. So far as he was concerned, young Rosalind was dead.

A day later came a crisp, terse letter from Mr. Barton in Chicago, which informed him that as three more street-car companies had gone into the hands of receivers he could expect for the present no further remittances. Last of all, on a dazed Sunday night, a telegram told him of Monsignor Darcy's sudden death in Philadelphia five days before.

He knew then what it was that he had perceived among the curtains of the room in Atlantic City.

V. THE EGOTIST BECOMES A PERSONAGE

'*A fathom deep in sleep I lie*
With old desires, restrained before,
To clamour lifeward with a cry,
As dark flies out the greying door;
And so in quest of creeds to share
I seek assertive day again . . .
But old monotony is there:
Endless avenues of rain.

Oh, might I rise again! Might I
Throw off the heat of that old wine,
See the new morning mass the sky
With fairy towers, line on line;
Find each mirage in the high air
A symbol, not a dream again . . .
But old monotony is there:
Endless avenues of rain.'

Under the glass portcullis of a theatre Amory stood, watching the first great drops of rain splatter down and flatten to dark stains on the sidewalk. The air became grey and opalescent; a solitary light suddenly outlined a window over the way; then another light; then a hundred more danced and glimmered into vision. Under his feet a thick, iron-studded skylight turned yellow; in the street the lamps of the taxi-cabs sent out glistening sheens along the already black pavement. The unwelcome November rain had perversely stolen the day's last hour and pawned it with that ancient fence, the night.

The silence of the theatre behind him ended with a

curious snapping sound, followed by the heavy roaring of a rising crowd and the interlaced clatter of many voices. The matinée was over.

He stood aside, edged a little into the rain to let the throng pass. A small boy rushed out, sniffed in the damp, fresh air and turned up the collar of his coat; came three or four couples in a great hurry; came a further scattering of people whose eyes as they emerged glanced invariably, first at the wet street, then at the rain-filled air, finally at the dismal sky; last a dense, strolling mass that depressed him with its heavy odour compounded of the tobacco smell of the men and the fetid sensuousness of stale powder on women. After the thick crowd came another scattering; a stray half-dozen; a man on crutches; finally the rattling bang of folding seats inside announced that the ushers were at work.

New York seemed not so much awakening as turning over in its bed. Pallid men rushed by, pinching together their coat-collars; a great swarm of tired, magpie girls from a department-store crowded along with shrieks of strident laughter, three to an umbrella; a squad of marching policemen passed, already miraculously protected by oilskin capes.

The rain gave Amory a feeling of detachment, and the numerous unpleasant aspects of city life without money occurred to him in threatening procession. There was the ghastly, stinking crush of the subway – the car cards thrusting themselves at one, leering out like dull bores who grab your arm with another story; the querulous worry as to whether some one isn't leaning on you; a man deciding not to give his seat to a woman, hating her for it; the woman hating him for not doing it; at worst a squalid phantasmagoria of breath, and old cloth on human bodies and the smells of the food men ate – at best just people – too hot or too cold, tired, worried.

He pictured the rooms where these people lived – where the patterns of the blistered wall-papers were heavy reiterated sunflowers on green and yellow backgrounds, where there were tin bathtubs and gloomy hallways and verdureless, unnamable spaces in back of the buildings; where even love dressed as seduction – a sordid murder around the corner, illicit motherhood in the flat above. And always there was the economical stuffiness of indoor winter, and the long summers, nightmares of perspiration between sticky enveloping walls . . . dirty restaurants where careless, tired people helped themselves to sugar with their own used coffee-spoons, leaving hard brown deposits in the bowl.

It was not so bad where there were only men or else only women; it was when they were vilely herded that it all seemed so rotten. It was some shame that women gave off at having men see them tired and poor – it was some disgust that men had for women who were tired and poor. It was dirtier than any battle-field he had seen, harder to contemplate than any actual hardship moulded of mire and sweat and danger, it was an atmosphere wherein birth and marriage and death were loathsome, secret things.

He remembered one day in the subway when a delivery boy had brought in a great funeral wreath of fresh flowers, how the smell of it had suddenly cleared the air and given every one in the car a momentary glow.

'I detest poor people,' thought Amory suddenly. 'I hate them for being poor. Poverty may have been beautiful once, but it's rotten now. It's the ugliest thing in the world. It's essentially cleaner to be corrupt and rich than it is to be innocent and poor.' He seemed to see again a figure whose significance had once impressed him – a well-dressed young man gazing from a club window on Fifth Avenue and saying something to his companion with a look of utter disgust. Probably, thought Amory, what he said was: 'My God! Aren't people horrible!'

Never before in his life had Amory considered poor people. He thought cynically how completely he was lacking in all human sympathy. O. Henry had found in these people romance, pathos, love, hate – Amory saw only coarseness, physical filth, and stupidity. He made no self-accusations: never any more did he reproach himself for feelings that were natural and sincere. He accepted all his reactions as a part of him, unchangeable, unmoral. This problem of poverty transformed, magnified, attached to some grander, more dignified attitude might some day even be his problem; at present it roused only his profound distaste.

He walked over to Fifth Avenue, dodging the blind, black menace of umbrellas, and standing in front of Delmonico's hailed an auto-bus. Buttoning his coat closely around him he climbed to the roof, where he rode in solitary state through the thin, persistent rain, stung into alertness by the cool moisture perpetually reborn on his cheek. Somewhere in his mind a conversation began, rather resumed its place in his attention. It was composed not of two voices, but of one, which acted alike as questioner and answerer:

Question.—Well – what's the situation?

Answer.—That I have about twenty-four dollars to my name.

Q.—You have the Lake Geneva estate.

A.—But I intend to keep it.

Q.—Can you live?

A.—I can't imagine not being able to. People make money in books and I've found that I can always do the things that people do in books. Really they are the only things I can do.

Q.—Be definite.

A.—I don't know what I'll do – nor have I much curiosity. To-morrow I'm going to leave New York for good. It's a bad town unless you're on top of it.

Q.—Do you want a lot of money?

A.—No. I am merely afraid of being poor.

Q.—Very afraid?

A.—Just passively afraid.

Q.—Where are you drifting?

A.—Don't ask *me*!

Q.—Don't you care?

A.—Rather. I don't want to commit moral suicide.

Q.—Have you no interests left?

A.—None. I've no more virtue to lose. Just as a cooling pot gives off heat, so all through youth and adolescence we give off calories of virtue. That's what's called ingenuousness.

Q.—An interesting idea.

A.—That's why a 'good man going wrong' attracts people. They stand around and literally *warm themselves* at the calories of virtue he gives off. Sarah makes an unsophisticated remark and the faces simper in delight – 'How *innocent* the poor child is!' They're warming themselves at her virtue. But Sarah sees the simper and never makes that remark again. Only she feels a little colder after that.

Q.—All your calories gone?

A.—All of them. I'm beginning to warm myself at other people's virtue.

Q.—Are you corrupt?

A.—I think so. I'm not sure. I'm not sure about good and evil at all any more.

Q.—Is that a bad sign in itself?

A.—Not necessarily.

Q.—What would be the test of corruption?

A.—Becoming really insincere – calling myself 'not such a bad fellow,' thinking I regretted my lost youth when I only envy the delights of losing it. Youth is like having a big plate of candy. Sentimentalists think they want to be in the pure, simple state they were in before they ate the candy. They don't. They just want the fun of eating it all over again. The matron doesn't want to repeat her girlhood – she wants to repeat her honeymoon. I don't want to repeat my innocence. I want the pleasure of losing it again.

Q.—Where are you drifting?

This dialogue merged grotesquely into his mind's most familiar state – a grotesque blending of desires, worries, exterior impressions and physical reactions.

One Hundred and Twenty-seventh Street – or One Hundred and Thirty-seventh Street . . . Two and three look alike – no, not much. Seat damp . . . are clothes absorbing wetness from seat, or seat absorbing dryness from clothes? . . . Sitting on wet substance gave appendicitis, so Froggy Parker's mother said. Well, he'd had it – I'll sue the steamboat company, Beatrice said, and my uncle has a quarter interest – did Beatrice go to heaven? . . . probably not – He represented Beatrice's immortality, also love-affairs of numerous dead men who surely had never thought of him . . . if it wasn't appendicitis, influenza maybe. What? One Hundred and Twentieth Street? That must have been One Hundred and Twelfth back there. One O Two instead of One Two Seven. Rosalind not like Beatrice, Eleanor like Beatrice, only wilder and brainier. Apartments along here expensive – probably hundred and fifty a month – maybe two hundred. Uncle had only paid hundred a month for whole great big house in Minneapolis. Question – were the stairs on the left or right as you came in? Anyway, in 12 Univee they were straight back and to the left. What a dirty river – want to go down there and see if it's dirty – French rivers all brown or black, so were Southern rivers. Twenty-four dollars meant four hundred and eighty doughnuts. He could live on it three months and sleep in the park. Wonder where Jill was – Jill Bayne, Fayne, Sayne – what the devil – neck hurts, darned uncomfortable seat. No desire to sleep with Jill, what could Alec see in her? Alec had a coarse taste in women. Own taste the best; Isabelle, Clara, Rosalind, Eleanor, were all-American. Eleanor would pitch, probably southpaw. Rosalind was outfield, wonderful hitter, Clara first base, maybe. Wonder what Humbird's body looked like now. If he himself hadn't been bayonet instructor he'd have gone up to line three months sooner, probably been killed. Where's the darned bell——

The street numbers of Riverside Drive were obscured by the mist and dripping trees from anything but the swiftest scrutiny, but Amory had finally caught sight of one – One Hundred and Twenty-seventh Street. He got off and with no distinct destination followed a winding, descending side-walk and came out facing the river, in particular a long pier and a partitioned litter of shipyards for miniature craft: small launches, canoes, rowboats, and catboats. He turned northward and followed the shore, jumped a small wire fence and found himself in a great disorderly yard adjoining

a dock. The hulls of many boats in various stages of repair
were around him; he smelled sawdust and paint and the
scarcely distinguishable flat odour of the Hudson. A man
approached through the heavy gloom.

'Hello,' said Amory.

'Got a pass?'

'No. Is this private?'

'This is the Hudson River Sporting and Yacht Club.'

'Oh! I didn't know. I'm just resting.'

'Well—' began the man dubiously.

'I'll go if you want me to.'

The man made non-committal noises in his throat and
passed on. Amory seated himself on an overturned boat and
leaned forward thoughtfully until his chin rested in his hand.

'Misfortune is liable to make me a damn bad man,' he
said slowly.

In the Drooping Hours

While the rain drizzled on Amory looked futilely back at
the stream of his life, all its glitterings and dirty shallows. To
begin with, he was still afraid – not physically afraid any
more, but afraid of people and prejudice and misery and
monotony. Yet, deep in his bitter heart, he wondered if he
was after all worse than this man or the next. He knew that
he could sophisticate himself finally into saying that his own
weakness was just the result of circumstances and environment; that often when he raged at himself as an egotist
something would whisper ingratiatingly: 'No. Genius!'
That was one manifestation of fear, that voice which whispered that he could not be both great and good, that genius
was the exact combination of those inexplicable grooves and
twists in his mind, that any discipline would curb it to
mediocrity. Probably more than any concrete vice or failing
Amory despised his own personality – he loathed knowing
that to-morrow and the thousand days after he would swell
pompously at a compliment and sulk at an ill word like a
third-rate musician or a first-class actor. He was ashamed of

the fact that very simple and honest people usually distrusted him; that he had been cruel, often, to those who had sunk their personalities in him – several girls, and a man here and there through college, that he had been an evil influence on; people who had followed him here and there into mental adventures from which he alone rebounded unscathed.

Usually, on nights like this, for there had been many lately, he could escape from this consuming introspection by thinking of children and the infinite possibilities of children – he leaned and listened and he heard a startled baby awake in a house across the street and lend a tiny whimper to the still night. Quick as a flash he turned away, wondering with a touch of panic whether something in the brooding despair of his mood had made a darkness in its tiny soul. He shivered. What if some day the balance was overturned, and he became a thing that frightened children and crept into rooms in the dark, approached dim communion with those phantoms who whispered shadowy secrets to the mad of that dark continent upon the moon. . . .

Amory smiled a bit.

'You're too much wrapped up in yourself,' he heard some one say. And again——

'Get out and do some real work——'

'Stop worrying——'

He fancied a possible future comment of his own.

'Yes – I was perhaps an egotist in youth, but I soon found it made me morbid to think too much about myself.'

Suddenly he felt an overwhelming desire to let himself go to the devil – not to go violently as a gentleman should, but to sink safely and sensuously out of sight. He pictured himself in an adobe house in Mexico, half-reclining on a rug-covered couch, his slender, artistic fingers closed on a cigarette while he listened to guitars strumming melancholy undertones to an age-old dirge of Castile and an olive-skinned, carmine-lipped girl caressed his hair. Here he might live a strange litany, delivered from right and wrong

and from the hound of heaven and from every God (except
the exotic Mexican one who was pretty slack himself and
rather addicted to Oriental scents) – delivered from success
and hope and poverty into that long chute of indulgence
which led, after all, only to the artificial lake of death.

There were so many places where one might deteriorate
pleasantly: Port Said, Shanghai, parts of Turkestan, Con-
stantinople, the South Seas – all lands of sad, haunting
music and many odours, where lust could be a mode and
expression of life, where the shades of night skies and sun-
sets would seem to reflect only moods of passion: the colours
of lips and poppies.

Still Weeding

Once he had been miraculously able to scent evil as a
horse detects a broken bridge at night, but the man with the
queer feet in Phœbe's room had diminished to the aura over
Jill. His instinct perceived the fetidness of poverty, but no
longer ferreted out the deeper evils in pride and sensuality.

There were no more wise men; there were no more
heroes; Burne Holiday was sunk from sight as though he
had never lived; Monsignor was dead. Amory had grown
up to a thousand books, a thousand lies; he had listened
eagerly to people who pretended to know, who knew
nothing. The mystical reveries of saints that had once filled
him with awe in the still hours of night, now vaguely repelled him. The Byrons and Brookes who had defied life
from mountain tops were in the end but flaneurs and
poseurs, at best mistaking the shadow of courage for the
substance of wisdom. The pageantry of his disillusion took
shape in a world-old procession of Prophets, Athenians,
Martyrs, Saints, Scientists, Don Juans, Jesuits, Puritans,
Fausts, Poets, Pacifists; like costumed alumni at a college
reunion they streamed before him as their dreams, personalities, and creeds had in turn thrown coloured lights on his
soul; each had tried to express the glory of life and the tremendous significance of man; each had boasted of

synchronizing what had gone before into his own rickety
generalities; each had depended after all on the set stage and
the convention of the theatre, which is that man in his hun-
ger for faith will feed his mind with the nearest and most
convenient food.

Women – of whom he had expected so much; whose
beauty he had hoped to transmute into modes of art; whose
unfathomable instincts, marvellously incoherent and inarticulate, he had thought to perpetuate in terms of experience –
had become merely consecrations to their own posterity.
Isabelle, Clara, Rosalind, Eleanor, were all removed by their
very beauty, around which men had swarmed, from the
possibility of contributing anything but a sick heart and a
page of puzzled words to write.

Amory based his loss of faith in help from others on
several sweeping syllogisms. Granted that his generation,
however bruised and decimated from this Victorian war,
were the heirs of progress. Waving aside petty differences of
conclusions which, although they might occasionally cause
the deaths of several millions of young men, might be explained away – supposing that after all Bernard Shaw and
Bernhardi, Bonar Law and Bethmann-Hollweg were mutual
heirs of progress if only in agreeing against the ducking of
witches – waiving the antitheses and approaching individually these men who seemed to be the leaders, he was repelled
by the discrepancies and contradictions in the men themselves.

There was, for example, Thornton Hancock, respected by
half the intellectual world as an authority on life, a man who
had verified and believed the code he lived by, an educator
of educators, an adviser to Presidents – yet Amory knew that
this man had, in his heart, leaned on the priest of another
religion.

And Monsignor, upon whom a cardinal rested, had
moments of strange and horrible insecurity – inexplicable
in a religion that explained even disbelief in terms of its own
faith: if you doubted the devil it was the devil that made you
doubt him. Amory had seen Monsignor go to the houses of

stolid philistines, read popular novels furiously, saturate himself in routine, to escape from that horror.

And this priest, a little wiser, somewhat purer, had been, Amory knew, not essentially older than he.

Amory was alone – he had escaped from a small enclosure into a great labyrinth. He was where Goethe was when he began 'Faust'; he was where Conrad was when he wrote 'Almayer's Folly.'

Amory said to himself that there were essentially two sorts of people who through natural clarity or disillusion left the enclosure and sought the labyrinth. There were men like Wells and Plato, who had, half unconsciously, a strange, hidden orthodoxy, who would accept for themselves only what could be accepted for all men – incurable romanticists who never, for all their efforts, could enter the labyrinth as stark souls; there were on the other hand sword-like pioneering personalities, Samuel Butler, Renan, Voltaire, who progressed much slower, yet eventually much further, not in the direct pessimistic line of speculative philosophy but concerned in the eternal attempt to attach a positive value to life. . . .

Amory stopped. He began for the first time in his life to have a strong distrust of all generalities and epigrams. They were too easy, too dangerous to the public mind. Yet all thought usually reached the public after thirty years in some such form: Benson and Chesterton had popularized Huysmans and Newman; Shaw had sugar-coated Nietzsche and Ibsen and Schopenhauer. The man in the street heard the conclusions of dead genius through some one else's clever paradoxes and didactic epigrams.

Life was a damned muddle . . . a football game with every one off-side and the referee gotten rid of – every one claiming the referee would have been on his side. . . .

Progress was a labyrinth . . . people plunging blindly in and then rushing wildly back, shouting that they had found it . . . the invisible king – the élan vital – the principle of evolution . . . writing a book, starting a war, founding a school. . . .

Amory, even had he not been a selfish man, would have started all inquiries with himself. He was his own best example – sitting in the rain, a human creature of sex and pride, foiled by chance and his own temperament of the balm of love and children, preserved to help in building up the living consciousness of the race.

In self-reproach and loneliness and disillusion he came to the entrance of the labyrinth.

Another dawn flung itself across the river; a belated taxi hurried along the street, its lamps still shining like burning eyes in a face white from a night's carouse. A melancholy siren sounded far down the river.

Monsignor

Amory kept thinking how Monsignor would have enjoyed his own funeral. It was magnificently Catholic and liturgical. Bishop O'Neill sang solemn high mass and the cardinal gave the final absolutions. Thornton Hancock, Mrs. Lawrence, the British and Italian ambassadors, the papal delegate, and a host of friends and priests were there – yet the inexorable shears had cut through all these threads that Monsignor had gathered into his hands. To Amory it was a haunting grief to see him lying in his coffin, with closed hands upon his purple vestments. His face had not changed, and, as he never knew he was dying, it showed no pain or fear. It was Amory's dear old friend, his and the others' – for the church was full of people with daft, staring faces, the most exalted seeming the most stricken.

The cardinal, like an archangel in cope and mitre, sprinkled the holy water; the organ broke into sound; the choir began to sing the *Requiem Eternam*.

All these people grieved because they had to some extent depended upon Monsignor. Their grief was more than sentiment for the 'crack in his voice or a certain break in his walk,' as Wells put it. These people had leaned on Monsignor's faith, his way of finding cheer, of making religion a thing of lights and shadows, making all light and shadow merely aspects of God. People felt safe when he was near.

Of Amory's attempted sacrifice had been born merely the full realization of his disillusion, but of Monsignor's funeral was born the romantic elf who was to enter the labyrinth with him. He found something that he wanted, had always wanted and always would want – not to be admired, as he had feared; not to be loved, as he had made himself believe; but to be necessary to people, to be indispensable; he remembered the sense of security he had found in Burne.

Life opened up in one of its amazing bursts of radiance and Amory suddenly and permanently rejected an old epigram that had been playing listlessly in his mind: 'Very few things matter and nothing matters very much.'

On the contrary, Amory felt an immense desire to give people a sense of security.

The Big Man with Goggles

On the day that Amory started on his walk to Princeton the sky was a colourless vault, cool, high and barren of the threat of rain. It was a grey day, that least fleshly of all weathers; a day of dreams and far hopes and clear visions. It was a day easily associated with those abstract truths and purities that dissolve in the sunshine or fade out in mocking laughter by the light of the moon. The trees and clouds were carved in classical severity; the sounds of the countryside had harmonized to a monotone, metallic as a trumpet, breathless as the Grecian urn.

The day had put Amory in such a contemplative mood that he caused much annoyance to several motorists who were forced to slow up considerably or else run him down. So engrossed in his thoughts was he that he was scarcely surprised at that strange phenomenon – cordiality manifested within fifty miles of Manhattan – when a passing car slowed down beside him and a voice hailed him. He looked up and saw a magnificent Locomobile in which sat two middle-aged men, one of them small and anxious-looking, apparently an

artificial growth on the other who was large and begoggled
and imposing.

'Do you want a lift?' asked the apparently artificial
growth, glancing from the corner of his eye at the imposing
man as if for some habitual, silent corroboration.

'You bet I do. Thanks.'

The chauffeur swung open the door, and, climbing in,
Amory settled himself in the middle of the back seat. He
took in his companions curiously. The chief characteristic of
the big man seemed to be a great confidence in himself set
off against a tremendous boredom with everything around
him. That part of his face which protruded under the
goggles was what is generally termed 'strong'; rolls of not
undignified fat had collected near his chin; somewhere
above was a wide thin mouth and the rough model for a
Roman nose, and, below, his shoulders collapsed without a
struggle into the powerful bulk of his chest and belly. He
was excellently and quietly dressed. Amory noticed that he
was inclined to stare straight at the back of the chauffeur's
head as if speculating steadily but hopelessly some baffling
hirsute problem.

The smaller man was remarkable only for his complete
submersion in the personality of the other. He was of that
lower secretarial type who at forty have engraved upon their
business cards: 'Assistant to the President,' and without a
sigh consecrate the rest of their lives to second-hand
mannerisms.

'Going far?' asked the smaller man in a pleasant dis-
interested way.

'Quite a stretch.'

'Hiking for exercise?'

'No,' responded Amory succinctly, 'I'm walking because
I can't afford to ride.'

'Oh.'

Then again:

'Are you looking for work? Because there's lots of work,'
he continued rather testily. 'All this talk of lack of work. The

West is especially short of labour.' He expressed the West with a sweeping, lateral gesture. Amory nodded politely.

'Have you a trade?'

No – Amory had no trade.

'Clerk, eh?'

No – Amory was not a clerk.

'Whatever your line is,' said the little man, seeming to agree wisely with something Amory had said, 'now is the time of opportunity and business openings.' He glanced again toward the big man, as a lawyer grilling a witness glances involuntarily at the jury.

Amory decided that he must say something and for the life of him could think of only one thing to say.

'Of course I want a great lot of money——'

The little man laughed mirthlessly but conscientiously.

'That's what every one wants nowadays, but they don't want to work for it.'

'A very natural, healthy desire. Almost all normal people want to be rich without great effort – except the financiers in problem plays, who want to "crash their way through." Don't you want easy money?'

'Of course not,' said the secretary indignantly.

'But,' continued Amory disregarding him, 'being very poor at present I am contemplating socialism as possibly my forte.'

Both men glanced at him curiously.

'These bomb throwers—' The little man ceased as words lurched ponderously from the big man's chest.

'If I thought you were a bomb thrower I'd run you over to the Newark jail. That's what I think of Socialists.'

Amory laughed.

'What are you,' asked the big man, 'one of these parlour Bolsheviks, one of these idealists? I must say I fail to see the difference. The idealists loaf around and write the stuff that stirs up the poor immigrants.'

'Well,' said Amory, 'if being an idealist is both safe and lucrative, I might try it.'

'What's your difficulty? Lost your job?'

'Not exactly, but – well, call it that.'

'What was it?'

'Writing copy for an advertising agency.'

'Lots of money in advertising.'

Amory smiled discreetly.

'Oh, I'll admit there's money in it eventually. Talent doesn't starve any more. Even art gets enough to eat these days. Artists draw your magazine covers, write your advertisements, hash out rag-time for your theatres. By the great commercializing of printing you've found a harmless, polite occupation for every genius who might have carved his own niche. But beware the artist who's an intellectual also. The artist who doesn't fit – the Rousseau, the Tolstoi, the Samuel Butler, the Amory Blaine——'

'Who's he?' demanded the little man suspiciously.

'Well,' said Amory, 'he's a – he's an intellectual personage not very well known at present.'

The little man laughed his conscientious laugh, and stopped rather suddenly as Amory's burning eyes turned on him.

'What are you laughing at?'

'These *intellectual* people——'

'Do you know what it means?'

The little man's eyes twitched nervously.

'Why, it *usually* means——'

'It *always* means brainy and well-educated,' interrupted Amory. 'It means having an active knowledge of the race's experience.' Amory decided to be very rude. He turned to the big man. 'The young man,' he indicated the secretary with his thumb, and said young man as one says bell-boy, with no implication of youth, 'has the usual muddled connotation of all popular words.'

'You object to the fact that capital controls printing?' said the big man, fixing him with his goggles.

'Yes – and I object to doing their mental work for them. It seemed to me that the root of all the business I saw around me consisted in overworking and underpaying a bunch of dubs who submitted to it.'

'Here now,' said the big man, 'you'll have to admit that the labouring man is certainly highly paid – five and six hour days – it's ridiculous. You can't buy an honest day's work from a man in the trades-unions.'

'You've brought it on yourselves,' insisted Amory. 'You people never make concessions until they're wrung out of you.'

'What people?'

'Your class; the class I belonged to until recently; those who by inheritance or industry or brains or dishonesty have become the moneyed class.'

'Do you imagine that if that road-mender over there had the money he'd be any more willing to give it up?'

'No, but what's that got to do with it?'

The older man considered.

'No, I'll admit it hasn't. It rather sounds as if it had though.'

'In fact,' continued Amory, 'he'd be worse. The lower classes are narrower, less pleasant and personally more selfish – certainly more stupid. But all that has nothing to do with the question.'

'Just exactly what is the question?'

Here Amory had to pause to consider exactly what the question was.

Amory Coins a Phrase

'When life gets hold of a brainy man of fair education,' began Amory slowly, 'that is, when he marries he becomes, nine times out of ten, a conservative as far as existing social conditions are concerned. He may be unselfish, kind-hearted, even just in his own way, but his first job is to provide and to hold fast. His wife shoos him on, from ten thousand a year to twenty thousand a year, on and on, in an enclosed treadmill that hasn't any windows. He's done! Life's got him! He's no help! He's a spiritually married man.'

Amory paused and decided that it wasn't such a bad phrase.

'Some men,' he continued, 'escape the grip. Maybe their wives have no social ambitions; maybe they've hit a sentence or two in a "dangerous book" that pleased them; maybe they started on the treadmill as I did and were knocked off. Anyway, they're the congressmen you can't bribe, the Presidents who aren't politicians, the writers, speakers, scientists, statesmen who aren't just popular grab-bags for a half-dozen women and children.'

'He's the natural radical?'

'Yes,' said Amory. 'He may vary from the disillusioned critic like old Thornton Hancock, all the way to Trotsky. Now this spiritually unmarried man hasn't direct power, for unfortunately the spiritually married man, as a by-product of his money chase, has garnered in the great newspaper, the popular magazine, the influential weekly – so that Mrs. Newspaper, Mrs. Magazine, Mrs. Weekly can have a better limousine than those oil people across the street or those cement people 'round the corner.'

'Why not?'

'It makes wealthy men the keepers of the world's intellectual conscience and, of course, a man who has money under one set of social institutions quite naturally can't risk his family's happiness by letting the clamour for another appear in his newspaper.'

'But it appears,' said the big man.

'Where? – in the discredited mediums. Rotten cheap-papered weeklies.'

'All right – go on.'

'Well, my first point is that through a mixture of conditions of which the family is the first, there are these two sorts of brains. One sort takes human nature as it finds it, uses its timidity, its weakness, and its strength for its own ends. Opposed is the man who, being spiritually unmarried, continually seeks for new systems that will control or counteract human nature. His problem is harder. It is not life that's complicated, it's the struggle to guide and control life. That is his struggle. He is a part of progress – the spiritually married man is not.'

The big man produced three big cigars, and proffered them on his huge palm. The little man took one, Amory shook his head and reached for a cigarette.

'Go on talking,' said the big man. 'I've been wanting to hear one of you fellows.'

Going Faster

'Modern life,' began Amory again, 'changes no longer century by century, but year by year, ten times faster than it ever has before – populations doubling, civilizations unified more closely with other civilizations, economic interdependence, racial questions, and – we're *dawdling* along. My idea is that we've got to go very much faster.' He slightly emphasized the last words and the chauffeur unconsciously increased the speed of the car. Amory and the big man laughed; the little man laughed, too, after a pause.

'Every child,' said Amory, 'should have an equal start. If his father can endow him with a good physique and his mother with some common sense in his early education, that should be his heritage. If the father can't give him a good physique, if the mother has spent in chasing men the years in which she should have been preparing herself to educate her children, so much the worse for the child. He shouldn't be artificially bolstered up with money, sent to these horrible tutoring schools, dragged through college . . . Every boy ought to have an equal start.'

'All right,' said the big man, his goggles indicating neither approval nor objection.

'Next I'd have a fair trial of government ownership of all industries.'

'That's been proven a failure.'

'No – it merely failed. If we had government ownership we'd have the best analytical business minds in the government working for something besides themselves. We'd have Mackays instead of Burlesons; we'd have Morgans in the

Treasury Department; we'd have Hills running interstate commerce. We'd have the best lawyers in the Senate.'

'They wouldn't give their best efforts for nothing. McAdoo——'

'No,' said Amory, shaking his head. 'Money isn't the only stimulous that brings out the best that's in a man, even in America.'

'You said a while ago that it was.'

'It is, right now. But if it were made illegal to have more than a certain amount the best men would all flock for the one other reward which attracts humanity – honour.'

The big man made a sound that was very like *boo*.

'That's the silliest thing you've said yet.'

'No, it isn't silly. It's quite plausible. If you'd gone to college you'd have been struck by the fact that the men there would work twice as hard for any one of a hundred petty honours as those other men did who were earning their way through.'

'Kids – child's play!' scoffed his antagonist.

'Not by a darned sight – unless we're all children. Did you ever see a grown man when he's trying for a secret society – or a rising family whose name is up at some club? They'll jump when they hear the sound of the word. The idea that to make a man work you've got to hold gold in front of his eyes is a growth, not an axiom. We've done that for so long that we've forgotten there's any other way. We've made a world where that's necessary. Let me tell you' – Amory became emphatic – 'if there were ten men insured against either wealth or starvation, and offered a green ribbon for five hours' work a day and a blue ribbon for ten hours' work a day, nine out of ten of them would be trying for the blue ribbon. That competitive instinct only wants a badge. If the size of their house is the badge they'll sweat their heads off for that. If it's only a blue ribbon, I damn near believe they'll work just as hard. They have in other ages.'

'I don't agree with you.'

'I know it,' said Amory nodding sadly. 'It doesn't matter

any more though. I think these people are going to come and take what they want pretty soon.'

A fierce hiss came from the little man.

'*Machine-guns!*'

'Ah, but you've taught them their use.'

The big man shook his head.

'In this country there are enough property owners not to permit that sort of thing.'

Amory wished he knew the statistics of property owners and non-property owners; he decided to change the subject.

But the big man was aroused.

'When you talk of "taking things away," you're on dangerous ground.'

'How can they get it without taking it? For years people have been stalled off with promises. Socialism may not be progress, but the threat of the red flag is certainly the inspiring force of all reform. You've got to be sensational to get attention.'

'Russia is your example of a beneficent violence, I suppose?'

'Quite possibly,' admitted Amory. 'Of course, it's overflowing just as the French Revolution did, but I've no doubt that it's really a great experiment and well worth while.'

'Don't you believe in moderation?'

'You won't listen to the moderates, and it's almost too late. The truth is that the public has done one of those startling and amazing things that they do about once in a hundred years. They've seized an idea.'

'What is it?'

'That however the brains and abilities of men may differ, their stomachs are essentially the same.'

The Little Man Gets His

'If you took all the money in the world,' said the little man with much profundity, 'and divided it up in equ——'

'Oh, shut up!' said Amory briskly and, paying no attention to the little man's enraged stare, he went on with his argument.

'The human stomach—' he began; but the big man interrupted rather impatiently.

'I'm letting you talk, you know,' he said, 'but please avoid stomachs. I've been feeling mine all day. Anyway, I don't agree with one-half you've said. Government ownership is the basis of your whole argument, and it's invariably a bee-hive of corruption. Men won't work for blue ribbons, that's all rot.'

When he ceased the little man spoke up with a determined nod, as if resolved this time to have his say out.

'There are certain things which are human nature,' he asserted with an owl-like look, 'which always have been and always will be, which can't be changed.'

Amory looked from the small man to the big man helplessly.

'Listen to that! *That's* what makes me discouraged with progress. *Listen* to that! I can name offhand over one hundred natural phenomena that have been changed by the will of man – a hundred instincts in man that have been wiped out or are now held in check by civilization. What this man here just said has been for thousands of years the last refuge of the associated mutton-heads of the world. It negates the efforts of every scientist, statesman, moralist, reformer, doctor, and philosopher that ever gave his life to humanity's service. It's a flat impeachment of all that's worth while in human nature. Every person over twenty-five years old who makes that statement in cold blood ought to be deprived of the franchise.'

The little man leaned back against the seat, his face purple with rage. Amory continued, addressing his remarks to the big man.

'These quarter-educated, stale-minded men such as your friend here, who *think* they think, every question that comes up, you'll find his type in the usual ghastly muddle. One minute it's "the brutality and inhumanity of these Prussians" – the next it's "we ought to exterminate the whole

German people." They always believe that "things are in a bad way now," but they "haven't any faith in these ideal-ists." One minute they call Wilson "just a dreamer, not practical" – a year later they rail at him for making his dreams realities. They haven't clear logical ideas on one single subject except a sturdy, stolid opposition to all change. They don't think uneducated people should be highly paid, but they won't see that if they don't pay the uneducated people their children are going to be uneducated too, and we're going round and round in a circle. That – is the great middle class!'

The big man with a broad grin on his face leaned over and smiled at the little man.

'You're catching it pretty heavy, Garvin; how do you feel?'

The little man made an attempt to smile and act as if the whole matter were so ridiculous as to be beneath notice. But Amory was not through.

'The theory that people are fit to govern themselves rests on this man. If he can be educated to think clearly, concisely, and logically, freed of his habit of taking refuge in platitudes and prejudices and sentimentalisms, then I'm a militant Socialist. If he can't, then I don't think it matters much what happens to man or his systems, now or hereafter.'

'I am both interested and amused,' said the big man. 'You are very young.'

'Which may only mean that I have neither been corrupted nor made timid by contemporary experience. I possess the most valuable experience, the experience of the race, for in spite of going to college I've managed to pick up a good education.'

'You talk glibly.'

'It's not all rubbish,' cried Amory passionately. 'This is the first time in my life I've argued Socialism. It's the only panacea I know. I'm restless. My whole generation is rest-less. I'm sick of a system where the richest man gets the most beautiful girl if he wants her, where the artist without an income has to sell his talents to a button manufacturer.

Even if I had no talents I'd not be content to work ten years, condemned either to celibacy or a furtive indulgence, to give some man's son an automobile.'

'But, if you're not sure——'

'That doesn't matter,' exclaimed Amory. 'My position couldn't be worse. A social revolution might land me on top. Of course I'm selfish. It seems to me I've been a fish out of water in too many outworn systems. I was probably one of the two dozen men in my class at college who got a decent education; still they'd let any well-tutored flathead play football and *I* was ineligible, because some silly old men thought we should *all* profit by conic sections. I loathed the army. I loathed business. I'm in love with change and I've killed my conscience——'

'So you'll go along crying that we must go faster.'

'That, at least, is true,' Amory insisted. 'Reform won't catch up to the needs of civilization unless it's made to. A laissez-faire policy is like spoiling a child by saying he'll turn out all right in the end. He will – if he's made to.'

'But you don't believe all this Socialist patter you talk.'

'I don't know. Until I talked to you I hadn't thought seriously about it. I wasn't sure of half of what I said.'

'You puzzle me,' said the big man, 'but you're all alike. They say Bernard Shaw, in spite of his doctrines, is the most exacting of all dramatists about his royalties. To the last farthing.'

'Well,' said Amory, 'I simply state that I'm a product of a versatile mind in a restless generation – with every reason to throw my mind and pen in with the radicals. Even if, deep in my heart, I thought we were all blind atoms in a world as limited as a stroke of a pendulum, I and my sort would struggle against tradition; try, at least, to displace old cants with new ones. I've thought I was right about life at various times, but faith is difficult. One thing I know. If living isn't a seeking for the grail it may be a damned amusing game.'

For a minute neither spoke and then the big man asked:

'What was your university?'

'Princeton.'

The big man became suddenly interested; the expression of his goggles altered slightly.

'I sent my son to Princeton.'

'Did you?'

'Perhaps you knew him. His name was Jesse Ferrenby. He was killed last year in France.'

'I knew him very well. In fact, he was one of my particular friends.'

'He was – a – quite a fine boy. We were very close.'

Amory began to perceive a resemblance between the father and the dead son and he told himself that there had been all along a sense of familiarity. Jesse Ferrenby, the man who in college had borne off the crown that he had aspired to. It was all so far away. What little boys they had been, working for blue ribbons——

The car slowed up at the entrance to a great estate, ringed around by a huge hedge and a tall iron fence.

'Won't you come in for lunch?'

Amory shook his head.

'Thank you, Mr. Ferrenby, but I've got to get on.'

The big man held out his hand. Amory saw that the fact that he had known Jesse more than outweighed any disfavour he had created by his opinions. What ghosts were people with which to work! Even the little man insisted on shaking hands.

'Good-bye!' shouted Mr. Ferrenby, as the car turned the corner and started up the drive. 'Good luck to you and bad luck to your theories.'

'Same to you, sir,' cried Amory, smiling and waving his hand.

'Out of the Fire, Out of the Little Room'

Eight hours from Princeton Amory sat down by the Jersey roadside and looked at the frost-bitten country. Nature as a rather coarse phenomenon composed largely of flowers that, when closely inspected, appeared moth-eaten, and of ants that endlessly traversed blades of grass, was always disillusioning; nature represented by skies and waters and far horizons was more likable. Frost and the promise of winter thrilled him now, made him think of a wild battle between St. Regis and Groton, ages ago, seven years ago – and of an autumn day in France twelve months before when he had lain in tall grass, his platoon flattened down close around him, waiting to tap the shoulders of a Lewis gunner. He saw the two pictures together with somewhat the same primitive exaltation – two games he had played, differing in quality of acerbity, linked in a way that differed them from Rosalind or the subject of labyrinths which were, after all, the business of life.

'I am selfish,' he thought.

'This is not a quality that will change when I "see human suffering" or "lose my parents" or "help others".

'This selfishness is not only part of me. It is the most living part.

'It is by somehow transcending rather than by avoiding that selfishness that I can bring poise and balance into my life.

'There is no virtue of unselfishness that I cannot use. I can make sacrifices, be charitable, give to a friend, endure for a friend, lay down my life for a friend – all because these things may be the best possible expression of myself; yet I have not one drop of the milk of human kindness.'

The problem of evil had solidified for Amory into the problem of sex. He was beginning to identify evil with the strong phallic worship in Brooke and the early Wells. Inseparably linked with evil was beauty – beauty, still a constant rising tumult; soft in Eleanor's voice, in an old song at night, rioting deliriously through life like superimposed waterfalls, half rhythm, half darkness. Amory knew that every time he had reached toward it longingly it had leered out at him with the grotesque face of evil. Beauty of great art, beauty of all joy, most of all the beauty of women.

After all, it had too many associations with licence and indulgence. Weak things were often beautiful, weak things were never good. And in this new loneness of his that had been selected for what greatness he might achieve, beauty must be relative or, itself a harmony, it would make only a discord.

In a sense this gradual renunciation of beauty was the second step after his disillusion had been made complete. He felt that he was leaving behind him his chance of being a certain type of artist. It seemed so much more important to be a certain sort of man.

His mind turned a corner suddenly and he found himself thinking of the Catholic Church. The idea was strong in him that there was a certain intrinsic lack in those to whom orthodox religion was necessary, and religion to Amory meant the Church of Rome. Quite conceivably it was an empty ritual but it was seemingly the only assimilative, traditionary bulwark against the decay of morals. Until the great mobs could be educated into a moral sense some one must cry: 'Thou shalt not!' Yet any acceptance was, for the present, impossible. He wanted time and the absence of ulterior pressure. He wanted to keep the tree without ornaments, realize fully the direction and momentum of this new start.

The afternoon waned from the purging good of three o'clock to the golden beauty of four. Afterwards he walked through the dull ache of a setting sun when even the clouds seemed bleeding and at twilight he came to a graveyard. There was a dusky, dreamy smell of flowers and the ghost of a new moon in the sky and shadows everywhere. On an impulse he considered trying to open the door of a rusty iron vault built into the side of a hill; a vault washed clean and covered with late-blooming, weepy watery-blue flowers that might have grown from dead eyes, sticky to the touch with a sickening odour.

Amory wanted to *feel* 'William Dayfield, 1864.'

He wondered that graves ever made people consider life in vain. Somehow he could find nothing hopeless in having lived. All the broken columns and clasped hands and doves and angels meant romances. He fancied that in a hundred years he would like having young people speculate as to whether his eyes were brown or blue, and he hoped quite passionately that his grave would have about it an air of many, many years ago. It seemed strange that out of a row of Union soldiers two or three made him think of dead loves and dead lovers, when they were exactly like the rest, even to the yellowish moss.

Long after midnight the towers and spires of Princeton were visible, with here and there a late-burning light – and suddenly out of the clear darkness the sound of bells. As an endless dream it went on; the spirit of the past brooding over a new generation, the chosen youth from the muddled, unchastened world, still fed romantically on the mistakes and half-forgotten dreams of dead statesmen and poets. Here was a new generation, shouting the old cries, learning the old creeds, through a revery of long days and nights; destined finally to go out into that dirty grey turmoil to follow love and pride; a new generation dedicated more than the last to the fear of poverty and the worship of success; grown up to find all Gods dead, all wars fought, all faiths in man shaken. . . .

Amory, sorry for them, was still not sorry for himself – art, politics, religion, whatever his medium should be, he knew he was safe now, free from all hysteria – he could accept what was acceptable, roam, grow, rebel, sleep deep through many nights. . . .

There was no God in his heart, he knew; his ideas were still in riot; there was ever the pain of memory; the regret for his lost youth – yet the waters of disillusion had left a deposit on his soul, responsibility and a love of life, the faint stirring of old ambitions and unrealized dreams. But – oh, Rosalind! Rosalind! . . .

'It's all a poor substitute at best,' he said sadly.

And he could not tell why the struggle was worth while, why he had determined to use to the utmost himself and his heritage from the personalities he had passed. . . .

He stretched out his arms to the crystalline, radiant sky.

'I know myself,' he cried, 'but that is all.'

THE CRACK-UP

and other
Autobiographical Pieces

WHO'S WHO—AND WHY

[1920]

THE HISTORY OF my life is the history of the struggle between an overwhelming urge to write and a combination of circumstances bent on keeping me from it.

When I lived in St Paul and was about twelve I wrote all through every class in school in the back of my geography book and first-year Latin and on the margins of themes and declensions and mathematics problems. Two years later a family congress decided that the only way to force me to study was to send me to boarding-school. This was a mistake. It took my mind off my writing. I decided to play football, to smoke, to go to college, to do all sorts of irrelevant things that had nothing to do with the real business of life, which, of course, was the proper mixture of description and dialogue in the short story.

But in school I went off on a new tack. I saw a musical comedy called *The Quaker Girl*, and from that day forth my desk bulged with Gilbert & Sullivan librettos and dozens of notebooks containing the germs of dozens of musical comedies.

Near the end of my last year at school I came across a new musical-comedy score lying on top of the piano. It was a show called *His Honor the Sultan*, and the title furnished the information that it had been presented by the Triangle Club of Princeton University.

That was enough for me. From then on the university question was settled. I was bound for Princeton.

I spent my entire Freshman year writing an operetta for the Triangle Club. To do this I failed in algebra, trigonometry, coordinate geometry, and hygiene. But the Triangle Club accepted my show, and by tutoring all through a stuffy August I managed to come back a Sophomore and act in it as a chorus girl. A little after this came a hiatus. My health broke down and I left college one December to spend the rest of the year recuperating in the West. Almost my final memory before I left was of writing a last lyric on that year's Triangle production while in bed in the infirmary with a high fever.

The next year, 1916–17, found me back in college, but by this time I had decided that poetry was the only thing worth while, so with my head ringing with the metres of Swinburne and the matters of Rupert Brooke I spent the spring doing sonnets, ballads, and rondels into the small hours. I had read somewhere that every great poet had written great poetry before he was twenty-one. I had only a year and, besides, war was impending. I must publish a book of startling verse before I was engulfed.

By autumn I was in an infantry officers' training camp at Fort Leavenworth, with poetry in the discard and a brand-new ambition—I was writing an immortal novel. Every evening, concealing my pad behind Small Problems for Infantry, I wrote paragraph after paragraph on a somewhat edited history of me and my imagination. The outline of twenty-two chapters, four of them in verse, was made, two chapters were completed; and then I was detected and the game was up. I could write no more during study period.

This was a distinct complication. I had only three months to live—in those days all infantry officers thought they had only three months to live—and I had left no mark on the world. But such consuming ambition was not to be thwarted by a mere war. Every Saturday at one o'clock when the week's work was over I hurried to the Officers' Club, and there, in a corner of a roomful of smoke, conversation, and rattling newspapers, I wrote a one-hundred-and-twenty-thousand-word novel on the consecutive week-ends of three months. There was no revising; there was no time for it. As I finished each chapter I sent it to a typist in Princeton.

Meanwhile I lived in its smeary pencil pages. The drills, marches, and Small Problems for Infantry were a shadowy dream. My whole heart was concentrated upon my book.

I went to my regiment happy. I had written a novel. The war could now go on. I forgot paragraphs and pentameters, similes and syllogisms. I got to be a first lieutenant, got my orders overseas—and then the publishers wrote me that though *The Romantic Egotist* was the most original manuscript they had received for years they couldn't publish it. It was crude and reached no conclusion.

It was six months after this that I arrived in New York and presented my card to the office boys of seven city editors asking to be taken on as a reporter. I had just turned twenty-two, the war was over, and I was going to trail murderers by day and do short stories by night. But the newspapers didn't need me. They sent their office boys out to tell me they didn't need me. They decided definitely and irrevocably by the sound of my name on a calling card that I was absolutely unfitted to be a reporter.

Instead I became an advertising man at ninety dollars a month, writing the slogans that while away the weary hours in rural trolley cars. After hours I wrote stories—from March to June. There were nineteen altogether; the quickest written in an hour and a half, the slowest in three days. No one bought them, no one sent personal letters. I had one hundred and twenty-two rejection slips pinned in a frieze about my room. I wrote movies. I wrote song lyrics. I wrote complicated advertising schemes. I wrote poems. I wrote sketches. I wrote jokes. Near the end of June I sold one story for thirty dollars.

On the Fourth of July, utterly disgusted with myself and all the editors, I went home to St Paul and informed family and friends that I had given up my position and had come home to write a novel. They nodded politely, changed the subject and spoke of me very gently. But this time I knew what I was doing. I had a novel to write at last, and all through two hot months I wrote and revised and compiled and boiled down. On 15th September *This Side of Paradise* was accepted by special delivery.

In the next two months I wrote eight stories and sold

nine. The ninth was accepted by the same magazine that had rejected it four months before. Then, in November, I sold my first story to the editors of *The Saturday Evening Post*. By February I had sold them half a dozen. Then my novel came out. Then I got married. Now I spend my time wondering how it happened.

In the words of the immortal Julius Caesar: 'That's all there is; there isn't any more.'

HOW TO LIVE
ON $36,000 A YEAR
[1924]

'YOU OUGHT TO start saving money,' The Young Man
With a Future assured me just the other day. 'You think it's
smart to live up to your income. Some day you'll land in the
poorhouse.'

I was bored, but I knew he was going to tell me anyhow,
so I asked him what I'd better do.

'It's very simple,' he answered impatiently; 'only you
establish a trust fund where you can't get your money if you
try.'

I had heard this before. It is System Number 999. I tried
System Number 1 at the very beginning of my literary
career four years ago. A month before I was married I went
to a broker and asked his advice about investing some
money.

'It's only a thousand,' I admitted, 'but I feel I ought to
begin to save right now.'

He considered.

'You don't want Liberty Bonds,' he said. 'They're too
easy to turn into cash. You want a good, sound, conservative
investment, but also you want it where you can't get at it
every five minutes.'

He finally selected a bond for me that paid 7 per cent and
wasn't listed on the market. I turned over my thousand
dollars, and my career of amassing capital began that day.

On that day, also, it ended.

The Heirloom No One Would Buy

My wife and I were married in New York in the spring of

277

1920, when prices were higher than they had been within the memory of man. In the light of after events it seems fitting that our career should have started at that precise point in time. I had just received a large cheque from the movies and I felt a little patronizing toward the millionaires riding down Fifth Avenue in their limousines—because my income had a way of doubling every month. This was actually the case. It had done so for several months—I had made only thirty-five dollars the previous August, while here in April I was making three thousand—and it seemed as if it was going to do so for ever. At the end of the year it must reach half a million. Of course with such a state of affairs, economy seemed a waste of time. So we went to live at the most expensive hotel in New York, intending to wait there until enough money accumulated for a trip abroad.

To make a long story short, after we had been married for three months I found one day to my horror that I didn't have a dollar in the world, and the weekly hotel bill for two hundred dollars would be due next day.

I remember the mixed feelings with which I issued from the bank on hearing the news.

'What's the matter?' demanded my wife anxiously, as I joined her on the sidewalk. 'You look depressed.'

'I'm not depressed,' I answered cheerfully; 'I'm just surprised. We haven't got any money.'

'Haven't got any money,' she repeated calmly, and we began to walk up the Avenue in a sort of trance. 'Well, let's go to the movies,' she suggested jovially.

It all seemed so tranquil that I was not a bit cast down. The cashier had not even scowled at me. I had walked in and said to him, 'How much money have I got?' And he looked in a big book and answered, 'None.'

That was all. There were no harsh words, no blows. And I knew that there was nothing to worry about. I was now a successful author, and when successful authors ran out of money all they had to do was to sign cheques. I wasn't poor— they couldn't fool me. Poverty meant being depressed and living in a small remote room and eating at a *rôtisserie* on the corner, while I—why, it was impossible that I should be poor! I was living at the best hotel in New York!

My first step was to try to sell my only possession—my $1,000 bond. It was the first of many times I made the attempt; in all financial crises I dig it out and with it go hopefully to the bank, supposing that, as it never fails to pay the proper interest, it has at last assumed a tangible value. But as I have never been able to sell it, it has gradually acquired the sacredness of a family heirloom. It is always referred to by my wife as 'your bond,' and it was once turned in at the Subway offices after I left it by accident on a car seat!

This particular crisis passed next morning when the dis-covery that publishers sometimes advanced royalties sent me hurriedly to mine. So the only lesson I learned from it was that my money usually turns up somewhere in time of need, and that at the worst you can always borrow—a lesson that would make Benjamin Franklin turn over in his grave.

For the first three years of our marriage our income aver-aged a little more than $20,000 a year. We indulged in such luxuries as a baby and a trip to Europe, and always money seemed to come easier and easier with less and less effort, until we felt that with just a little more margin to come and go on, we could begin to save.

Plans

We left the Middle West and moved East to a town about fifteen miles from New York, where we rented a house for $300 a month. We hired a nurse for $90 a month; a man and his wife—they acted as butler, chauffeur, yard man, cook, parlour maid and chambermaid—for $160 a month; and a laundress, who came twice a week, for $36 a month. This year of 1923, we told each other, was to be our saving year. We were going to earn $24,000, and live on $18.000, thus giving us a surplus of $6,000 with which to buy safety and security for our old age. We were going to do better at last.

Now as everyone knows, when you want to do better you first buy a book and print your name in the front of it in capital letters. So my wife bought a book, and every bill that came to the house was carefully entered in it, so that we could watch living expenses and cut them away to almost nothing—or at least to $1,500 a month.

We had, however, reckoned without our town. It is one of those little towns springing up on all sides of New York which are built especially for those who have made money suddenly but have never had money before.

My wife and I are, of course, members of this newly rich class. That is to say, five years ago we had no money at all, and what we now do away with would have seemed like inestimable riches to us then. I have at times suspected that we are the only newly rich people in America, that in fact we are the very couple at whom all the articles about the newly rich were aimed.

Now when you say 'newly rich' you picture a middle-aged and corpulent man who has a tendency to remove his collar at formal dinners and is in perpetual hot water with his ambitious wife and her titled friends. As a member of the newly rich class, I assure you that this picture is entirely libellous. I myself, for example, am a mild, slightly used young man of twenty-seven, and what corpulence I may have developed is for the present a strictly confidential matter between my tailor and me. We once dined with a bona fide nobleman, but we were both far too frightened to take off our collars or even to demand corned beef and cabbage. Nevertheless we live in a town prepared for keeping money in circulation.

When we came here, a year ago, there were, all together, seven merchants engaged in the purveyance of food—three grocers, three butchers, and a fisherman. But when the word went around in food-purveying circles that the town was filling up with the recently enriched as fast as houses could be built for them, the rush of butchers, grocers, fishmen and delicatessen men became enormous. Train-loads of them arrived daily with signs and scales in hand to stake out a claim and sprinkle sawdust upon it. It was like the gold rush of '49, or a big bonanza of the seventies. Older and larger cities were denuded of their stores. Inside of a year eighteen food dealers had set up shop in our main street and might be seen any day waiting in their doorways with alluring and deceitful smiles.

Having long been somewhat overcharged by the seven previous food purveyors we all naturally rushed to the new men, who made it known by large numerical signs in their windows that they intended practically to give food away. But once we were snared, the prices began to rise alarmingly, until all of us scurried like frightened mice from one new man to another, seeking only justice, and seeking it in vain.

Great Expectations

What had happened, of course, was that there were too many food purveyors for the population. It was absolutely impossible for eighteen of them to subsist in the town and at the same time to charge moderate prices. So each was waiting for some of the others to give up and move away; meanwhile the only way the rest of them could carry their loans from the banks was by selling things at two or three times the prices in the city fifteen miles away. And that is how our town became the most expensive one in the world.

Now in magazine articles people always get together and found community stores, but none of us would consider such a step. It would absolutely ruin us with our neighbours, who would suspect that we actually cared about our money. When I suggested one day to a local lady of wealth—whose husband, by the way, is reputed to have made his money by vending illicit liquids—that I start a community store known as 'F. Scott Fitzgerald—Fresh Meats', she was horrified. So the idea was abandoned.

But in spite of the groceries, we began the year in high hopes. My first play was to be presented in the autumn, and even if living in the East forced our expenses a little over $1,500 a month, the play would easily make up for the difference. We knew what colossal sums were earned on play royalties, and just to be sure, we asked several playwrights what was the maximum that could be earned on a year's run. I never allowed myself to be rash. I took a sum halfway between the maximum and the minimum, and put that down as what we could fairly count on its earning. I think my figures came to about $100,000.

It was a pleasant year; we always had this delightful event of the play to look forward to. When the play succeeded we could buy a house, and saving money would be so easy that we could do it blindfolded with both hands tied behind our backs.

As if in happy anticipation we had a small windfall in March from an unexpected source—a moving picture—and for almost the first time in our lives we had enough surplus to buy some bonds. Of course we had 'my' bond, and every six months I clipped the little coupon and cashed it, but we were so used to it that we never counted it as money. It was simply a warning never to tie up cash where we couldn't get at it in time of need.

No, the thing to buy was Liberty Bonds, and we bought four of them. It was a very exciting business. I descended to a shining and impressive room downstairs, and under the chaperonage of a guard deposited my $4,000 in Liberty Bonds, together with 'my' bond, in a little tin box to which I alone had the key.

Less Cash Than Company

I left the bank, feeling decidedly solid. I had at last accumulated a capital. I hadn't exactly accumulated it, but there it was anyhow, and if I had died next day it would have yielded my wife $212 a year for life—or for just as long as she cared to live on that amount.

'That,' I said to myself with some satisfaction, 'is what is called providing for the wife and children. Now all I have to do is deposit the $100,000 from my play and then we're through with worry for ever.'

I found that from this time on I had less tendency to worry about current expenses. What if we did spend a few hundred too much now and then? What if our grocery bills did vary mysteriously from $85 to $165 a month, according as to how closely we watched the kitchen? Didn't I have bonds in the bank? Trying to keep under $1,500 a month the way things were going was merely niggardly. We were going to save on a scale that would make such petty economies seem like counting pennies.

The coupons on 'my' bond are always sent to an office on lower Broadway. Where Liberty Bond coupons are sent I never had a chance to find out, as I didn't have the pleasure of clipping any. Two of them I was unfortunately compelled to dispose of just one month after I first locked them up. I had begun a new novel, you see, and it occurred to me it would be much better business in the end to keep at the novel and live on the Liberty Bonds while I was writing it. Unfortunately the novel progressed slowly, while the Liberty Bonds went at an alarming rate of speed. The novel was interrupted whenever there was any sound above a whisper in the house, while the Liberty Bonds were never interrupted at all.

And the summer drifted too. It was an exquisite summer and it became a habit with many world-weary New Yorkers to pass their week-ends at the Fitzgerald house in the country. Along near the end of a balmy and insidious August I realized with a shock that only three chapters of my novel were done—and in the little tin safety-deposit vault, only 'my' bond remained. There it lay—paying storage on itself and a few dollars more. But never mind; in a little while the box would be bursting with savings. I'd have to hire a twin box next door.

But the play was going into rehearsal in two months. To tide over the interval there were two courses open to me—I could sit down and write some short stories or I could continue to work on the novel and borrow the money to live on. Lulled into a sense of security by our sanguine anticipations I decided on the latter course, and my publishers lent me enough to pay our bills until the opening night.

So I went back to my novel, and the months and money

melted away; but one morning in October I sat in the cold interior of a New York theatre and heard the cast read through the first act of my play. It was magnificent; my estimate had been too low. I could almost hear the people scrambling for seats, hear the ghostly voices of the movie magnates as they bid against one another for the picture rights. The novel was now laid aside; my days were spent at the theatre and my nights in revising and improving the two or three little weak spots in what was to be the success of the year.

The time approached and life became a breathless affair. The November bills came in, were glanced at, and punched onto a bill file on the bookcase. More important questions were in the air. A disgusted letter arrived from an editor telling me I had written only two short stories during the entire year. But what did that matter? The main thing was that our second comedian got the wrong intonation in his first-act exit line.

The play opened in Atlantic City in November. It was a colossal frost. People left their seats and walked out, people rustled their programmes and talked audibly in bored impatient whispers. After the second act I wanted to stop the show and say it was all a mistake but the actors struggled heroically on.

There was a fruitless week of patching and revising, and then we gave up and came home. To my profound astonishment the year, the great year, was almost over. I was $5,000 in debt, and my one idea was to get in touch with a reliable poorhouse where we could hire a room and bath for nothing a week. But one satisfaction nobody could take from us. We had spent $36,000, and purchased for one year the right to be members of the newly rich class. What more can money buy?

Taking Account of Stock

The first move, of course, was to get out 'my' bond, take it to the bank and offer it for sale. A very nice old man at a shining table was firm as to its value as security, but he

promised that if I became overdrawn he would call me up
on the phone and give me a chance to make good. No, he
never went to lunch with depositors. He considered writers
a shiftless class, he said, and assured me that the whole bank
was absolutely burglarproof from cellar to roof.

Too discouraged even to put the bond back in the now
yawning deposit box, I tucked it gloomily into my pocket
and went home. There was no help for it—I must go to
work. I had exhausted my resources and there was nothing
else to do. In the train I listed all our possessions on which, if
it came to that, we could possibly raise money. Here is the
list:

1 Oil stove, damaged
9 Electric lamps, all varieties
2 Bookcases with books to match
1 Cigarette humidor, made by a convict
2 Framed crayon portraits of my wife and me
1 Medium-priced automobile, 1921 model
1 Bond, par value $1,000; actual value unknown

'Let's cut down expenses right away,' began my wife
when I reached home. 'There's a new grocery in town
where you pay cash and everything costs only half what it
does anywhere else. I can take the car every morning
and ———'

'Cash!' I began to laugh at this. 'Cash!'

The one thing it was impossible for us to do now was to
pay cash. It was too late to pay cash. We had no cash to pay.
We should rather have gone down on our knees and thanked
the butcher and grocer for letting us charge. An enormous
economic fact became clear to me at that moment—the rarity
of cash, the latitude of choice that cash allows.

'Well,' she remarked thoughtfully, 'that's too bad. But at
least we don't need three servants. We'll get a Japanese to do
general housework, and I'll be nurse for a while until you get
us out of danger.'

'Let them go?' I demanded incredulously. 'But we can

let them go! We'd have to pay them an extra two weeks each.
Why, to get them out of the house would cost us $125—in
cash! Besides, it's nice to have the butler; if we have an
awful smash we can send him up to New York to hold us a
place in the bread line.'

'Well, then, how can we economize?'

'We can't. We're too poor to economize. Economy is a
luxury. We could have economized last summer—but now
our only salvation is in extravagance.'

'How about a smaller house?'

'Impossible! Moving is the most expensive thing in the
world; and besides, I couldn't work during the confusion.
No,' I went on, 'I'll just have to get out of this mess the only
way I know how, by making more money. Then when we've
got something in the bank we can decide what we'd better
do.'

Over our garage is a large bare room whither I now retired with pencil, paper and the oil stove, emerging the next
afternoon at five o'clock with a 7,000-word story. That was
something; it would pay the rent and last month's overdue
bills. It took twelve hours a day for five weeks to rise from
abject poverty back into the middle class, but within that
time we had paid our debts, and the cause for immediate
worry was over.

But I was far from satisfied with the whole affair. A
young man can work at excessive speed with no ill effects,
but youth is unfortunately not a permanent condition of life.

I wanted to find out where the $36,000 had gone. Thirty-
six thousand is not very wealthy—not yacht-and-Palm-
Beach wealthy—but it sounds to me as though it should buy
a roomy house full of furniture, a trip to Europe once a year,
and a bond or two besides. But our $36,000 had bought
nothing at all.

So I dug up my miscellaneous account books, and
my wife dug up her complete household record for the
year 1923, and we made out the monthly average.
Here it is:

HOUSEHOLD EXPENSES

					Apportioned per Month
Income tax	..	..	..	..	$ 198·00
Food	..	..	..	..	202·00
Rent	..	..	..	..	300·00
Coal, wood, ice, gas, light, phone, and water				..	114·50
Servants	..	..	..	..	295·00
Golf clubs	..	..	..	..	105·50
Clothes—three people	..	..	..	158·00
Doctor and dentist	..	..	..	42·50
Drugs and cigarettes	..	..	..	32·50
Automobile	..	..	..	..	25·00
Books	..	..	..	..	14·50
All other household expenses		..	..	112·50
Total	..	..	..	..	$1,600·00

'Well, that's not bad,' we thought when we had got thus far. 'Some of the items are pretty high, especially food and servants. But there's about everything accounted for, and it's only a little more than half our income.'

Then we worked out the average monthly expenditures that could be included under pleasure.

Hotel bills—this meant spending the night or charging meals in New York			..	..	$ 51·00
Trips—only two, but apportioned per month				43·00
Theatre tickets	..	..	..	..	55·00
Barber and hairdresser	..	..	..	25·00
Charity and loans	..	..	..	15·00
Taxis	..	..	..	..	15·00
Gambling—this dark heading covers bridge, craps, and football bets			..	..	33·00
Restaurant parties	..	..	..	70·00
Entertaining	..	..	..	..	70·00
Miscellaneous	..	..	..	..	23·00
Total	..	..	..	..	$400·00

Some of these items were pretty high. They will seem higher to a Westerner than to a New Yorker. Fifty-five dollars for theatre tickets means between three and five shows a month, depending on the type of show and how long it's been running. Football games are also included in this, as well as ringside seats to the Dempsey-Firpo fight. As for the amount marked 'restaurant parties'—$70 would perhaps take three couples to a popular after-theatre cabaret—but it would be a close shave.

We added the items marked 'pleasure' to the items marked 'household expenses', and obtained a monthly total.

'Fine', I said. 'just $3,000. Now at least we'll know where to cut down, because we know where it goes.'

She frowned; then a puzzled, awed expression passed over her face.

'What's the matter?' I demanded. 'Isn't it all right? Are some of the items wrong?'

'It isn't the items,' she said staggeringly; 'it's the total. This only adds up to $2,000 a month."

I was incredulous, but she nodded.

'But listen,' I protested; 'my bank statements show that we've spent $3,000 a month. You don't mean to say that every month we lose 1,000 dollars?'

'This only adds up to $2,000,' she protested, 'so we must have.'

'Give me the pencil.'

For an hour I worked over the accounts in silence, but to no avail.

'Why, this is impossible!' I insisted. 'People don't lose $12,000 in a year. It's just—it's just missing.'

There was a ring at the doorbell and I walked over to answer it, still dazed by these figures. It was the Banklands, our neighbours from over the way.

'Good heavens!' I announced. 'We've just lost $12,000!'

Bankland stepped back alertly.

'Burglars?' he inquired.

'Ghosts,' answered my wife.

Mrs Bankland looked nervously around.

'Really?'

We explained the situation, the mysterious third of our income that had vanished into thin air.

'Well, what we do,' said Mrs Bankland, 'is, we have a budget.'

'We have a budget,' agreed Bankland, 'and we stick absolutely to it. If the skies fall we don't go over any item of that budget. That's the only way to live sensibly and save money.'

'That's what we ought to do,' I agreed.

Mrs Bankland nodded enthusiastically.

'It's a wonderful scheme,' she went on. 'We make a certain deposit every month, and all I save on it I can have for myself to do anything I want with.'

I could see that my wife was visibly excited.

'That's what I want to do,' she broke out suddenly. 'Have a budget. Everybody does it that has any sense.'

'I pity anyone that doesn't use that system,' said Bankland solemnly. 'Think of the inducement to economy—the extra money my wife'll have for clothes.'

'How much have you saved so far?' my wife inquired eagerly of Mrs Bankland.

'So far?' repeated Mrs Bankland. 'Oh, I haven't had a chance so far. You see we only began the system yesterday.'

'Yesterday!' we cried.

'Just yesterday,' agreed Bankland darkly. 'But I wish to heaven I'd started it a year ago. I've been working over our accounts all week, and do you know, Fitzgerald, every month there's $2,000 I can't account for to save my soul.'

Headed Toward Easy Street

Our financial troubles are now over. We have permanently left the newly rich class and installed the budget system. It is simple and sensible, and I can explain it to you in a few words. You consider your income as an enormous pie all cut up into slices, each slice representing one class of expenses. Somebody has worked it all out; so you know just what proportion of your income you can spend on each slice. There is

10

even a slice for founding universities, if you go in for that.

For instance, the amount you spend on the theatre should be half your drug-store bill. This will enable us to see one play every five and a half months, or two and a half plays a year. We have already picked out the first one, but if it isn't running five and a half months from now we shall be that much ahead. Our allowance for newspapers should be only a quarter of what we spend on self-improvement, so we are considering whether to get the Sunday paper once a month or to subscribe for an almanac.

According to the budget we will be allowed only three-quarters of a servant, so we are on the lookout for a one-legged cook who can come six days a week. And apparently the author of the budget lives in a town where you can still go to the movies for a nickel and get a shave for a dime. But we are going to give up the expenditure called 'Foreign missions, etc.,' and apply it to the life of crime instead. Altogether, outside of the fact that there is no slice allowed for 'missing' it seems to be a very complete book, and according to the testimonials in the back, if we make $36,000 again this year, the chances are that we'll save at least $35.000.

'But we can't get any of that first $36,000 back,' I complained around the house. 'If we just had something to show for it I wouldn't feel so absurd.'

My wife thought a long while.

'The only thing you can do,' she said finally, 'is to write a magazine article and call it How to Live on $36,000 a Year.'

'What a silly suggestion!' I replied coldly.

HOW TO LIVE ON
PRACTICALLY NOTHING
A YEAR
[1924]

'ALL RIGHT,' I said hopefully, 'what did it come to
for the month?' 'Two thousand three hundred and twenty
dollars and eighty-two cents.' It was the fifth of five long
months during which we had tried every device we knew
to bring the figure of our expenditures safely below the
figure of our income. We had succeeded in buying less
clothes, less food and fewer luxuries; in fact we had succeeded in everything except saving money.

'Let's give up,' said my wife gloomily. 'Look, here's another bill I haven't even opened.'

'It isn't a bill; it's got a French stamp.'

It was a letter. I read it aloud, and when I finished we
looked at each other in a wild, expectant way.

'I don't see why everybody doesn't come over here,'
it said. 'I am now writing from a little inn in France
where I just had a meal fit for a king, washed down with
champagne, for the absurd sum of sixty-one cents. It costs
about one-tenth as much to live over here. From where
I sit I can see the smoky peaks of the Alps rising behind a town that was old before Alexander the Great was
born. . . .'

By the time we had read the letter for the third time we
were in our car bound for New York. As we rushed into the
steamship office half an hour later, overturning a rolltop desk
and bumping an office boy up against the wall, the agent
looked up with mild surprise.

Off to the Riviera to Economize

'Don't utter a word,' he said. 'You're the twelfth this

morning and I understand. You've just got a letter from a friend in Europe telling you how cheap everything is and you want to sail right away. How many?'

'One child,' we told him breathlessly.

'Good!' he exclaimed, spreading out a deck of cards on his flat table. 'The suits read that you are going on a long, unexpected journey, that you have illness ahead of you and that you will soon meet a number of dark men and women who mean you no good.'

As we threw him heavily from the window his voice floated up to us somewhere between the sixteenth storey and the street:

'You sail one week from tomorrow.'

Now when a family goes abroad to economize, they don't go to the Wembley exhibition or the Olympic games; in fact they don't go to London and Paris at all, but hasten to the Riviera, which is the southern coast of France and which is reputed to be the cheapest as well as the most beautiful locality in the world. Moreover we were going to the Riviera out of season, which is something like going to Palm Beach for July.

When the Riviera season finishes in late spring, all the wealthy British and Americans move up to Deauville and Trouville, and all the gambling houses and fashionable milliners and jewellers and second-storey men close up their establishments and follow their quarry north. Immediately prices fall. The native Rivierans, who have been living on rice and fish all winter, come out of their caves and buy a bottle of red wine and splash about for a bit in their own blue sea.

For two reformed spendthrifts, the Riviera in summer had exactly the right sound. So we put our house in the hands of six real-estate agents and steamed off to France amid the deafening applause of a crowd of friends on the pier—both of whom waved wildly until we were out of sight.

We felt that we had escaped from extravagance and clamour and from all the wild extremes among which we had dwelt for five hectic years, from the tradesman who laid for us and the nurse who bullied us and the couple who kept our house for us and knew us all too well. We were going to the Old World to find a new rhythm for our lives, with a true conviction that we had left our old selves behind for ever—and with a capital of just over seven thousand dollars.

The sun coming through high french windows woke us one week later. Outside we could hear the high, clear honk of strange auto horns and we remembered that we were in Paris.

The baby was already sitting up in her cot, ringing the bells which summoned the different *fonctionnaires* of the hotel as though she had determined to start the day immediately. It was indeed her day, for we were in Paris for no other reason than to get her a nurse.

'*Entrez!*' we shouted together as there was a knock at the door.

The Governess We Did Not Engage

A handsome waiter opened it and stepped inside, whereupon our child ceased her harmonizing upon the bells and regarded him with a marked disfavour.

'Iss a mademoiselle who waited out in the street,' he remarked.

'Speak French,' I said sternly. 'We're all French here.'

He spoke French for some time.

'All right,' I interrupted after a moment. 'Now say that again very slowly in English; I didn't quite understand.'

'His name's Entrez,' remarked the baby helpfully.

'Be that as it may,' I flared up, 'his French strikes me as very bad.'

We discovered finally that an English governess was outside to answer our advertisment in the paper.

'Tell her to come in.'

After an interval, a tall, languid person in a Rue de la Paix hat strolled into the room and we tried to look as dignified as is possible when sitting up in bed.

'You're Americans?' she said, seating herself with scornful care.

'Yes.'

'I understand you want a nurse. Is this the child?'

'Yes, ma'am.'

Here is some high-born lady of the English court, we thought, in temporarily reduced circumstances.

'I've had a great deal of experience,' she said, advancing upon our child and attempting unsuccessfully to take her hand. 'I'm practically a trained nurse; I'm a lady born and I never complain.'

'Complain of what?' demanded my wife.

The applicant waved her hand vaguely.

'Oh, the food, for example.'

'Look here,' I asked suspiciously, 'before we go any farther, let me ask what salary you've been getting.'

'For you,' she hesitated, 'one hundred dollars a month.'

'Oh, you wouldn't have to do the cooking too,' we assured her; 'it's just to take care of one child.'

She arose and adjusted her feather boa with a fine scorn.

'You'd better get a French nurse,' she said, 'if you're that kind of people. She won't open the windows at night and your baby will never learn the French word for "tub", but you'll only have to pay her ten dollars a month.'

'Good-bye,' we said together.

'I'll come for fifty.'

'Good-bye,' we repeated.

'For forty—and I'll do the baby's washing.'

'We wouldn't take you for your board.'

The hotel trembled slightly as she closed the door.

'Where's the lady gone?' asked our child.

'She's hunting Americans', we said. 'She looked in the hotel register and thought she saw Chicago written after our names.'

We are always witty like that with the baby. She considers us the most amusing couple she has ever known.

The Hot, Sweet South of France

After breakfast I went to the Paris branch of our American bank to get money; but I had no sooner entered it than I wished myself at the hotel, or at least that I had gone in by the back way, for I had evidently been recognized and an enormous crowd began to gather outside. The crowd grew, and I considered going to the window and making them a speech; but I thought that might only increase the disturbance, so I looked around intending to ask someone's advice. I recognized no one, however, except one of the bank officials and a Mr and Mrs Douglas Fairbanks from America, who were buying francs at a counter in the rear. So I decided not to show myself; and by the time I had cashed my cheque the crowd had given up and melted away.

I think now that we did well to get away from Paris in nine days, which, after all, was only a week more than we had intended. Every morning a new boatload of Americans poured into the boulevards, and every afternoon our room at the hotel was filled with familiar faces until—except that there was no faint taste of wood alcohol in the refreshments—we might have been in New York. But at last, with six thousand five hundred dollars remaining, and with an English nurse whom we engaged for twenty-six dollars a month, we boarded the train for the Riviera, the hot, sweet South of France.

When your eyes first fall upon the Mediterranean you know at once why it was here that man first stood erect and stretched out his arms toward the sun. It is a blue sea; or rather it is too blue for that hackneyed phrase which has described every muddy pool from pole to pole. It is the fairy blue of Maxfield Parrish's pictures; blue like blue books, blue oil, blue eyes, and in the shadow of the mountains a green belt of land runs along the coast for a hundred miles and makes a playground for the world. The Riviera! The names of its resorts, Cannes, Nice, Monte Carlo, call up the memory of a hundred kings and princes who have lost their thrones and come here to die, of mysterious rajahs and beys flinging blue diamonds to English dancing girls, of Russian millionaires tossing away fortunes at roulette in the lost caviar days before the war.

From Charles Dickens to Catherine de' Medici, from Prince Edward of Wales in the height of his popularity, to Oscar Wilde in the depth of his disgrace, the whole world has come here to forget or to rejoice, to hide its face or have

its fling, to build white palaces out of the spoils of oppres-
sion or to write the books which sometimes batter those
palaces down. Under striped awnings beside the sea grand
dukes and gamblers and diplomats and noble courtesans and
Balkan czars smoked their slow cigarettes while 1913 drifted
into 1914 without a quiver of the calendar, and the fury
gathered in the north that was to sweep three-fourths of
them away.

Floundering in Flawless French

We reached Hyères, the town of our destination, in the
blazing noon, aware immediately of the tropic's breath as it
oozed out of the massed pines. A cabby with a large egg-
shaped carbuncle in the centre of his forehead struggled with
a uniformed hotel porter for the possession of our grips.

'Je suis a stranger here,' I said in flawless French. 'Je
veux aller to le best hotel dans le town.'

The porter pointed to an imposing auto-bus in the station
drive.

'Which is the best?' I asked.

For answer, he picked up our heaviest grip, balanced it a
moment in his hand, hit the cabby a crashing blow on the
forehead—I immediately understood the gradual growth of
the carbuncle—and then pressed us firmly toward the car. I
tossed several nickels—or rather francs—upon the pros-
trate carbuncular man.

'Isn't it hot,' remarked the nurse.

'I like it very much indeed,' I responded, mopping my
forehead and attempting a cool smile. I felt that the moral
responsibility was with me. I had picked out Hyères for no
more reason than that a friend had once spent a winter there.
Besides, we hadn't come here to keep cool; we had come
here to economize, to live on practically nothing a year.

'Nevertheless, it's hot,' said my wife, and a moment later
the child shouted, 'Coat off!' in no uncertain voice.

'He must think we want to see the town,' I said when,
after driving for a mile along a palm-lined road, we stopped
in an ancient Mexican-looking square. 'Hold on!'

This last was in alarm, for he was hurriedly disembarking our baggage in front of a dilapidated quick-lunch emporium.

'Is this a joke?' I demanded. 'Did I tell you to go to the best hotel in town?'

'Here it is,' he said.

'No, it isn't. This is the worst hotel I ever saw.'

'I am the proprietor,' he said.

'I'm sorry, but we've got a baby here'—the nurse obligingly held up the baby—'and we want a more modern hotel, with a bath.'

'We have a bath.'

'I mean a private bath.'

'We will not use while you are here. All the big hotels have shut up themselves for during the summer.'

'I don't believe him for a minute,' said my wife.

I looked around helplessly. Two scanty, hungry women had come out of the door and were looking voraciously at our baggage. Suddenly I heard the sound of slow hoofs, and glancing up I beheld the carbuncular man driving disconsolately up the dusty street.

'What's le best hotel dans le town?' I shouted at him.

'Non, non, non, non!' he cried, waving his reins excitedly. 'Jardin Hôtel open!'

As the proprietor dropped my grip and started toward the cabby at a run, I turned to the hungry women accusingly.

'What do you mean by having a bus like this?' I demanded.

I felt very American and superior; I intimated that if the morals of the French people were in this decadent state I regretted that we had ever entered the war.

'Daddy's hot too,' remarked the baby irrelevantly.

'I am not hot!'

'Daddy had better stop talking and find us a hotel,' remarked the English nurse, 'before we all melt away.'

It was the work of but an hour to pay off the proprietor, to add damages for his wounded feelings and to install ourselves in the Hôtel du Jardin, on the edge of town.

'Hyères,' says my guidebook, 'is the very oldest and

warmest of the Riviera winter resorts and is now frequented
almost exclusively by the English.'

But when we arrived there late in May, even the English,
except the very oldest and warmest, had moved away. At
dinner, only a superannuated dozen, a slowly decaying dozen,
a solemn and dispirited dozen remained. But we were to be
there merely while we searched for a villa, and it had the
advantage of being amazingly cheap for a first-class hotel.
The rate for four of us, including meals, was one hundred
and fifty francs—less than eight dollars a day.

The real-estate agent, an energetic young gentleman with
his pants buttoned snugly around his chest, called on us next
morning.

'Dozens of villas,' he said enthusiastically. 'We will take
the horse and buggy and go see.'

It was a simmering morning, but the streets already
swarmed with the faces of Southern France—dark faces, for
there is an Arab streak along the Riviera, left from turbulent,
forgotten centuries. Once the Moors harried the coast for
gain, and later, as they swept up through Spain in mad
glory, they threw out frontier towns along the shores as
outposts for their conquest of the world. They were not the
first people, or the last, that have tried to overrun France.
All that remains now for proud Moslem hopes is an occasional Moorish tower and the tragic glint of black Eastern
eyes.

'Now this villa rents for thirty dollars a month,' said the
real-estate agent as we stopped at a small house on the edge
of town.

'What's the matter with it ?' asked my wife suspiciously.

'Nothing at all. It is superb. It has six rooms and a well.'

'A well ?'

'A fine well.'

'Do you mean it has no bathroom ?'

'Not what you would call an actual bathroom.'

'Drive on,' we said.

It was obvious by noon that there were no villas to be let
in Hyères. Those we saw were all too hot, too small, too

HOW TO LIVE ON PRACTICALLY NOTHING A YEAR 299

dirty, or too *triste*, an expressive word which implies that the mad marquis still walks through the halls in his shroud.

'Yes, we have no villas today,' remarked the agent, smiling.

'That's a very old played-out joke,' I said, 'and I am too hot to laugh.'

Extracting Information

Our clothes were hanging on us like wet towels, but when I had established our identity by a scar on my left hand we were admitted to the hotel. I decided to ask one of the lingering Englishmen if there was perhaps another quiet town near by.

Now, asking something of an American or a Frenchman is a definite thing: the only difference is that you can understand the American's reply. But getting an answer from an Englishman is about as complicated as borrowing a match from the Secretary of State. The first one I approached dropped his paper, looked at me in horror and bolted precipitately from the room. This disconcerted me for a moment, but luckily my eyes fell on a man whom I had seen being wheeled in to dinner.

'Good morning,' I said, 'Could you tell me—' He jerked spasmodically, but to my relief, he was unable to leave his seat. 'I wonder if you know a town where I could get a villa for the summer.'

'Don't know any at all,' he said coldly. 'And I wouldn't tell you if I did.'

He didn't exactly pronounce the last sentence, but I could read the words as they were issued from his eyes.

'I suppose you're a newcomer too,' I suggested.

'I've been here every winter for sixteen years.'

Pretending to detect an invitation in this, I drew up my chair.

'Then you must know some town,' I assured him.

'Cannes, Nice, Monte Carlo.'

'But they're too expensive. I want a quiet place to do a lot of work.'

'Cannes, Nice, Monte Carlo. All quiet in summer. Don't

know any others. Wouldn't tell you if I did. Good day.'

Upstairs, the nurse was counting the mosquito bites on the baby, all received during the night, and my wife was adding them up in a big book.

'Cannes, Nice, Monte Carlo,' I said.

'I'm glad we're going to leave this broiling town,' remarked the nurse.

'I think we'd better try Cannes.'

'I think so too,' said my wife eagerly. 'I hear it's very gay— I mean, it's no economy to stay where you can't work, and I don't believe we can get a villa here after all.'

'Let's go on the big boat,' said the baby suddenly.

'Silence! We've come to the Riviera and we're here to stay.'

The Villa of Our Dreams

So we decided to leave the nurse and baby in Hyères and run up to Cannes, which is a more fashionable town in a more northerly situation along the shore. Now when you run up to somewhere you have to have an automobile, so we bought the only new one in town next day. It had the power of six horses—the age of the horses was not stated—and it was so small that we loomed out of it like giants; so small that you could run it under the veranda for the night. It had no lock, no speedometer, no gauge, and its cost, including the parcel-post charge, was seven hundred and fifty dollars. We started for Cannes in it, and except for the warm exhaust when other cars drove over us, we found the trip comparatively cool.

All the celebrities of Europe have spent a season in Cannes; even the Man with the Iron Mask whiled away twelve years on an island off its shore. Its gorgeous villas are built of stone so soft that it is sawed instead of hewed. We looked at four of them next morning. They were small, neat and clean; you could have matched them in any suburb of Los Angeles. They rented at sixty-five dollars a month.

'I like them,' said my wife firmly. 'Let's rent one. They look awfully easy to run.'

'We didn't come abroad to find a house that was easy to

run,' I objected. 'How could I write looking out on a'—
I glanced out the window and my eyes met a splendid view
of the sea—'where I'd hear every whisper in the house.'

So we moved on to the fourth villa, the wonderful fourth
villa the memory of which still causes me to lie awake and
hope that some bright day will find me there. It rose in white
marble out of a great hill, like a château, like a castle of old.
The very taxicab that took us there had romance in its front
seat.

'Did you notice our driver?' said the agent, leaning
toward me. 'He used to be a Russian millionaire.'

We peered through the glass at him—a thin dispirited
man who ordered the gears about with a lordly air.

'The town is full of them,' said the agent. 'They're glad
to get jobs as chauffeurs, butlers or waiters. The women
work as *femmes de chambre* in the hotels.'

'Why don't they open tea rooms like Americans do?'

'Many of them aren't fit for anything. We're awfully sorry
for them, but—' He leaned forward and tapped on the glass.
'Would you mind driving a little faster? We haven't got all
day.'

'Look,' he said when we reached the château on the hill.
'There's the Grand Duke Michael's villa next door.'

'You mean he's the butler there?'

'Oh no; he's got money. He's gone north for the summer.'

When we had entered through scrolled brass gates that
creaked massively as gates should for a king, and when the
blinds had been drawn, we were in a high central hall hung
with ancestral portraits of knights in armour and courtiers in
satin and brocade. It was like a movie set. Flights of marble
stairs rose in solid dignity to form a grand gallery into which
light dropped through blue figured glass upon a mosaic
floor. It was modern, too, with huge clean beds and a model
kitchen and three bathrooms and a solemn, silent study
overlooking the sea.

'It belonged to a Russian general,' said the agent; 'killed
in Silesia during the war.'

'How much is it?'

'For the summer, one hundred and ten dollars a month.'

'Done!' I said. 'Fix up the lease right away. My wife will go to Hyères immediately to get the—'

'Just a minute,' she said, frowning. 'How many servants will it take to run this house?'

'Why, I should say,'—the agent glanced at us sharply and hesitated—'about five.'

'I should say about eight.' She turned to me. 'Let's go to Newport and rent the Vanderbilt house instead.'

'Remember,' said the agent, 'you've got the Grand Duke Michael on your left'.

'Will he come to see us?' I inquired.

'He would of course,' explained the agent, 'only you see, he's gone away.'

We held debate upon the mosaic floor. My theory was that I couldn't work in the little houses and that this would be a real investment because of its romantic inspiration. My wife's theory was that eight servants eat a lot of food and that it simply wouldn't do. We apologized to the agent, shook hands respectfully with the millionaire taxi driver and gave him five francs, and in a state of great dejection returned to Hyères.

'Here's the hotel bill,' said my wife as we went despondently in to dinner.

'Thank heaven, it's only fifty-five dollars.'

I opened it. To my amazement, tax after tax had been added beneath the bill—government tax, city tax, a ten per cent tax to retip the servants.

I looked gloomily at a nameless piece of meat soaked in a lifeless gravy which reclined on my plate.

'I think it's goat's meat,' said the nurse, following my eyes. She turned to my wife. 'Did you ever taste goat's meat, Mrs Fitzgerald?'

But Mrs Fitzgerald had never tasted goat's meat and Mrs Fitzgerald had fled.

Hunting His Majesty

As I wandered dismally about the hotel the next day, hoping

that our house on Long Island hadn't been rented so that we could go home for the summer, I noticed that the halls were even more deserted than usual. There seemed to be more old copies of the *Illustrated London News* about, and more empty chairs. At dinner we had the goat again. As I looked around the empty dining-room I suddenly realized that the last Englishman had taken his cane and his conscience and fled to London. The management was keeping open a two-hundred-room hotel for us alone!

Hyères grew warmer and we rested there in a helpless daze. We knew now why Catherine de' Medici had chosen it for her favourite resort. A month of it in the summer and she must have returned to Paris with a dozen St Bartholomew's sizzling in her head. In vain we took trips to Nice, to Antibes, to St Maximim—we were worried now; a fourth of our seven thousand had slipped away. Then one morning just five weeks after we had left New York we got off the train at a little town that we had never considered before. It was a red little town built close to the sea, with gay red-roofed houses and an air of repressed carnival about it; carnival that would venture forth into the streets before night. We knew that we would love to live in it and we asked a citizen the whereabouts of the real-estate agency.

'Ah, for that you had far better ask the king,' he exclaimed.

A principality! A second Monaco! We had not known there were two of them along the French shore.

'And a bank that will cash a letter of credit?'

'For that, too, you must ask the king.'

He pointed the way toward the palace down a long shady street, and my wife hurriedly produced a mirror and began powdering her face.

'But our dusty clothes,' I said modestly. 'Do you think the king will—'

He considered.

'I'm not sure about clothes,' he answered. 'But I think—yes, I think the king will attend to that for you too.'

I hadn't meant that, but we thanked him and with much

inward trepidation proceeded toward the imperial domain. After half an hour, when the royal turrets had failed to rise against the sky, I stopped another man.

'Can you tell us the way to the imperial palace?'

'The what?'

'We want to get an interview with his majesty—his majesty the king.'

The word 'king' caught his attention. His mouth opened understandingly and he pointed to a sign over our heads:

'W. F. King,' I read, 'Anglo-American Bank, Real-Estate Agency, Railroad Tickets, Insurance, Tours and Excursions, Circulating Library.'

Where Things are so Cheap

The potentate turned out to be a brisk, efficient Englishman of middle age who had gradually acquired the little town to himself over a period of twenty years.

'We are Americans come to Europe to economize,' I told him. 'We've combed the Riviera from Nice to Hyères and haven't been able to find a villa. Meanwhile our money is leaking gradually away.'

He leaned back and pressed a button and almost immediately a lean, gaunt woman appeared in the door.

'This is Marthe,' he said, 'your cook.'

We could hardly believe our ears.

'Do you mean you have a villa for us?'

'I have already selected one,' he said. 'My agents saw you getting off the train.'

He pressed another button and another woman stood respectfully beside the first.

'This is Jeanne, your *femme de chambre*. She does the mending, too, and waits on the table. You pay her thirteen dollars a month and you pay Marthe sixteen dollars. Marthe does the marketing, however, and expects to make a little on the side for herself.'

'But the villa?'

'The lease is being made out now. The price is seventy-nine dollars a month and your cheque is good with me. We move you in tomorrow.'

Within an hour we had seen our home, a clean cool villa set in a large garden on a hill above town. It was what we had been looking for all along. There was a summerhouse and a sand pile and two bathrooms and roses for breakfast and a gardener who called me milord. When we had paid the rent, only thirty-five hundred dollars, half our original capital, remained. But we felt at last we could begin to live on practically nothing a year.

In the late afternoon of 1st September, 1924, a distinguished-looking young man, accompanied by a young lady might have been seen lounging on a sandy beach in France. Both of them were burned to a deep chocolate brown, so that at first they seemed to be of Egyptian origin; but closer inspection showed that their faces had an Aryan cast and that their voices, when they spoke, had a faintly nasal, North American ring. Near them played a small black child with cotton-white hair who from time to time beat a tin spoon upon a pail and shouted, '*Regardez-moi!*' in no uncertain voice.

Out of the casino near by drifted weird rococo music—a song dealing with the non-possession of a specific yellow fruit in a certain otherwise well-stocked store. Waiters, both Senegalese and European, rushed around among the bathers with many-coloured drinks, pausing now and then to chase away the children of the poor, who were dressing and undressing with neither modesty nor self-consciousness, upon the sand.

'Hasn't it been a good summer!' said the young man lazily. 'We've become absolutely French.'

'And the French are such an aesthetic people,' said the young lady, listening for a moment to the banana music. 'They know how to live. Think of all the nice things they have to eat!'

'Delicious things! Heavenly things!' exclaimed the young man, spreading some American devilled ham on some

biscuits marked Springfield, Illinois. 'But then they've
studied the food question for two thousand years.'

'And things are so cheap here!' cried the young lady
enthusiastically. 'Think of perfume! Perfume that would
cost fifteen dollars in New York, you can get here for five.'

The young man struck a Swedish match and lit an American cigarette.

'The trouble with most Americans in France,' he remarked sonorously, 'is that they won't lead a real French
life. They hang around the big hotels and exchange opinions
fresh from the States.'

'I know,' she agreed. 'That's exactly what it said in the
New York Times this morning.'

The American music ended and the English nurse arose,
implying that it was time the child went home to supper.
With a sigh, the young man arose, too, and shook himself,
violently, scattering a great quantity of sand.

'We've got to stop on the way and get some Arizon-oil
gasoline,' he said. 'That last stuff was awful.'

'The check, suh,' said a Senegalese waiter with an accent
from well below the Mason-Dixon Line. 'That'll be ten
francs fo' two glasses of beer.'

The young man handed him the equivalent of seventy
cents in the gold-coloured hat checks of France. Beer was
perhaps a little higher than in America, but then he had had
the privilege of hearing the historic banana song on a real, or
almost real, jazz band. And waiting for him at home was a
regular French supper—baked beans from the quaint old
Norman town of Akron, Ohio, an omelet fragrant with la
Chicago bacon and a cup of English tea.

But perhaps you have already recognized in these two
cultured Europeans the same barbaric Americans who had
left America just five months before; and perhaps you wonder
that the change could have come about so quickly. The
secret is that they had entered fully into the life of the Old
World. Instead of patronizing tourist hotels they had made
excursions to quaint little out-of-the-way restaurants,   with
the real French atmosphere, where supper for two rarely

came to more than ten or fifteen dollars. Not for them the glittering capitals—Paris, Brussels, Rome. They were content with short trips to beautiful historic old towns, such as Monte Carlo, where they once left their automobile with a kindly garage man who paid their hotel bill and bought them tickets home.

The High Cost of Economizing

Yes, our summer had been a complete success. And we had lived on practically nothing—that is, on practically nothing except our original seven thousand dollars. It was all gone.

The trouble is that we had come to the Riviera out of season—that is, out of one season, but in the middle of another. For in summer the people who are trying to economize come South, and the shrewd French know that this class is the very easiest game of all, as people who are trying to get something for nothing are very liable to be.

Exactly where the money went we don't know—we never do. There were the servants, for example. I was very fond of Marthe and Jeanne—and afterwards of their sisters Eugénie and Serpolette, who came in to help—but on my own initiative it would never have occurred to me to insure them all. Yet that was the law. If Jeanne suffocated in her mosquito netting, if Marthe tripped over a bone and broke her thumb, I was responsible. I wouldn't have minded so much except that the little on the side that Marthe made in doing our marketing amounted, as I figure, to about forty-five per cent.

Our weekly bills at the grocer's and the butcher's averaged sixty-five dollars, or higher than they had ever been in an expensive Long Island town. Whatever the meat actually cost, it was almost invariably inedible; while as for the milk, every drop of it had to be boiled, because the cows were tubercular in France. For fresh vegetables we had tomatoes and a little asparagus; that was all—the only garlic that can be put over on us must be administered in sleep. I wondered often how the Riviera middle class—the bank clerk, say, who supports a family on from forty to seventy dollars a month—manages to keep alive.

'It's even worse in winter,' a little French girl told us on the beach. 'The English and Americans drive the prices up until we can't buy and we don't know what to do. My sister has had to go to Marseilles and find work, and she's only fourteen. Next winter I'll go too.'

No Money and No Regrets

There simply isn't enough to go around; and the Americans who, because of their own high standard of material comfort, want the best obtainable, naturally have to pay. And in addition, the sharp French tradesmen are always ready to take advantage of a careless American eye.

'I don't like this bill,' I said to the food-and-ice deliverer. 'I arranged to pay you five francs and not eight francs a day.'

He became unintelligible for a moment to gain time.

'My wife added it up,' he said.

Those valuable Riviera wives! Always they are adding up their husbands' accounts, and the dear ladies simply don't know one figure from another. Such a talent in the wife of a railroad president would be an asset worth many million dollars.

It is twilight as I write this, and out of my window darkening banks of trees, set one clump behind another in many greens, slope down to the evening sea. The flaming sun has collapsed behind the peaks of the Estérels and the moon already hovers over the Roman aqueducts of Fréjus, five miles away. In half an hour René and Bobbé, officers of aviation, are coming to dinner in their white ducks; and René, who is only twenty-three and has never recovered from having missed the war, will tell us romantically how he wants to smoke opium in Peking and how he writes a few things 'for myself alone.' Afterwards, in the garden, their white uniforms will grow dimmer as the more liquid dark comes down, until they, like the heavy roses and the nightingales in the pines, will seem to take an essential and indivisible part in the beauty of this proud gay land.

And though we have saved nothing, we have danced the *carmagnole*; and, except for the day when my wife took the mosquito lotion for a mouth wash, and the time when I tried to smoke a French cigarette, and, as Ring Lardner would say, swooned, we haven't yet been sorry that we came.

The dark-brown child is knocking at the door to bid me good night.

'Going on the big boat, daddy?' she says in broken English.

'No.'

'Why?'

'Because we're going to try it for another year, and besides —think of perfume.'

We are always like that with the baby. She considers us the wittiest couple she has ever known.

HOW TO WASTE
MATERIAL: A NOTE ON
MY GENERATION
[1926]

EVER SINCE IRVING'S preoccupation with the necessity for an American background, for some square miles of cleared territory on which colourful variants might presently arise, the question of material has hampered the American writer. For one Dreiser who made a single-minded and irreproachable choice there have been a dozen like Henry James who have stupid-got with worry over the matter, and yet another dozen who, blinded by the fading tail of Walt Whitman's comet, have botched their books by the insincere compulsion to write 'significantly' about America.

Insincere because it is not a compulsion found in themselves—it is 'literary' in the most belittling sense. During the past seven years we have had at least half a dozen treatments of the American farmer, ranging from New England to Nebraska; at least a dozen canny books about youth, some of them with surveys of the American universities for background; more than a dozen novels reflecting various aspects of New York, Chicago, Washington, Detroit, Indianapolis, Wilmington, and Richmond; innumerable novels dealing with American politics, business, society, science, racial problems, art, literature, and moving pictures, and with Americans abroad at peace or in war; finally several novels of change and growth, tracing the swift decades for their own sweet lavender or protesting vaguely and ineffectually against the industrialization of our beautiful old American life. We have had an Arnold Bennett for every five

310

towns—surely by this time the foundations have been laid! Are we competent only to toil forever upon a never completed first floor whose specifications change from year to year?

In any case we are running through our material like spendthrifts—just as we have done before. In the 'nineties there began a feverish search for any period of American history that hadn't been 'used', and once found it was immediately debauched into a pretty and romantic story. These past seven years have seen the same sort of literary gold rush; and for all our boasted sincerity and sophistication the material is being turned out raw and undigested in much the same way. One author goes to a midland farm for three months to obtain the material for an epic of the American husbandmen! Another sets off on a like errand to the Blue Ridge Mountains, a third departs with a Corona for the West Indies—one is justified in the belief that what they get hold of will weigh no more than the journalistic loot brought back by Richard Harding Davis and John Fox, Jr, twenty years ago.

Worse, the result will be doctored up to give it a literary flavour. The farm story will be sprayed with faint dilution of ideas and sensory impressions from Thomas Hardy; the novel of the Jewish tenement block will be festooned with wreaths from *Ulysses* and the later Gertrude Stein; the document of dreamy youth will be prevented from fluttering entirely away by means of great and half-great names— Marx, Spencer, Wells, Edward Fitzgerald—dropped like paperweights here and there upon the pages. Finally the novel of business will be cudgelled into being satire by the questionable but constantly reiterated implication that the author and his readers don't partake of the American commercial instinct and aren't a little jealous.

And most of it—the literary beginnings of what was to have been a golden age—is as dead as if it had never been written. Scarcely one of those who put so much effort and enthusiasm, even intelligence, into it, got hold of any material at all.

To a limited extent this was the fault of two men—one of

whom, H. L. Mencken, has yet done more for American letters than any man alive. What Mencken felt the absence of, what he wanted, and justly, back in 1920, got away from him, got twisted in his hand. Not because the 'literary revolution' went beyond him but because his idea had always been ethical rather than aesthetic. In the history of culture no pure aesthetic idea has ever served as an offensive weapon. Mencken's invective, sharp as Swift's, made its point by the use of the most forceful prose style now written in English. Immediately, instead of committing himself to an infinite series of pronouncements upon the American novel, he should have modulated his tone to the more urbane, more critical one of his early essay on Dreiser.

But perhaps it was already too late. Already he had begotten a family of hammer-and-tongs men—insensitive, suspicious of glamour, preoccupied exclusively with the external, the contemptible, the 'national', and the drab, whose style was a debasement of his least effective manner and who, like glib children, played continually with his themes in his maternal shadow. These were the men who manufactured enthusiasm when each new mass of raw data was dumped on the literary platform—mistaking incoherence for vitality, chaos for vitality. It was the 'new poetry movement' over again, only that this time its victims were worth the saving. Every week some new novel gave its author membership in 'that little band who are producing a worthy American literature'. As one of the charter members of that little band I am proud to state that it has now swollen to seventy or eighty members.

And through a curious misconception of his work, Sherwood Anderson must take part of the blame for this enthusiastic march up a blind alley in the dark. To this day reviewers solemnly speak of him as an inarticulate, fumbling man, bursting with ideas—when, on the contrary, he is the possessor of a brilliant and almost inimitable prose style, and of scarcely any ideas at all. Just as the prose of Joyce in the hands of, say, Waldo Frank becomes insignificant and idiotic, so the Anderson admirers set up Hergesheimer as an anti-Christ and then proceed to imitate Anderson's lapses from that difficult simplicity they are unable to understand. And here again critics support them by discovering merits in the very disorganization that is to bring their books to a timely and unregretted doom.

Now the business is over. 'Wolf' has been cried too often. The public, weary of being fooled, has gone back to its Englishmen, its memoirs, and its prophets. Some of the late brilliant boys are on lecture tours (a circular informs me that most of them are to speak upon 'the literary revolution'!), some are writing pot-boilers, a few have definitely abandoned the literary life—they were never sufficiently aware that material, however closely observed, is as elusive as the moment in which it has its existence unless it is purified by an incorruptible style and by the catharsis of a passionate emotion.

Of all the work by the young men who have sprung up since 1920 one book survives—*The Enormous Room* by E. E. Cummings. It is scarcely a novel; it doesn't deal with the American scene; it was swamped in the mediocre downpour, isolated—forgotten. But it lives on, because those few who cause books to live have not been able to endure the thought of its mortality. Two other books, both about the war, complete the possible salvage from the work of the younger generation—*Through the Wheat* and *Three Soldiers*, but the former despite its fine last chapters doesn't stand up as well as *Le Croix de Bois* and *The Red Badge of Courage*, while the latter is marred by its pervasive flavour of contemporary indignation. But as an augury that some one has profited by this dismal record of high hope and stale failure comes the first work of Ernest Hemingway.

II

In Our Time consists of fourteen stories, short and long, with fifteen vivid miniatures interpolated between them.

When I try to think of any contemporary American short stories as good as *Big Two-Hearted River*, the last one in the book, only Gertrude Stein's *Melanctha*, Anderson's *The Egg*, and Lardner's *Golden Honeymoon* come to mind. It is the account of a boy on a fishing trip—he hikes, pitches his tent, cooks dinner, sleeps, and next morning casts for trout. Nothing more—but I read it with the most breathless unwilling interest I have experienced since Conrad first bent my reluctant eyes upon the sea.

The hero, Nick, runs through nearly all the stories, until the book takes on almost an autobiographical tint—in fact *My Old Man*, one of the two in which this element seems entirely absent, is the least successful of all. Some of the stories show influences but they are invariably absorbed and transmuted, while in *My Old Man* there is an echo of Anderson's way of thinking in those sentimental 'horse stories', which inaugurated his respectability and also his decline four years ago.

But with *The Doctor and the Doctor's Wife*, *The End of Something*, *The Three Day Blow*, *Mr and Mrs Elliot*, and *Soldier's Home* you are immediately aware of something temperamentally new. In the first of these a man is backed down by a half-breed Indian after committing himself to a fight. The quality of humiliation in the story is so intense that it immediately calls up every such incident in the reader's past. Without the aid of a comment or a pointing finger one knows exactly the sharp emotion of young Nick who watches the scene.

The next two stories describe an experience at the last edge of adolescence. You are constantly aware of the continual snapping of ties that is going on around Nick. In the half stewed, immature conversation before the fire you watch the awakening of that vast unrest that descends upon the emotional type at about eighteen. Again there is not a single recourse to exposition. As in *Big Two-Hearted River*, a picture—sharp, nostalgic, tense—develops before your eyes. When the picture is complete a light seems to snap out, the story is over. There is no tail, no sudden change of pace at the end to throw into relief what has gone before.

Nick leaves home penniless; you have a glimpse of him lying wounded in the street of a battered Italian town, and later of a love affair with a nurse on a hospital roof in Milan. Then in one of the best of the stories he is home again. The last glimpse of him is when his mother asks him, with all the bitter world in his heart, to kneel down beside her in the dining room in Puritan prayer.

Anyone who first looks through the short interpolated sketches will hardly fail to read the stories themselves. *The Garden at Mons* and *The Barricade* are profound essays upon the English officer, written on a postage stamp. *The King of Greece's Tea Party*, *The Shooting of the Cabinet Ministers*, and *The Cigar-Store Robbery* particularly fascinated me, as they did when Edmund Wilson first showed them to me in an earlier pamphlet, over two years ago.

Disregard the rather ill-considered blurbs on the cover. It is sufficient that here is no raw food served up by the railroad restaurants of California and Wisconsin. In the best of these dishes there is not a bit to spare. And many of us who have grown weary of admonitions to 'watch this man or that' have felt a sort of renewal of excitement of these stories wherein Ernest Hemingway turns a corner into the street.

IN PREPARATORY SCHOOL and up to the middle of sophomore year in college, it worried me that I wasn't going and hadn't gone to Yale. Was I missing a great American secret? There was a gloss upon Yale that Princeton lacked; Princeton's flannels hadn't been pressed for a week, its hair always blew a little in the wind. Nothing was ever carried through at Princeton with the same perfection as the Yale Junior Prom or the elections to their senior societies. From the ragged squabble of club elections with its scars of snobbishness and adolescent heartbreak, to the enigma that faced you at the end of senior year as to what Princeton *was* and what, bunk and cant aside, it really stood for, it never presented itself with Yale's hard, neat, fascinating brightness. Only when you tried to tear part of your past out of your heart, as I once did, were you aware of its power of arousing a deep and imperishable love.

Princeton men take Princeton for granted and resent any attempt at analysis. As early as 1899 Jesse Lynch Williams was anathematized for reporting that Princeton wine helped to make the 'nineties golden. If the Princetonian had wanted to assert in sturdy chorus that his college was the true flower of American democracy, was deliberately and passionately America's norm in ideals of conduct and success, he would have gone to Yale. His brother and many of the men from his school went there. Contrariwise he chooses Princeton because at seventeen the furies that whip on American youth have become too coercive for his taste. He wants something quieter, mellower, and less exigent. He sees himself being caught up into a wild competition that will lead him headlong into New Haven and dump him pell-mell out into the

316

world. The series of badges which reward the winner of each
sprint are no doubt desirable, but he seeks the taste of
pleasant pastures and a moment to breathe deep and rumi-
nate before he goes into the clamorous struggle of American
life. He finds at Princeton other men like himself and thus is
begotten Princeton's scoffing and mildly ironic attitude toward Yale.

Harvard has never existed as a conception at Princeton.
Harvard men were 'Bostonians with affected accents,' or
they were 'That Isaacs fellow who got the high school scho-
larship out home.' Lee Higginson & Company hired their
athletes for them but no matter how much one did for
Harvard one couldn't belong to 'Fly' or 'Porcellian' without
going to Grotton or St Mark's. Such ideas were satisfying
if inaccurate, for Cambridge, in more senses than one, was
many miles away. Harvard was a series of sporadic
relationships, sometimes pleasant, sometimes hostile—that
was all.

Princeton is in the flat midlands of New Jersey, rising, a
green Phoenix, out of the ugliest country in the world. Sordid Trenton sweats and festers a few miles south; northward
are Elizabeth and the Erie Railroad and the suburban slums
of New York; westward the dreary upper purlieus of the
Delaware River. But around Princeton, shielding her, is a
ring of silence—certified milk dairies, great estates with pea-
cocks and deer parks, pleasant farms and woodlands which
we paced off and mapped down in the spring of 1917 in
preparation for the war. The busy East has already dropped
away when the branch train rattles familiarly from the junction. Two tall spires and then suddenly all around you
spreads out the loveliest riot of Gothic architecture in
America, battlement linked on to battlement, hall to hall,
arch-broken, vine-covered—luxuriant and lovely over two
square miles of green grass. Here is no monotony, no feeling
that it was all built yesterday at the whim of last week's
millionaire; Nassau Hall was already thirty years old when
Hessian bullets pierced its sides.

Alfred Noyes has compared Princeton to Oxford. To me

the two are sharply different. Princeton is thinner and fresher, at once less profound and more elusive. For all its past, Nassau Hall stands there hollow and barren, not like a mother who has borne sons and wears the scars of her travail but like a patient old nurse, sceptical and affectionate with these foster children who, as Americans, can belong to no place under the sun.

In my romantic days I tried to conjure up the Princeton of Aaron Burr, Philip Freneau, James Madison, and Light Horse Harry Lee, to tie on, so to speak, to the eighteenth century, to the history of man. But the chain parted at the Civil War, always the broken link in the continuity of American life. Colonial Princeton was, after all, a small denominational college. The Princeton I knew and belonged to grew from President McCosh's great shadow in the 'seventies, grew with the great *post bellum* fortunes of New York and Philadelphia to include coaching parties and keg parties and the later American conscience and Booth Tarkington's Triangle Club and Wilson's cloistered plans for an educational utopia. Bound up with it somewhere was the rise of American football.

For at Princeton, as at Yale, football became, back in the 'nineties, a sort of symbol. Symbol of what ? Of the eternal violence of American life ? Of the eternal immaturity of the race ? The failure of a culture within the walls ? Who knows ? It became something at first satisfactory, then essential and beautiful. It became, long before the insatiable millions took it, with Gertrude Ederle and Mrs Snyder, to its heart, the most intense and dramatic spectacle since the Olympic games. The death of Johnny Poe with the Black Watch in Flanders starts the cymbals crashing for me, plucks the strings of nervous violins as no adventure of the mind that Princeton ever offered. A year ago in the Champs Elysées I passed a slender dark-haired young man with an indolent characteristic walk. Something stopped inside me; I turned and looked after him. It was the romantic Buzz Law whom I had last seen one cold fall twilight in 1915, kicking from behind his goal line with a bloody bandage round his head.

After the beauty of its towers and the drama of its arenas, the widely known feature of Princeton is its 'clientele'.

A large proportion of such gilded youth as will absorb an education drifts to Princeton. Goulds, Rockefellers, Harrimans, Morgans, Fricks, Firestones, Perkinses, Pynes, McCormicks, Wanamakers, Cudahys and Du Ponts light there for a season, well or less well regarded. The names of Pell, Biddle, Van Rensselaer, Stuyvesant, Schuyler and Cooke titillate second generation mammas and papas with a social row to hoe in Philadelphia or New York. An average class is composed of three dozen boys from such Midas academies as St Paul's, St Mark's, St George's, Pomfret, and Grotton, a hundred and fifty more from Lawrenceville, Hotchkiss, Exeter, Andover, and Hill, and perhaps another two hundred from less widely known preparatory schools. The remaining twenty per cent enter from the high schools and these last furnish a large proportion of the eventual leaders. For them the business of getting to Princeton has been more arduous, financially as well as scholastically. They are trained and eager for the fray.

In my time, a decade ago, the mid-winter examinations in freshman year meant a great winnowing. The duller athletes, the rich boys of thicker skulls than their forebears, fell in droves by the wayside. Often they had attained the gates at twenty or twenty-one and with the aid of a tutoring school only to find the first test too hard. They were usually a pleasant fifty or sixty, those first flunk-outs. They left many regrets behind.

Nowadays only a few boys of that calibre ever enter. Under the new system of admissions they are spotted by their early scholastic writhings and balkings and informed that Princeton has space only for those whose brains are of normal weight. This is because a few years ago the necessity arose of limiting the enrolment. The war prosperity made college possible for many boys and by 1921 the number of candidates, who each year satisfied the minimum scholastic requirements for Princeton, was far beyond the university's capacity.

So, in addition to the college board examinations, the candidate must present his scholastic record, the good word of his schools, of two Princeton alumni, and must take a psychological test for general intelligence. The six hundred or so who with these credentials make the most favourable impression on the admissions committee are admitted. A man who is deficient in one scholastic subject may succeed in some cases over a man who has passed them all. A boy with a really excellent record, in, say science and mathematics, and a poor one in English, is admitted in preference to a boy with a fair general average and no special aptitude. The plan has raised the standard of scholarships and kept out such men as A, who in my time turned up in four different classes as a sort of perennial insult to the intelligence.

Whether the proverbially narrow judgments of headmasters upon adolescents will serve to keep out the Goldsmiths, the Byrons, the Whitmans, and the O'Neills it is too early to tell.

I can't help hoping that a few disreputable characters will slip in to salt the salt of the earth. Priggishness sits ill on Princeton. It was typified in my day by the Polity Club. This was a group that once a fortnight sat gravely at the feet of Mr Schwab or Judge Gary or some other pard-like spirit imported for the occasion. Had these inspired plutocrats disclosed trade secrets or even remained on the key of brisk business cynicism the occasion might have retained dignity, but the Polity Club were treated to the warmed-over straw soup of the house organ and the production picnic, with a few hot sops thrown in about 'future leaders of men'. Looking through a copy of the latest year book I do not find the Polity Club at all. Perhaps it now serves worthier purposes.

President Hibben is a mixture of 'normalcy' and discernment, of staunch allegiance to the *status quo* and of a fine tolerance amounting almost to intellectual curiosity. I have heard him in a speech mask with rhetoric statements of incredible shallowness; yet I have never known him to take a mean, narrow or short-sighted stand within Princeton's walls. He fell heir to the throne in 1912 during the reaction to the Wilson idealism, and I believe that, learning vicariously, he has pushed out his horizon amazingly since then. His situation was not unlike Harding's ten years later, but, surrounding himself with such men as Gauss, Heermance, and Alexander Smith, he has abjured the merely passive and conducted a progressive and often brilliant administration.

Under him functions a fine philosophy department, an excellent department of classics, fathered by the venerable Dean West, a scientific faculty starred by such names as Oswald Veblen and Conklin; and a surprisingly pallid English department, top-heavy, undistinguished and with an uncanny knack of making literature distasteful to young men. Dr Spaeth, one of several exceptions, coached the crew in the afternoon and in the morning aroused interest and even enthusiasm for the romantic poets, an interest later killed in the preceptorial rooms where mildly poetic gentlemen resented any warmth of discussion and called the prominent men of the class by their first names.

The *Nassau Literary Magazine* is the oldest college publication in America. In its files you can find the original Craig Kennedy story, as well as prose or poetry by Woodrow Wilson, John Grier Hibben, Henry van Dyke, David Graham Phillips, Stephen French Whitman, Booth Tarkington, Struthers Burt, Jesse Lynch Williams—almost every Princeton writer save Eugene O'Neill. To Princeton's misfortune, O'Neill's career terminated by request three years too soon. The *Princetonian*, the daily, is a conventional enough affair, though its editorial policy occasionally embodies coherent ideas, notably under James Bruce, Forrestal, and John Martin, now of *Time*. The *Tiger*, the comic, is generally speaking inferior to the *Lampoon*, the *Record*, and the *Widow*. When it was late to press, John Biggs and I used to write whole issues in the interval between darkness and dawn.

The Triangle Club (acting, singing and dancing) is Princeton's most characteristic organization. Founded by Booth Tarkington with the production of his libretto, *The Honorable Julius Caesar*, it blooms in a dozen cities every Christmastide. On the whole it represents a remarkable effort and under the wing of Donald Clive Stuart, it has become, unlike

11

the Mask and Wig Club of Pennsylvania, entirely an intra-mural affair. Its best years have been due to the residence of such talented improvisers as Tarkington, Roy Durstine, Walker Ellis, Ken Clark, or Erdman Harris. In my day it had a rowdy side but now the inebriated comedians and the all-night rehearsals are no more. It furnishes a stamping ground for the multiplying virtuosos of jazz, and the com-petition for places in the cast and chorus testifies to its popularity and power.

Princeton's sacred tradition is the honour system, a method of pledging that to the amazement of outsiders actually works, with consequent elimination of suspicion and supervision. It is handed over as something humanly precious to the freshmen within a week of their entrance. Personally I have never seen or heard of a Princeton man cheating in an exami-nation, though I am told a few such cases have been merci-lessly and summarily dealt with. I can think of a dozen times when a page of notes glanced at in a wash room would have made the difference between failure and success for me, but I can't recall any moral struggles in the matter. It simply doesn't occur to you, any more than it would occur to you to rifle your room-mate's pocketbook. Perhaps the thing that struck deepest in the last autumn's unfortunate *Lampoon* was the mention of the honour system with an insinuation and a sneer.

No freshmen allowed on Prospect Street; these are the eighteen upper class clubs. I first heard of them in an article by, I think, Owen Johnson, in the *Saturday Evening Post* nearly twenty years ago. Pictures of Ivy, Cottage, Tiger Inn, and Cap and Gown smiled from the page not like the tombs of robber barons on the Rhine but like friendly and dis-tinguished havens where juniors and seniors might eat three semi-private meals a day. Later I remember Prospect Street as the red torchlight of the freshman parade flickered over the imposing façades of the houses and the white shirt fronts of the upper classmen, and gleamed in the champagne gob-lets raised to toast the already prominent members of my class.

There are no fraternities at Princeton; toward the end of each year the eighteen clubs take in an average of about twenty-five sophomores each, seventy-five per cent of the class. The remaining twenty-five per cent continue to eat in the university dining halls and this situation has been the cause of revolutions, protests, petitions, and innumerable editorials in the *Alumni Weekly*. But the clubs represent an alumni investment of two million dollars—the clubs remain.

The Ivy Club was founded in 1879 and four years out of every five it is the most coveted club in Princeton. Its prestige is that, broadly speaking, it can invite twenty boys out of every class and get fifteen of them. Not infrequently it has its debacles. Cottage, Tiger Inn or Cap and Gown— these three with Ivy have long been known as the 'big' clubs—will take ten or fifteen of the boys that Ivy wants and Ivy will be left with a skeleton section of a dozen and considerable bitterness toward its successful rival. The University Cottage Club, feared and hated politically, has made several such raids. Architecturally the most sumptuous of the clubs, Cottage was founded in 1887. It has a large Southern following, particularly in St Louis and Baltimore. Unlike these two, Tiger Inn cultivates a bluff simplicity. Its membership is largely athletic and while it pretends to disdain social qualifications it has a sharp exclusiveness of its own. The fourth big club, Cap and Gown, began as an organization of earnest and somewhat religious young men, but during the last ten years social and political successes have overshadowed its original purpose. As late as 1916 its president could still sway a wavering crowd of sophomores with the happy slogan of 'Join Cap and Gown and Meet God'.

Of the others Colonial, an old club with a history of ups and downs, Charter, a comparative newcomer, and Quadrangle, the only club with a distinctly intellectual flavour, are the most influential. One club vanished in the confusion of the War. Two have been founded since, both of them in a little old building which has seen the birth of many. The special characteristics of the clubs vary so that it is hazardous to describe them. One whose members in my day were indefatigable patrons of the Nassau Inn Bar, is now, I am told, a sort of restaurant for the Philadelphian Society.

The Philadelphian Society is Princeton's Y.M.C.A., and in more sagacious moments it is content to function as such. Occasionally, though, it becomes inspired with a Messianic urge to evangelize the university. In my day for example, it imported for the purpose a noted rabble-rouser, one Dr X, who brought along in all seriousness a reformed Bad Example. Such students as out of piety or curiosity could be assembled were herded into Alexander Hall and there ensued one of the most grotesque orgies ever held in the shadow of a great educational institution. When Dr X's sermon had risen to an inspirational chant, several dozen boys rose, staunch as coloured gentlemen, and went forward to be saved. Among them was a popular free thinker and wine bibber whose sincerity we later probed but never determined. The climax of the occasion was the Bad Example's account of his past excesses, culminating in his descent into an actual stone gutter, his conversion and his rise to the position of Bad Example for Dr X's travelling circus.

By this time the tenderer spirits in the audience had become uncomfortable, the tougher ones riotous; a few left the hall. The unctuousness of the proceedings was too much even for those more timorous days, and later there were protests on the grounds of sheer good taste. Last year 'Buchmanism', a milder form of the same melodrama, came in for some outspoken and impatient criticism in the university press.

There is so much of Princeton that I have omitted to touch. Perhaps to be specific for a moment will be a method of being most general. Vivid lights played on the whole colourful picture during the winter and early spring of 1917, just before the War.

Never had the forces which compose the university been so strong and so in evidence. Four score sophomores had democratically refused to join clubs, under the leadership of David Bruce (a son of Senator Bruce), Richard Cleveland (a

son of President Cleveland), and Henry Hyacinth Strater of
Louisville, Kentucky. Not content with this, the latter, the
first man in his class to make the *Princetonian* and an ardent
devotee of Tolstoy and Edward Carpenter, came out as a
pacifist. He was brilliant and deeply popular; he was much
patronized, somewhat disapproved of but never in the slightest degree persecuted. He made a few converts who joined
the Quakers and remained pacifists to the end.

The *Nassau Literary Magazine* under John Peale Bishop
made a sudden successful bid for popular attention. Jack
Newlin, later killed in France, drew Beardsley-like pictures
for frontispieces; I wrote stories about current prom girls,
stories that were later incorporated into a novel; John Biggs
imagined the War with sufficient virtuosity to deceive vete-
rans; and John Bishop made a last metrical effort to link up
the current crusade with the revolution—while we all, waiting to go to training camps, found time heartily to despise
the bombast and rhetoric of the day. We published a satirical
number, a parody on the *Cosmopolitan Magazine*, which
infuriated the less nimble-witted members of the English
department. We—this time the board of the *Tiger*—issued
an irreverent number which burlesqued the faculty, the anti-
club movement, and then the clubs themselves, by their real
names. Everything around us seemed to be breaking up.
These were the great days; battle was on the horizon; nothing was ever going to be the same again and nothing mat-
tered. And for the next two years nothing did matter. Five
per cent of my class, twenty-one boys, were killed in the
war.

That spring I remember late nights at the Nassau Inn
with Bill Coan, the proctor, waiting outside to hale selected
specimens before the dean next morning. I remember the
long afternoons of military drill on the soccer fields, side by
side perhaps with an instructor of the morning. We used to
snicker at Professor Wardlaw Miles's attempts to reconcile
the snap of the drill manual with his own precise and pedantic English. There were no snickers two years later when he
returned from France with a leg missing and his breast

bright with decorations. A thousand boys cheered him to his home. I remember the last June night when, with two-thirds of us in uniform, our class sang its final song on the steps of Nassau Hall and some of us wept because we knew we'd never be quite so young any more as we had been here. And I seem to remember a host of more intimate things that are now as blurred and dim as our cigarette smoke or the ivy on Nassau Hall that last night.

Princeton is itself. Williams College is not 'what Princeton used to be'. Williams is for guided boys whose female relatives want them protected from reality. Princeton is of the world; it is somehow on the 'grand scale'; and for sixty years it has been approximately the same. There is less singing and more dancing. The keg parties are over but the stags line up for a hundred yards to cut in on young Lois Moran. There is no Elizabethan Club as at Yale to make a taste for poetry respectable, sometimes too respectable; exceptional talent must create its own public at Princeton, as it must in life. In spite of all persuasions the varsity man conservatively wears his P on the inside of his sweater, but so far no Attorney-General Palmers or Judge Thayers have bobbed up among the alumni. President Hibben sometimes disagrees aloud with Secretary Mellon and only ninety-two members of the senior class proclaimed themselves dry last year.

Looking back over a decade one sees the ideal of a university become a myth, a vision, a meadow lark among the smoke stacks. Yet perhaps it is there at Princeton, only more elusive than under the skies of the Prussian Rhineland or Oxfordshire; or perhaps some men come upon it suddenly and possess it, while others wander forever outside. Even these seek in vain through middle age for any corner of the republic that preserves so much of what is fair, gracious, charming, and honourable in American life.

TEN YEARS IN THE
ADVERTISING BUSINESS
[1929]

'WELL MR FITZGERALD, what can I do for you today?'
It was a high office with a view of that gold building.

'I want a raise, Mr Cakebook,' I said.

'Why?'

'I'm about to get married. You're only paying me ninety-
five dollars a month and, of course, with a family to support I've got to think of money.'

Into his grey eyes came a far-away look.

'Ninety-five dollars is a pretty good salary. By the way,
let me see that laundry slogan as it stands now.'

'Here it is,' I said, with eager pride. 'Listen: "We keep
you clean in Muskateen." How's that? Good, isn't it. "We
keep——"'

'Wait a minute,' he interrupted. 'Look here, Mr Fitzgerald. You're too temperamental. Your ideas are too fancy,
too imaginative. You ought to keep your feet on the ground.
Now let me see that layout.'

He worked over it for a moment, his large brain bulging a
little from time to time, his lips moving as to melody.

'Now listen to this,' he said, 'I've got something good:
"Muskateen Laundry—we clean and press." Listen Miss
Schwartz, take that down right away. "Muskateen Laundry
—we clean and press."'

Obsequiously I congratulated him—when he began to
beam I returned to my thesis.

'Well, how about money?'

... 'I don't know,' he mused. 'Of course we try to be fair.
How much do you want?'

I thought for a moment.

'Suppose you name an amount.'

'I'll tell you, Mr Fitzgerald,' he said, 'we don't like to argue about money with anybody. You let us use your picture and your name as one of the judges in this contest and we'll call it a thousand dollars.'

'But it'll take a couple of hours,' I objected, 'and, of course, with a family to support I've got to think of money.'

'I realize that. We'll call it fifteen hundred.'

'And it's understood that I'm in no sense to endorse this product.'

'Perfectly. You merely pick the prettiest girl.'

. We stood up and I looked out the window at that gold building.

'Did I understand you to say you're about to get married?' he asked.

'Oh, no, I've been married ten years. That was back before those little dots.'

'It must have been some other couple.'

'It was,' I assured him. 'Only the names were the same. The issues change every decade. Good-bye, Mr Cakebook.'

'Good-bye, Mr Fitzgerald.'

ECHOES OF THE
JAZZ AGE
[1931]

IT IS TOO SOON to write about the Jazz Age with perspective, and without being suspected of premature arteriosclerosis. Many people still succumb to violent retching when they happen upon any of its characteristic words—words which have since yielded in vividness to the coinages of the underworld. It is as dead as were the Yellow Nineties in 1902. Yet the present writer already looks back to it with nostalgia. It bore him up, flattered him and gave him more money than he had dreamed of, simply for telling people that he felt as they did, that something had to be done with all the nervous energy stored up and unexpended in the War.

The ten-year period that, as if reluctant to die outmoded in its bed, leaped to a spectacular death in October, 1929, began about the time of the May Day riots in 1919. When the police rode down the demobilized country boys gaping at the orators in Madison Square, it was the sort of measure bound to alienate the more intelligent young men from the prevailing order. We didn't remember anything about the Bill of Rights until Mencken began plugging it, but we did know that such tyranny belonged in the jittery little countries of South Europe. If goose-livered business men had this effect on the government, then maybe we had gone to war for J. P. Morgan's loans after all. But, because we were tired of Great Causes, there was no more than a short outbreak of moral indignation, typified by Dos Passos' *Three Soldiers*. Presently we began to have slices of the national cake, and our idealism only flared up when the newspapers made melodrama out of such stories as Harding and the Ohio Gang or Sacco and Vanzetti. The events of 1919 left

329

us cynical rather than revolutionary, in spite of the fact that now we are all rummaging around in our trunks wondering where in hell we left the liberty cap—'I know I *had* it'—and the moujik blouse. It was characteristic of the Jazz Age that it had no interest in politics at all.

It was an age of miracles, it was an age of art, it was an age of excess, and it was an age of satire. A Stuffed Shirt, squirming to blackmail in a lifelike way, sat upon the throne of the United States; a stylish young man hurried over to represent to us the throne of England. A world of girls yearned for the young Englishman; the old American groaned in his sleep as he waited to be poisoned by his wife, upon the advice of the female Rasputin who then made the ultimate decision in our national affairs. But such matters apart, we had things our way at last. With Americans ordering suits by the gross in London, the Bond Street tailors perforce agreed to moderate their cut to the American long-waisted figure and loose-fitting taste, something subtle passed to America, the style of man. During the Renaissance Francis the First looked to Florence to trim his leg. Seventeenth-century England aped the court of France, and fifty years ago the German Guards officer bought his civilian clothes in London. Gentlemen's clothes—symbol of 'the power that man must hold and that passes from race to race.'

We were the most powerful nation. Who could tell us any longer what was fashionable and what was fun? Isolated during the European War, we had begun combing the unknown South and West for folkways and pastimes, and there were more ready to hand.

The first social revelation created a sensation out of all proportion to its novelty. As far back as 1915 the unchaperoned young people of the smaller cities had discovered the mobile privacy of that automobile given to young Bill at sixteen to make him 'self-reliant.' At first petting was a desperate adventure even under such favourable conditions, but presently confidences were exchanged and the old commandment broke down. As early as 1917 there were references to such sweet and casual dalliance in any number of the *Yale Record* or the *Princeton Tiger*.

But petting in its more audacious manifestations was confined to the wealthier classes—among other young people the old standard prevailed until after the War, and a kiss meant that a proposal was expected, as young officers in strange cities sometimes discovered to their dismay. Only in 1920 did the veil finally fall—the Jazz Age was in flower.

Scarcely had the staider citizens of the republic caught their breaths when the wildest of all generations, the generation which had been adolescent during the confusion of the War, brusquely shouldered my contemporaries out of the way and danced into the limelight. This was the generation whose girls dramatized themselves as flappers, the generation that corrupted its elders and eventually overreached itself less through lack of morals than through lack of taste. May one offer in exhibit the year 1922! That was the peak of the younger generation, for though the Jazz Age continued, it became less and less an affair of youth.

The sequel was like a children's party taken over by the elders, leaving the children puzzled and rather neglected and rather taken aback. By 1923 their elders, tired of watching the carnival with ill-concealed envy, had discovered that young liquor will take the place of young blood, and with a whoop the orgy began. The younger generation was starred no longer.

A whole race going hedonistic, deciding on pleasure. The precocious intimacies of the younger generation would have come about with or without prohibition—they were implicit in the attempt to adapt English customs to American conditions. (Our South, for example, is tropical and early maturing—it has never been part of the wisdom of France and Spain to let young girls go unchaperoned at sixteen and seventeen.) But the general decision to be amused that began with the cocktail parties of 1921 had more complicated origins.

The word jazz in its progress toward respectability has

meant first sex, then dancing, then music. It is associated with a state of nervous stimulation, not unlike that of big cities behind the lines of a war. To many English the War still goes on because all the forces that menace them are still active—Wherefore eat, drink and be merry, for to-morrow we die. But different causes had now brought about a corresponding state in America—though there were entire classes (people over fifty, for example) who spent a whole decade denying its existence even when its puckish face peered into the family circle. Never did they dream that they had contributed to it. The honest citizens of every class, who believed in a strict public morality and were powerful enough to enforce the necessary legislation, did not know that they would necessarily be served by criminals and quacks, and do not really believe it to-day. Rich righteousness had always been able to buy honest and intelligent servants to free the slaves or the Cubans, so when this attempt collapsed our elders stood firm with all the stubbornness of people involved in a weak case, pre-serving their righteousness and losing their children. Silver-haired women and men with fine old faces, people who never did a consciously dishonest thing in their lives, still assure each other in the apartment hotels of New York and Boston and Washington that 'there's a whole generation growing up that will never know the taste of liquor.' Mean-while their granddaughters pass the well-thumbed copy of *Lady Chatterley's Lover* around the boarding-school and, if they get about at all, know the taste of gin or corn at sixteen. But the generation who reached maturity between 1875 and 1895 continued to believe what they want to believe.

Even the intervening generations were incredulous. In 1920 Heywood Broun announced that all this hubbub was nonsense, that young men didn't kiss but told anyhow. But very shortly people over twenty-five came in for an intensive education. Let me trace some of the revelations vouch-safed them by reference to a dozen works written for various types of mentality during the decade. We begin with the suggestion that Don Juan leads an interesting life (*Jurgen*, 1919); then we learn that there's a lot of sex around if we only knew it (*Winesburg, Ohio*, 1920), that adolescents lead very amorous lives (*This Side of Paradise*, 1920), that there are a lot of neglected Anglo-Saxon words (*Ulysses*, 1921), that older people don't always resist sudden temptations (*Cytherea*, 1922), that girls are sometimes seduced without being ruined (*Flaming Youth*, 1922), that even rape often turns out well (*The Sheik*, 1922), that glamorous English ladies are often promiscuous (*The Green Hat*, 1924), that in fact they devote most of their time to it (*The Vortex*, 1926), that it's a damn good thing too (*Lady Chatterley's Lover*, 1928), and finally that there are abnormal variations (*The Well of Loneliness*, 1928, and *Sodom and Gomorrah*, 1929).

In my opinion the erotic element in these works, even *The Sheik* written for children in the key of *Peter Rabbit*, did not one particle of harm. Everything they described, and much more, was familiar in our contemporary life. The majority of the theses were honest and elucidating—their effect was to restore some dignity to the male as opposed to the he-man in American life. ('And what is a "He-man"?' demanded Gertrude Stein one day. 'Isn't it a large enough order to fill out to the dimensions of all that "a man" has meant in the past? A "*He*-man"!') The married woman can now discover whether she is being cheated, or whether sex is just something to be endured, and her compensation should be to establish a tyranny of the spirit, as her mother may have hinted. Perhaps many women found that love was meant to be fun. Anyhow the objectors lost their tawdry little case, which is one reason why our literature is now the most living in the world.

Contrary to popular opinion, the movies of the Jazz Age had no effect upon its morals. The social attitude of the producers was timid, behind the times, and banal—for example, no picture mirrored even faintly the younger generation until 1923, when magazines had already been started to celebrate it and it had long ceased to be news. There were a few feeble splutters and then Clara Bow in

Flaming Youth; promptly the Hollywood hacks ran the theme into its cinematographic grave. Throughout the Jazz Age the movies got no farther than Mrs. Jiggs, keeping up with its most blatant superficialities. This was no doubt due to the censorship as well as to innate conditions in the industry. In any case, the Jazz Age now raced along under its own power, served by great filling stations full of money.

The people over thirty, the people all the way up to fifty, had joined the dance. We greybeards (to tread down F.P.A.) remember the uproar when in 1912 grandmothers of forty tossed away their crutches and took lessons in the Tango and the Castle-Walk. A dozen years later a woman might pack the Green Hat with her other affairs as she set off for Europe or New York, but Savonarola was too busy flogging dead horses in Augean stables of his own creation to notice. Society, even in small cities, now dined in separate chambers, and the sober table learned about the gay table only from hearsay. There were very few people left at the sober table. One of its former glories, the less sought-after girls who had become resigned to sublimating a probable celibacy, came across Freud and Jung in seeking their intellectual recompense and came tearing back into the fray.

By 1926 the universal preoccupation with sex had become a nuisance. (I remember a perfectly mated, contented young mother asking my wife's advice about 'having an affair right away,' though she had no one especially in mind, 'because don't you think it's sort of undignified when you get much over thirty?') For a while bootleg Negro records with their phallic euphemisms made everything suggestive, and simultaneously came a wave of erotic plays—young girls from finishing-schools packed the galleries to hear about the romance of being a Lesbian and George Jean Nathan protested. Then one young producer lost his head entirely, drank a beauty's alcoholic bath-water and went to the penitentiary. Somehow his pathetic attempt at romance belongs to the Jazz Age, while his contemporary in prison, Ruth Snyder, had to be hoisted into it by the tabloids— she was, as *The Daily News* hinted deliciously to gourmets, about 'to cook, *and sizzle*, *AND FRY !'* in the electric chair.

The gay elements of society had divided into two main streams, one flowing toward Palm Beach and Deauville, and the other, much smaller, toward the summer Riviera. One could get away with more on the summer Riviera, and whatever happened seemed to have something to do with art. From 1926 to 1929, the great years of the Cap d'Antibes, this corner of France was dominated by a group quite distinct from that American society which is dominated by Europeans. Pretty much of anything went at Antibes—by 1929, at the most gorgeous paradise for swimmers on the Mediterranean no one swam any more, save for a short hang-over dip at noon. There was a picturesque graduation of steep rocks over the sea and somebody's valet and an occasional English girl used to dive from them, but the Americans were content to discuss each other in the bar. This was indicative of something that was taking place in the homeland—Americans were getting soft. There were signs everywhere: we still won the Olympic games but with champions whose names had few vowels in them—teams composed, like the fighting Irish combination of Notre Dame, of fresh overseas blood. Once the French became really interested, the Davis Cup gravitated automatically to their intensity in competition. The vacant lots of the Middle-Western cities were built up now—except for a short period in school, we were not turning out to be an athletic people like the British, after all. The hare and the tortoise. Of course if we wanted to we could be in a minute; we still had all those reserves of ancestral vitality, but one day in 1926 we looked down and found we had flabby arms and a fat pot and couldn't say boop-boop-a-doop to a Sicilian. Shades of Van Bibber!—no Utopian ideal, God knows. Even golf, once considered an effeminate game, had seemed very strenuous of late—an emasculated form appeared and proved just right.

By 1927 a widespread neurosis began to be evident, faintly signalled, like a nervous beating of the feet, by the popularity of crossword puzzles. I remember a fellow ex-patriate opening a letter from a mutual friend of ours, urging him to come home and be revitalized by the hardy, bracing qualities of the native soil. It was a strong letter and it affected us both deeply, until we noticed that it was headed from a nerve sanatorium in Pennsylvania.

By this time contemporaries of mine had begun to disappear into the dark maw of violence. A classmate killed his wife and himself on Long Island, another tumbled 'accidentally' from a skyscraper in Philadelphia, another purposely from a skyscraper in New York. One was killed in a speak-easy in Chicago; another was beaten to death in a speak-easy in New York and crawled home to the Princeton Club to die; still another had his skull crushed by a maniac's axe in an insane asylum where he was confined. These are not catastrophes that I went out of my way to look for—these were my friends; moreover, these things happened not during the depression but during the boom.

In the spring of '27, something bright and alien flashed across the sky. A young Minnesotan who seemed to have had nothing to do with his generation did a heroic thing, and for a moment people set down their glasses in country clubs and speak-easies and thought of their old best dreams. Maybe there was a way out by flying, maybe our restless blood could find frontiers in the illimitable air. But by that time we were all pretty well committed; and the Jazz Age continued; we would all have one more.

Nevertheless, Americans were wandering ever more widely—friends seemed eternally bound for Russia, Persia, Abyssinia, and Central Africa. And by 1928 Paris had grown suffocating. With each new shipment of Americans spewed up by the boom the quality fell off, until toward the end there was something sinister about the crazy boatloads. They were no longer the simple pa and ma and son and daughter, infinitely superior in their qualities of kindness and curiosity to the corresponding class in Europe, but fantastic neanderthals who believed something, something vague, that you remembered from a very cheap novel. I remember an Italian on a steamer who promenaded the deck in an American Reserve Officer's uniform picking quarrels in broken English with Americans who criticized their own institutions in the bar. I remember a fat Jewess, inlaid with diamonds, who sat behind us at the Russian ballet and said as the curtain rose, 'Thad's luffly, dey ought to baint a bicture of it.' This was low comedy, but it was evident that money and power were falling into the hands of people in comparison with whom the leader of a village Soviet would be a gold-mine of judgment and culture. There were citizens travelling in luxury in 1928 and 1929, who, in the distortion of their new condition, had the human value of Pekinese, bivalves, cretins, goats. I remember the Judge from some New York district who had taken his daughter to see the Bayeux Tapestries and made a scene in the papers advocating their segregation because one scene was immoral. But in those days life was like the race in *Alice in Wonderland*, there was a prize for every one.

The Jazz Age had had a wild youth and a heady middle age. There was the phase of the necking parties, the Leopold-Loeb murder (I remember the time my wife was arrested on Queensborough Bridge on the suspicion of being the 'Bob-haired Bandit') and the John Held Clothes. In the second phase such phenomena as sex and murder became more mature, if much more conventional. Middle age must be served and pyjamas came to the beach to save fat thighs and flabby calves from competition with the one-piece bathing-suit. Finally skirts came down and everything was concealed. Everybody was at scratch now. Let's go—

But it was not to be. Somebody had blundered and the most expensive orgy in history was over.

It ended two years ago,* because the utter confidence which was its essential prop received an enormous jolt, and it didn't take long for the flimsy structure to settle earth-ward. And after two years the Jazz Age seems as far away as the days before the War. It was borrowed time anyhow —the whole upper tenth of a nation living with the in-souciance of grand dukes and the casualness of chorus girls.

* 1929.

But moralizing is easy now and it was pleasant to be in one's twenties in such a certain and unworried time. Even when you were broke you didn't worry about money, because it was in such profusion around you. Toward the end one had a struggle to pay one's share; it was almost a favour to accept hospitality that required any travelling. Charm, notoriety, mere good manners weighed more than money as a social asset. This was rather splendid, but things were getting thinner and thinner as the eternal necessary human values tried to spread over all that expansion. Writers were geniuses on the strength of one respectable book or play; just as during the War officers of four months' experience commanded hundreds of men, so there were now many little fish lording it over great big bowls. In the theatrical world extravagant productions were carried by a few second-rate stars, and so on up the scale into politics, where it was difficult to interest good men in positions of the highest importance and responsibility, importance and responsibility far exceeding that of business executives but which paid only five or six thousand a year.

Now once more the belt is tight and we summon the proper expression of horror as we look back at our wasted youth. Sometimes, though, there is a ghostly rumble among the drums, an asthmatic whisper in the trombones that swings me back into the early 'twenties when we drank wood alcohol and every day in every way grew better and better, and there was a first abortive shortening of the skirts, and girls all looked alike in sweater dresses, and people you didn't want to know said 'Yes, we have no bananas,' and it seemed only a question of a few years before the older people would step aside and let the world be run by those who saw things as they were—and it all seems rosy and romantic to us who were young then, because we will never feel quite so intensely about our surroundings any more.

MY LOST CITY

[1932]

THERE WAS FIRST THE ferry boat moving softly from the Jersey shore at dawn—the moment crystallized into my first symbol of New York. Five years later when I was fifteen I went into the city from school to see Ina Claire in *The Quaker Girl* and Gertrude Bryan in *Little Boy Blue*. Confused by my hopeless and melancholy love for them both, I was unable to choose between them—so they blurred into one lovely entity, the girl. She was my second symbol of New York. The ferry boat stood for triumph, the girl for romance. In time I was to achieve some of both, but there was a third symbol that I have lost somewhere, and lost for ever.

I found it on a dark April afternoon after five more years. 'Oh, Bunny,' I yelled. '*Bunny!*'

He did not hear me—my taxi lost him, picked him up again half a block down the street. There were black spots of rain on the sidewalk and I saw him walking briskly through the crowd wearing a tan raincoat over his inevitable brown get-up; I noted with a shock that he was carrying a light cane.

'Bunny!' I called again, and stopped. I was still an undergraduate at Princeton while he had become a New Yorker. This was his afternoon walk, this hurry along with his stick through the gathering rain, and as I was not to meet him for an hour it seemed an intrusion to happen upon him engrossed in his private life. But the taxi kept pace with him and as I continued to watch I was impressed: he was no longer the shy little scholar of Holder Court—he walked

339

with confidence, wrapped in his thoughts and looking straight ahead, and it was obvious that his new background was entirely sufficient to him. I knew that he had an apartment where he lived with three other men, released now from all undergraduate taboos, but there was something else that was nourishing him and I got my first impression of that new thing—the Metropolitan spirit.

Up to this time I had seen only the New York that offered itself for inspection—I was Dick Whittington up from the country gaping at the trained bears, or a youth of the Midi dazzled by the boulevards of Paris. I had come only to stare at the show, though the designers of the Woolworth Building and the Chariot Race Sign, the producers of musical comedies and problem plays, could ask for no more appreciative spectator, for I took the style and glitter of New York even above its own valuation. But I had never accepted any of the practically anonymous invitations to debutante balls that turned up in an undergraduate's mail, perhaps because I felt that no actuality could live up to my conception of New York's splendour. Moreover, she to whom I fatuously referred as 'my girl' was a Middle Westerner, a fact which kept the warm centre of the world out there, so I thought of New York as essentially cynical and heartless—save for one night when she made luminous the Ritz Roof on a brief passage through.

Lately, however, I had definitely lost her and I wanted a man's world, and this sight of Bunny made me see New York as just that. A week before, Monsignor Fay had taken me to the Lafayette where there was spread before us a brilliant flag of food, called an *hors d'œuvre*, and with it we drank claret that was as brave as Bunny's confident cane—but after all it was a restaurant, and afterwards we would drive back over a bridge into the hinterland. The New York of undergraduate dissipation, of Bustanoby's, Shanley's, Jack's, had become a horror, and though I returned to it, alas, through many an alcoholic mist, I felt each time a betrayal of a persistent idealism. My participance was prurient rather than licentious and scarcely one pleasant

memory of it remains from those days; as Ernest Hemingway once remarked, the sole purpose of the cabaret is for
unattached men to find complaisant women. All the rest is a
wasting of time in bad air.

But that night, in Bunny's apartment, life was mellow
and safe, a finer distillation of all that I had come to love at
Princeton. The gentle playing of an oboe mingled with city
noises from the street outside, which penetrated into the
room with difficulty through great barricades of books; only
the crisp tearing open of invitations by one man was a discordant note. I had found a third symbol of New York and
I began wondering about the rent of such apartments and
casting about for the appropriate friends to share one with
me.

Fat chance—for the next two years I had as much control
over my own destiny as a convict over the cut of his clothes.
When I got back to New York in 1919 I was so entangled in
life that a period of mellow monasticism in Washington
Square was not to be dreamed of. The thing was to make
enough money in the advertising business to rent a stuffy
apartment for two in the Bronx. The girl concerned had
never seen New York but she was wise enough to be rather
reluctant. And in a haze of anxiety and unhappiness I
passed the four most impressionable months of my life.

New York had all the iridescence of the beginning of the
world. The returning troops marched up Fifth Avenue and
girls were instinctively drawn east and north toward them
—this was the greatest nation and there was gala in the air.
As I hovered ghost-like in the Plaza Red Room of a Saturday afternoon, or went to lush and liquid garden parties in
the East Sixties or tippled with Princetonians in the Biltmore Bar, I was haunted always by my other life—my drab
room in the Bronx, my square foot of the subway, my
fixation upon the day's letter from Alabama—would it come
and what would it say?—my shabby suits, my poverty, and
love. While my friends were launching decently into life I
had muscled my inadequate bark into midstream. The
gilded youth circling around young Constance Bennett in

the Club de Vingt, the classmates in the Yale-Princeton
Club whooping up our first after-the-war reunion, the atmosphere of the millionaires' houses that I sometimes
frequented—these things were empty for me, though I recognized them as impressive scenery and regretted that I
was committed to other romance. The most hilarious
luncheon table or the most moony cabaret—it was all the
same; from them I returned eagerly to my home on Clare-
mont Avenue—home because there might be a letter
waiting outside the door. One by one my great dreams of
New York became tainted. The remembered charm of
Bunny's apartment faded with the rest when I interviewed
a blowsy landlady in Greenwich Village. She told me I
could bring girls to the room, and the idea filled me with
dismay—why should I want to bring girls to my room?—
I had a girl. I wandered through the town of 127th Street,
resenting its vibrant life; or else I bought cheap theatre
seats at Gray's drugstore and tried to lose myself for a few
hours in my old passion for Broadway. I was a failure—
mediocre at advertising work and unable to get started as a
writer. Hating the city, I got roaring, weeping drunk on my
last penny and went home. . . .

. . . Incalculable city. What ensued was only one of a
thousand success stories of those gaudy days, but it plays a
part in my own movie of New York. When I returned six
months later the offices of editors and publishers were open
to me, impresarios begged plays, the movies panted for
screen material. To my bewilderment, I was adopted, not as
a Middle Westerner, not even as a detached observer, but as
the archetype of what New York wanted. This statement
requires some account of the metropolis in 1920.

There was already the tall white city of to-day, already
the feverish activity of the boom, but there was a general
inarticulateness. As much as anyone the columnist F.P.A.
guessed the pulse of the individual crowd, but shyly, as one
watching from a window. Society and the native arts had
not mingled—Ellen Mackay was not yet married to Irving
Berlin. Many of Peter Arno's people would have been

meaningless to the citizen of 1920, and save for F.P.A.'s column there was no forum for metropolitan urbanity.

Then, for just a moment, the 'younger generation' idea became a fusion of many elements in New York life. People of fifty might pretend there was still a four hundred, or Maxwell Bodenheim might pretend there was a Bohemia worth its paint and pencils—but the blending of the bright, gay, vigorous elements began then, and for the first time there appeared a society a little livelier than the solid-mahogany dinner parties of Emily Price Post. If this society produced the cocktail party, it also evolved Park Avenue wit, and for the first time an educated European could envisage a trip to New York as something more amusing than a gold-trek into a formalized Australian Bush.

For just a moment, before it was demonstrated that I was unable to play the role, I, who knew less of New York than any reporter of six months' standing and less of its society than any hall-room boy in a Ritz stag line, was pushed into the position not only of spokesman for the time but of the typical product of that same moment. I, or rather it was 'we' now, did not know exactly what New York expected of us and found it rather confusing. Within a few months after our embarkation on the Metropolitan venture we scarcely knew any more who we were and we hadn't a notion what we were. A dive into a civic fountain, a casual brush with the law, was enough to get us into the gossip columns, and we were quoted on a variety of subjects we knew nothing about. Actually our 'contacts' included half a dozen unmarried college friends and a few new literary acquaintances—I remember a lonesome Christmas when we had not one friend in the city, nor one house we could go to. Finding no nucleus to which we could cling, we became a small nucleus ourselves and gradually we fitted our dis-ruptive personalities into the contemporary scene of New York. Or rather New York forgot us and let us stay.

This is not an account of the city's changes but of the changes in this writer's feeling for the city. From the con-fusion of the year 1920 I remember riding on top of a taxicab along deserted Fifth Avenue on a hot Sunday night, and a luncheon in the cool Japanese gardens at the Ritz with the wistful Kay Laurel and George Jean Nathan, and writing all night again and again, and paying too much for minute apartments, and buying magnificent but broken-down cars. The first speak-easies had arrived, the toddle was *passé*, the Montmartre was the smart place to dance and Lillian Tash-man's fair hair weaved around the floor among the en-liquored college boys. The plays were *Declassée* and *Sacred and Profane Love*, and at the Midnight Frolic you danced elbow to elbow with Marion Davies and perhaps picked out the vivacious Mary Hay in the pony chorus. We thought we were apart from all that; perhaps everyone thinks they are apart from their milieu. We felt like small children in a great bright unexplored barn. Summoned out to Griffith's studio on Long Island, we trembled in the presence of the familiar face of the *Birth of a Nation*; later I realized that behind much of the entertainment that the city poured forth into the nation there were only a lot of rather lost and lonely people. The world of the picture actors was like our own in that it was in New York and not of it. It had little sense of itself and no centre: when I first met Dorothy Gish I had the feeling that we were both standing on the North Pole and it was snowing. Since then they have found a home but it was not destined to be New York.

When bored we took our city with a Huysmans-like per-versity. An afternoon alone in our 'apartment' eating olive sandwiches and drinking a quart of Bushmill's whisky presented by Zoë Atkins, then out into the freshly be-witched city, through strange doors into strange apartments with intermittent swings along in taxis through the soft nights. At last we were one with New York, pulling it after us through every portal. Even now I go into many flats with the sense that I have been there before or in the one above or below—was it the night I tried to disrobe in the *Scandals*, or the night when (as I read with astonishment in the paper next morning) 'Fitzgerald Knocks Officer This Side of Paradise'? Successful scrapping not being among my accomplishments, I tried in vain to reconstruct the sequence of events which led up to this dénouement in Webster Hall. And lastly from that period I remember riding in a taxi one afternoon between very tall buildings under a mauve and rosy sky; I began to bawl because I had everything I wanted and knew I would never be so happy again.

It was typical of our precarious position in New York that when our child was to be born we played safe and went home to St. Paul—it seemed inappropriate to bring a baby into all that glamour and loneliness. But in a year we were back and we began doing the same things over again and not liking them so much. We had run through a lot, though we had retained an almost theatrical innocence by preferring the role of the observed to that of the observer. But innocence is no end in itself and as our minds unwillingly matured we began to see New York whole and try to save some of it for the selves we would inevitably become.

It was too late—or too soon. For us the city was inevitably linked up with Bacchic diversions, mild or fantastic. We could organize ourselves only on our return to Long Island and not always there. We had no incentive to meet the city half way. My first symbol was now a memory, for I knew that triumph is in oneself; my second one had grown commonplace—two of the actresses whom I had worshipped from afar in 1913 had dined in our house. But it filled me with a certain fear that even the third symbol had grown dim—the tranquillity of Bunny's apartment was not to be found in the ever-quickening city. Bunny himself was married, and about to become a father, other friends had gone to Europe, and the bachelors had become cadets of houses larger and more social than ours. By this time we 'knew everybody'—which is to say most of those whom Ralph Barton would draw as in the orchestra on an opening night.

But we were no longer important. The flapper, upon whose activities the popularity of my first books was based, had become *passé* by 1923—anyhow in the East. I decided to crash Broadway with a play, but Broadway sent its scouts to Atlantic City and quashed the idea in advance, so I felt that, for the moment, the city and I had little to offer each other. I would take the Long Island atmosphere that I had familiarly breathed and materialize it beneath unfamiliar skies.

It was three years before we saw New York again. As the ship glided up the river, the city burst thunderously upon us in the early dusk—the white glacier of lower New York swooping down like a strand of a bridge to rise into uptown New York, a miracle of foamy light suspended by the stars. A band started to play on deck, but the majesty of the city made the march trivial and tinkling. From that moment I knew that New York, however often I might leave it, was home.

The tempo of the city had changed sharply. The uncertainties of 1920 were drowned in a steady golden roar and many of our friends had grown wealthy. But the restlessness of New York in 1927 approached hysteria. The parties were bigger—those of Condé Nast, for example, rivalled in their way the fabled balls of the 'nineties; the place was faster—the catering to dissipation set an example to Paris; the shows were broader, the buildings were higher, the morals were looser and the liquor was cheaper; but all these benefits did not really minister to much delight. Young people wore out early—they were hard and languid at twenty-one, and save for Peter Arno none of them contributed anything new; perhaps Peter Arno and his collaborators said everything there was to say about the boom days in New York that couldn't be said by a jazz band. Many people who were not alcoholics were lit up four days out of seven, and frayed nerves were strewn everywhere; groups were held together by a generic nervousness and the hangover became a part of the day as well allowed-for as the Spanish siesta. Most of my friends drank too much—the more they were in tune to the times the more they drank. And so effort *per se* had no dignity against the mere bounty of those days in New York, a depreciatory word was found for it: a successful programme became a racket—I was in the literary racket.

We settled a few hours from New York and I found that every time I came to the city I was caught into a complication of events that deposited me a few days later in a somewhat exhausted state on the train for Delaware. Whole sections of the city had grown rather poisonous, but invariably I found a moment of utter peace in riding south through Central Park at dark toward where the façade of 59th Street thrusts its lights through the trees. There again was my lost city, wrapped cool in its mystery and promise. But that detachment never lasted long—as the toiler must live in the city's belly, so I was compelled to live in its disordered mind.

Instead there were the speak-easies—the moving from luxurious bars, which advertised in the campus publications of Yale and Princeton, to the beer gardens where the snarling face of the underworld peered through the German good nature of the entertainment, then on to strange and even more sinister localities where one was eyed by granite-faced boys and there was nothing left of joviality but only a brutishness that corrupted the new day into which one presently went out. Back in 1920 I shocked a rising young business man by suggesting a cocktail before lunch. In 1929 there was liquor in half the downtown offices, and a speak-easy in half the large buildings.

One was increasingly conscious of the speak-easy and of Park Avenue. In the past decade Greenwich Village, Washington Square, Murray Hill, the chateaux of Fifth Avenue had somehow disappeared, or become unexpressive of anything. The city was bloated, glutted, stupid with cake and circuses, and a new expression 'Oh yeah?' summed up all the enthusiasm evoked by the announcement of the last super-skyscrapers. My barber retired on a half million bet in the market and I was conscious that the head waiters who bowed me, or failed to bow me, to my table were far, far wealthier than I. This was no fun—once again I had enough of New York and it was good to be safe on shipboard where the ceaseless revelry remained in the bar in transport to the fleecing rooms of France.

'What news from New York?'

'Stocks go up. A baby murdered a gangster.'

'Nothing more?'

'Nothing. Radios blare in the street.'

I once thought that there were no second acts in American lives, but there was certainly to be a second act to New York's boom days. We were somewhere in North Africa when we heard a dull distant crash which echoed to the farthest wastes of the desert.

'What was that?'

'Did you hear it?'

'It was nothing'

'Do you think we ought to go home and see?'

'No—it was nothing.'

In the dark autumn of two years later we saw New York again. We passed through curiously polite customs agents, and then with bowed head and hat in hand I walked reverently through the echoing tomb. Among the ruins a few childish wraiths still played to keep up the pretence that they were alive, betraying by their feverish voices and hectic cheeks the thinness of the masquerade. Cocktail parties, a last hollow survival from the days of carnival, echoed to the plaints of the wounded: 'Shoot me, for the love of God, someone shoot me!', and the groans and wails of the dying: 'Did you see that United States Steel is down three more points?' My barber was back at work in his shop; again the head waiters bowed people to their tables, if there were people to be bowed. From the ruins, lonely and inexplicable as the sphinx, rose the Empire State Building and, just as it had been a tradition of mine to climb to the Plaza Roof to take leave of the beautiful city, extending as far as eyes could reach, so now I went to the roof of the last and most magnificent of towers. Then I understood—everything was explained: I had discovered the crowning error of the city, its Pandora's box. Full of vaunting pride the New Yorker had climbed here and seen with dismay what he had never suspected, that the city was not the endless succession of canyons that he had supposed but that *it had limits*—from the tallest structure he saw for the first time that it faded out into the country on all sides, into an expanse of green and blue that alone was limitless. And with the awful realization that New York was a city after all and not a universe, the whole shining edifice that he had reared in his imagination came crashing to the ground. That was the rash gift of Alfred W. Smith to the citizens of New York.

Thus I take leave of my lost city. Seen from the ferry boat in the early morning, it no longer whispers of fantastic success and eternal youth. The whoopee mamas who prance before its empty parquets do not suggest to me the ineffable beauty of my dream girls of 1914. And Bunny, swinging along confidently with his cane toward his cloister in a carnival, has gone over to Communism and frets about the wrongs of southern mill workers and western farmers whose voices, fifteen years ago, would not have penetrated his study walls.

All is lost save memory, yet sometimes I imagine myself reading, with curious interest, a *Daily News* of the issue of 1945:

MAN OF FIFTY RUNS AMUCK IN NEW YORK
*Fitzgerald Feathered Many Love Nests Cutie Avers
Bumped Off By Outraged Gunman*

So perhaps I am destined to return some day and find in the city new experiences that so far I have only read about. For the moment I can only cry out that I have lost my splendid mirage. Come back, come back, O glittering and white!

'CRACK!' GOES THE pistol and off starts this entry. Sometimes he has caught it just right; more often he has jumped the gun. On these occasions, if he is lucky, he runs only a dozen yards, looks around and jogs sheepishly back to the starting place. But too frequently he makes the entire circuit of the track under the impression that he is leading the field, and reaches the finish to find he has no following. The race must be run all over again.

A little more training, take a long walk, cut out that night-cap, no meat at dinner, and stop worrying about politics—

So runs an interview with one of the champion false starters of the writing profession—myself. Opening a leather-bound waste-basket which I fatuously refer to as my 'note-book', I pick out at random a small, triangular piece of wrapping paper with a cancelled stamp on one side. On the other side is written:

Boopsie Dee was cute.

Nothing more. No cue as to what was intended to follow that preposterous statement. Boopsie Dee, indeed, confronting me with this single dogmatic fact about herself. Never will I know what happened to her, where and when she picked up her revolting name, and whether her cuteness got her into much trouble.

I pick out another scrap:

Article: Unattractive Things Girls Do, to pair with counter article by woman: Unattractive Things Men Do. No. 1. Remove glass eye at dinner table.

350

That's all there is on that scrap. Evidently, an idea that had dissolved into hilarity before it had fairly got under way. I try to revive it seriously. What unattractive things do girls do—I mean universally nowadays—or what unattractive things do a great majority of them do, or a strong minority? I have a few feeble ideas, but no, the notion is dead. I can only think of an article I read somewhere about a woman who divorced her husband because of the way he stalked a chop, and wondering at the time why she didn't try him out on a chop before she married him. No, that all belongs to a gilded age when people could afford to have nervous breakdowns because of the squeak in daddy's shoes.

Lines to an Old Favourite

There are hundreds of these hunches. Not all of them have to do with literature. Some are hunches about importing a troupe of Ouled Naïl dancers from Africa, about bringing the Grand-Guignol from Paris to New York, about resuscitating football at Princeton—I have two scoring plays that will make a coach's reputation in one season—and there is a faded note 'explain to D. W. Griffith why costume plays are sure to come back.' Also my plan for a film version of H. G. Wells's *History of the World*.

These little flurries caused me no travail—they were opium eater's illusions, vanishing with the smoke of the pipe, or you know what I mean. The pleasure of thinking about them was the exact equivalent of having accomplished them. It is the six-page, ten-page, thirty-page globs of paper that grieve me professionally, like unsuccessful oil shafts; they represent my false starts.

There is, for example, one false start which I have made at least a dozen times. It is—or rather has tried to take shape as—a short story. At one time or another, I have written as many words on it as would make a presentable novel, yet the present version is only about twenty-five hundred words long and hasn't been touched for two years. Its present name —it has gone under various aliases—is *The Barnaby Family*.

From childhood I have had a daydream—what a word

for one whose entire life is spent noting them down—about starting at scratch on a desert island and building a comparatively high state of civilization out of the materials at hand. I have always felt that Robinson Crusoe cheated when he rescued the tools from the wreck, and this applies equally to the Swiss Family Robinson, the Two Little Savages, and the balloon castaways of *The Mysterious Island*. In my story, not only would no convenient grain of wheat, repeating rifle, 4,000 H.P. Diesel engine or technocratic butler be washed ashore but even my characters would be helpless city dwellers with no more wood lore than a cuckoo out of a clock.

The creation of such characters was easy, and it was easy washing them ashore:

For three long hours they were prostrated on the beach. Then Donald sat up.

'Well, here we are,' he said with sleepy vagueness.

'Where?' his wife demanded eagerly.

'It couldn't be America and it couldn't be the Philippines,' he said, 'because we started from one and haven't got to the other.'

'I'm thirsty,' said the child.

Donald's eyes went quickly to the shore.

'Where's the raft?' He looked rather accusingly at Vivian. 'Where's the raft?'

'It was gone when I woke up.'

'It would be,' he exclaimed bitterly. 'Somebody might have thought of bringing the jug of water ashore. If I don't do it, nothing is done in this house—I mean this family.'

All right, go on from there. Anybody—you back there in the tenth row—step up! Don't be afraid. Just go on with the story. If you get stuck, you can look up tropical fauna and flora in the encyclopedia, or call up a neighbour who has been shipwrecked.

Anyhow, that's the exact point where my story—and I

still think it's a great plot—begins to creak and groan with unreality. I turn around after a while with a sense of uneasiness—how could anybody believe that rubbish about monkeys throwing coconuts?—trot back to the starting place, and I resume my crouch for days and days.

A Murder That Didn't Jell

During such days I sometimes examine a clot of pages which is headed Ideas for Possible Stories. Among others, I find the following.

> Bath water in Princeton or Florida
> Plot—suicide, indulgence, hate, liver and circumstance
> Snubbing or having somebody
> Dancer who found she could fly

Oddly enough, all these are intelligible, if not enlightening, suggestions to me. But they are all old—old. I am as apt to be stimulated by them as by my signature or the beat of my feet pacing the floor. There is one that for years has puzzled me, that is as great a mystery as Boopsie Dee.

Story: THE WINTER WAS COLD

CHARACTERS

Victoria Cuomo

Mark de Vinci

Jason Tenweather

Ambulance surgeon

Stark, a watchman

What was this about? Who were these people? I have no doubt that one of them was to be murdered or else to be a murderer. But all else about the plot I have forgotten long ago.

I turn over a little. Here is something over which I linger longer; a false start that wasn't bad, that might have been run out.

12

WORDS

When you consider the more expensive article and finally decide on the cheaper one, the salesman is usually thoughtful enough to make it all right for you. 'You'll probably get the most wear out of this,' he says consolingly, or even, 'That's the one I'd choose myself.'

The Trimbles were like that. They were specialists in the neat promotion of the next best into the best.

'It'll do to wear around the house,' they used to say; or, 'We want to wait until we can get a really nice one.'

It was at this point that I decided I couldn't write about the Trimbles. They were very nice and I would have enjoyed somebody else's story of how they made out, but I couldn't get under the surface of their lives—what kept them content to make the best of things instead of changing things. So I gave them up.

There is the question of dog stories. I like dogs and would like to write at least one dog story in the style of Mr Terhune but see what happens when I take pen in hand.

DOG

THE STORY OF A LITTLE DOG

Only a newsboy with a wizened face, selling his papers on the corner. A big dog fancier, standing on the curb, laughed contemptuously and twitched up the collar of his Airedale coat. Another rich dog man gave a little bark of scorn from a passing taxi-cab.

But the newsboy was interested in the animal that had crept close to his feet. He was only a cur; his fuzzy coat was inherited from his mother, who had been a fashionable poodle, while in stature he resembled his father, a Great Dane. And somewhere there was a canary concerned, for a spray of yellow feathers projected from his backbone—

You see, I couldn't go on like that. Think of dog owners writing in to the editors from all over the country, protesting that I was no man for that job.

I am thirty-six years old. For eighteen years, save for a short space during the war, writing has been my chief interest in life, and I am in every sense a professional.

Yet even now when, at the recurrent cry of 'Baby needs shoes,' I sit down facing my sharpened pencils and block of legal-sized paper, I have a feeling of utter helplessness. I may write my story in three days or, as is more frequently the case, it may be six weeks before I have assembled anything worthy to be sent out. I can open a volume from a criminal-law library and find a thousand plots. I can go into highway and byway, parlour and kitchen, and listen to personal revelations that, at the hands of other writers, might endure forever. But all that is nothing—not even enough for a false start.

Twice-Told Tales

Mostly, we authors must repeat ourselves—that's the truth. We have two or three great and moving experiences in our lives—experiences so great and moving that it doesn't seem at the time that anyone else has been so caught up and pounded and dazzled and astonished and beaten and broken and rescued and illuminated and rewarded and humbled in just that way ever before.

Then we learn our trade, well or less well, and we tell our two or three stories—each time in a new disguise—maybe ten times, maybe a hundred, as long as people will listen.

If this were otherwise, one would have to confess to having no individuality at all. And each time I honestly believe that, because I have found a new background and a novel twist, I have really got away from the two or three fundamental tales I have to tell. But it is rather like Ed Wynn's famous anecdote about the painter of boats who was begged to paint some ancestors for a client. The bargain was arranged, but with the painter's final warning that the ancestors would all turn out to look like boats.

When I face the fact that all my stories are going to have a certain family resemblance, I am taking a step toward avoiding false starts. If a friend says he's got a story for me and launches into a tale of being robbed by Brazilian pirates in a swaying straw hut on the edge of a smoking volcano in the Andes, with his fiancée bound and gagged on the roof, I can well believe there were various human emotions involved; but having successfully avoided pirates, volcanoes, and fiancées who get themselves bound and gagged on roofs, I can't feel them. Whether it's something that happened twenty years ago or only yesterday, I must start out with an emotion—one that's close to me and that I can understand.

It's an Ill Wind

Last summer I was hauled to the hospital with high fever and a tentative diagnosis of typhoid. My affairs were in no better shape than yours are, reader. There was a story I should have written to pay my current debts, and I was haunted by the fact that I hadn't made a will. If I had really had typhoid I wouldn't have worried about such things, nor made that scene at the hospital when the nurses tried to plump me into an ice bath. I didn't have either the typhoid or the bath, but I continued to rail against my luck that just at this crucial moment I should have to waste two weeks in bed, answering the baby talk of nurses and getting nothing done at all. But three days after I was discharged I had finished a story about a hospital.

The material was soaking in and I didn't know it. I was profoundly moved by fear, apprehension, worry, impatience; every sense was acute, and that is the best way of accumulating material for a story. Unfortunately, it does not always come so easily. I say to myself—looking at the awful blank block of paper—'Now, here's this man Swankins that I've known and liked for ten years. I am privy to all his private affairs, and some of them are wows. I've threatened to write about him, and he says to go ahead and do my worst.'

But can I? I've been in as many jams as Swankins, but I

didn't look at them the same way, nor would it ever have occurred to me to extricate myself from the Chinese police or from the clutches of that woman in the way Swankins chose. I could write some fine paragraphs about Swankins, but build a story around him that would have an ounce of feeling in it—impossible.

Or into my distraught imagination wanders a girl named Elsie about whom I was almost suicidal for a month, in 1916.

'How about me?' Elsie says. 'Surely you swore to a lot of emotions back there in the past. Have you forgotten?'

'No, Elsie, I haven't forgotten.'

'Well, then, write a story about me. You haven't seen me for twelve years, so you don't know how fat I am now and how boring I often seem to my husband.'

'No, Elsie, I——'

'Oh, come on. Surely I must be worth a story. Why, you used to hang around saying good-bye with your face so miserable and comic that I thought I'd go crazy myself before I got rid of you. And now you're afraid even to start a story about me. Your feeling must have been pretty thin if you can't revive it for a few hours.'

'No Elsie; you don't understand. I have written about you a dozen times. That funny little rabbit curl to your lip, I used in a story six years ago. The way your face all changed just when you were going to laugh—I gave that characteristic to one of the first girls I ever wrote about. The way I stayed around trying to say good night, knowing that you'd rush to the phone as soon as the front door closed behind me—all that was in a book that I wrote once upon a time.'

'I see. Just because I didn't respond to you, you broke me into bits and used me up piecemeal.'

'I'm afraid so, Elsie. You see, you never so much as kissed me, except that once with a kind of a shove at the same time, so there really isn't any story.'

Plots without emotions, emotions without plots. So it goes sometimes. Let me suppose, however, that I have got under way; two days' work, two thousand words are finished and being typed for a first revision. And suddenly doubts overtake me.

A Jury of One

What if I'm just horsing around? What's going on in this regatta anyhow? Who could care what happens to the girl, when the sawdust is obviously leaking out of her moment by moment? How did I get the plot all tangled up? I am alone in the privacy of my faded blue room with my sick cat, the bare February branches waving at the window, an ironic paperweight that says Business is Good, a New England conscience—developed in Minnesota—and my greatest problem:

'Shall I run it out? Or shall I turn back?'

Shall I say:

'I know I had something to prove, and it may develop farther along in the story?'

Or:

'This is just bullheadedness. Better throw it away and start over.'

The latter is one of the most difficult decisions that an author must make. To make it philosophically, before he has exhausted himself in a hundred-hour effort to resuscitate a corpse or disentangle innumerable wet snarls, is a test whether or not he is really a professional. There are often occasions when such a decision is doubly difficult. In the last stages of a novel, for instance, where there is no question of junking the whole, but when an entire favourite character has to be hauled out by the heels, screeching, and dragging half a dozen good scenes with him.

It is here that these confessions tie up with a general problem as well as with those peculiar to a writer. The decision as to when to quit, as to when one is merely floundering around and causing other people trouble, has to be made frequently in a lifetime. In youth we are taught the rather simple rule never to quit, because we are presumably following programmes made by people wiser than ourselves. My own conclusion is that when one has embarked on a course that grows increasingly doubtful and feels the vital forces beginning to be used up, it is best to ask advice, if decent advice is within range. Columbus didn't and Lindbergh couldn't. So my statement at first seems heretical toward the idea that it is pleasantest to live with—the idea of heroism. But I make a sharp division between one's professional life, when, after the period of apprenticeship, not more than 10 per cent of advice is worth a hoot, and one's private and worldly life, when often almost anyone's judgment is better than one's own.

Once, not so long ago, when my work was hampered by so many false starts that I thought the game was up at last, and when my personal life was even more thoroughly obfuscated, I asked an old Alabama Negro:

'Uncle Bob, when things get so bad that there isn't any way out, what do you do then?'

Homely Advice But Sound

The heat from the kitchen stove stirred his white sideburns as he warmed himself. If I cynically expected a platitudinous answer, a reflection of something remembered from Uncle Remus, I was disappointed.

'Mr Fitzgerald,' he said, 'when things get that-away I wuks.'

It was good advice. Work is almost everything. But it would be nice to be able to distinguish useful work from mere labour expended. Perhaps that is part of work itself—to find the difference. Perhaps my frequent, solitary sprints around the track are profitable. Shall I tell you about another one? Very well. You see, I had this hunch—But in counting the pages, I find that my time is up and I must put my book of mistakes away. On the fire? No! I put it weakly back in the drawer. These old mistakes are now only toys—and expensive ones at that—give them a toy's cupboard and then hurry back into the serious business of my profession. Joseph Conrad defined it more clearly, more vividly than any man of our time:

'My task is by the power of the written word to make

you hear, to make you feel—it is, before all, to make
you see.'

It's not very difficult to run back and start over again—
especially in private. What you aim at is to get in a good
race or two when the crowd is in the stand.

FOR A YEAR AND A HALF the writer of this appreciation
was Ring Lardner's most familiar companion; after that,
geography made separations and our contacts were rare.
When my wife and I last saw him in 1931, he looked already
like a man on his deathbed—it was terribly sad to see that six
feet three inches of kindness stretched out ineffectual in the
hospital room. His fingers trembled with a match, the tight
skin on his handsome skull was marked as a mask of misery
and nervous pain.

He gave a very different impression when we first saw
him in 1921—he seemed to have an abundance of quiet
vitality that would enable him to outlast anyone, to take
himself for long spurts of work or play that would ruin any
ordinary constitution. He had recently convulsed the country with the famous kitten-and-coat saga (it had to do with
a world's series bet and with the impending conversion of
some kittens into fur), and the evidence of the betting, a
beautiful sable, was worn by his wife at the time. In those
days he was interested in people, sports, bridge, music, the
stage, the newspapers, the magazines, the books. But
though I did not know it, the change in him had already
begun—the impenetrable despair that dogged him for a
dozen years to his death.

He had practically given up sleeping, save on short
vacations deliberately consecrated to simple pleasures, most
frequently golf with his friends, Grantland Rice or John
Wheeler. Many a night we talked over a case of Canadian
ale until bright dawn, when Ring would rise and yawn:
'Well, I guess the children have left for school by this
time—I might as well go home.'

The woes of many people haunted him—for example, the
doctor's death sentence pronounced upon Tad, the car-
toonist (who, in fact, nearly outlived Ring)—it was as if
he believed he could and ought to do something about such
things. And as he struggled to fulfil his contracts, one of
which, a comic strip based on the character of 'the busher,'
was a terror, indeed, it was obvious that he felt his work to
be directionless, merely 'copy'. So he was inclined to turn
his cosmic sense of responsibility into the channel of
solving other people's problems—finding someone an
introduction to a theatrical manager, placing a friend in a
job, manœuvring a man into a gold club. The effort made
was often out of proportion to the situation; the truth back
of it was that Ring was getting off—he was a faithful and
conscientious workman to the end, but he had stopped
finding any fun in his work ten years before he died.

About that time (1922) a publisher undertook to reissue
his old books and collect his recent stories and this gave him
a sense of existing in the literary world as well as with the
public, and he got some satisfaction from the reiterated
statements of Mencken and F.P.A. as to his true stature as a
writer. But I don't think he cared then—it is hard to understand, but I don't think he really gave a damn about anything except his personal relations with a few people. A
case in point was his attitude to those imitators who lifted
everything except the shirt off his back—only Hemingway has been so thoroughly frisked—it worried the imitators more than it worried Ring. His attitude was that if
they got stuck in the process he'd help them over any tough
place.

Throughout this period of huge earnings and an increasingly solid reputation on top and beneath, there were two
ambitions more important to Ring than the work by which
he will be remembered; he wanted to be a musician—
sometimes he dramatized himself ironically as a thwarted
composer—and he wanted to write shows. His dealings
with managers would make a whole story: they were always
commissioning him to do work which they promptly forgot

they had ordered, and accepting librettos that they never
produced. (Ring left a short ironic record of Ziegfeld.)
Only with the aid of the practical George Kaufman did he
achieve his ambition, and by then he was too far gone in
illness to get a proper satisfaction from it.

The point of these paragraphs is that, whatever Ring's
achievement was, it fell short of the achievement he was
capable of, and this because of a cynical attitude toward his
work. How far back did that attitude go?—back to his
youth in a Michigan village? Certainly back to his days with
the Cubs. During those years, when most men of promise
achieve an adult education, if only in the school of war,
Ring moved in the company of a few dozen illiterates playing a boy's game. A boy's game, with no more possibilities
in it than a boy could master, a game bounded by walls
which kept out novelty or danger, change or adventure.
This material, the observation of it under such circumstances, was the text of Ring's schooling during the most
formative period of the mind. A writer can spin on about his
adventures after thirty, after forty, after fifty, but the criteria by which these adventures are weighed and valued are
irrevocably settled at the age of twenty-five. However
deeply Ring might cut into it, his cake had exactly the
diameter of Frank Chance's diamond.

Here was his artistic problem, and it promised future
trouble. So long as he wrote within that enclosure the result
was magnificent: within it he heard and recorded the voice
of a continent. But when, inevitably, he outgrew his interest
in it, what was Ring left with?

He was left with his fine linguistic technique—and he
was left rather helpless in those few acres. He had been
formed by the very world on which his hilarious irony had
released itself. He had fought his way through to knowing
what people's motives are and what means they are likely
to resort to in order to attain their goals. But now he had
a new problem—what to do about it. He went on seeing,
and the sights travelled back to the optic nerve, but no longer
to be thrown off in fiction, because they were no longer

sights that could be weighed and valued by the old criteria. It was never that he was completely sold on athletic virtuosity as the be-all and end-all of problems; the trouble was that he could find nothing finer. Imagine life conceived as a business of beautiful muscular organization—an arising, an effort, a good break, a sweat, a bath, a meal, a love, a sleep—imagine it achieved; then imagine trying to apply that standard to the horribly complicated mess of living, where nothing, even the greatest conceptions and workings and achievements, is else but messy, spotty, tortuous—and then one can imagine the confusion that Ring faced on coming out of the ball park.

He kept on recording but he no longer projected, and this accumulation, which he has taken with him to the grave, crippled his spirit in the latter years. It was not the fear of Niles, Michigan, that hampered him—it was the habit of silence, formed in the presence of the 'ivory' with which he lived and worked. Remember it was not humble ivory— Ring has demonstrated that—it was arrogant, imperative, often megalomaniacal ivory. He got the habit of silence, then the habit of repression that finally took the form of his odd little crusade in the *New Yorker* against pornographic songs. He had agreed with himself to speak only a small portion of his mind.

The present writer once suggested to him that he organize some *cadre* within which he could adequately display his talents, suggesting that it should be something deeply personal, and something on which Ring could take his time, but he dismissed the idea lightly; he was a disillusioned idealist but he had served his Fates well, and no other ones could be casually created for him—'This is something that can be printed,' he reasoned; 'this, however, belongs with that bunch of stuff that can never be written.'

He covered himself in such cases with protests of his inability to bring off anything big, but this was specious, for he was a proud man and had no reason to rate his abilities cheaply. He refused to 'tell all' because in a crucial period of his life he had formed the habit of not doing it—and

this he had elevated gradually into a standard of taste. It
never satisfied him by a damn sight.

So one is haunted not only by a sense of personal loss but
by a conviction that Ring got less percentage of himself on
paper than any other American of the first flight. There is
' *You Know Me, Al,*' and there are about a dozen wonderful
short stories (my God, he hadn't even saved them—the
material of *How to Write Short Stories* was obtained by
photographing old issues in the public library!), and there
is some of the most uproarious and inspired nonsense since
Lewis Carroll. Most of the rest is mediocre stuff, with
flashes, and I would do Ring a disservice to suggest it
should be set upon an altar and worshipped, as have been
the most casual relics of Mark Twain. Those three volumes
should seem enough—to everyone who didn't know Ring.
But I venture that no one who knew him but will agree
that the personality of the man overlapped it. Proud, shy,
solemn, shrewd, polite, brave, kind, merciful, honourable
—with the affection these qualities aroused he created in
addition a certain awe in people. His intentions, his will,
once in motion, were formidable factors in dealing with
him—he always did every single thing he said he would
do. Frequently he was the melancholy Jaques, and sad
company indeed, but under any conditions a noble dignity
flowed from him, so that time in his presence always seemed
well spent.

On my desk, at the moment, I have the letters Ring
wrote to us; here is a letter one thousand words long, here
is one of two thousand words—theatrical gossip, literary
shop talk, flashes of wit but not much wit, for he was
feeling thin and saving the best of that for his work,
anecdotes of his activities. I reprint the most typical one
I can find:

'The Dutch Treat show was a week ago Friday night.
Grant Rice and I had reserved a table, and a table holds ten
people and no more. Well, I had invited, as one guest,
Jerry Kern, but he telephoned at the last moment that he
couldn't come. I then consulted with Grant Rice, who said

he had no substitute in mind, but that it was a shame to waste our extra ticket when tickets were at a premium. So I called up Jones, and Jones said yes, and would it be all right for him to bring along a former Senator who was a pal of his and had been good to him in Washington. I said I was sorry, but our table was filled and, besides, we didn't have an extra ticket. "Maybe I could dig up another ticket somewhere," said Jones. "I don't believe so," I said, "but anyway the point is that we haven't room at our table." "Well," said Jones, "I could have the Senator eat some-where else and join us in time for the show." "Yes," I said, "but we have no ticket for him." "Well, I'll think up something," he said. Well, what he thought up was to bring himself and the Senator and I had a hell of a time getting an extra ticket and shoving the Senator in at another table where he wasn't wanted, and later in the evening, the Senator thanked Jones and said he was the greatest fella in the world and all I got was goodnight.

'Well, I must close and nibble on a carrot. R.W.L.'

Even in a telegram Ring could compress a lot of himself. Here is one: WHEN ARE YOU COMING BACK AND WHY PLEASE ANSWER RING LARDNER

This is not the moment to recollect Ring's convivial as-pects, especially as he had, long before his death, ceased to find amusement in dissipation, or indeed in the whole range of what is called entertainment—save for his perennial interest in songs. By grace of the radio and of the many musicians who, drawn by his enormous magnetism, made pilgrimages to his bedside, he had a consolation in the last days, and he made the most of it, hilariously rewriting Cole Porter's lyrics in the *New Yorker*. But it would be an eva-sion for the present writer not to say that when he was Ring's neighbour a decade ago, they tucked a lot under their belts in many weathers, and spent many words on many men and things. At no time did I feel that I had known him enough, or that anyone knew him—it was not the feeling that there was more stuff in him and that it should come out, it was rather a qualitative difference, it was rather as though, due to some inadequacy in one's self, one had not penetrated to something unsolved, new and unsaid. That is why one wishes that Ring had written down a larger proportion of what was in his mind and heart. It would have saved him longer for us, and that in itself would be something. But I would like to know what it was, and now I will go on wishing—what did Ring want, how did he want things to be, how did he think things were?

A great and good American is dead. Let us not obscure him by the flowers, but walk up and look at that fine medallion, all abraded by sorrows that perhaps we are not equipped to understand. Ring made no enemies, because he was kind, and to many millions he gave release and delight.

SLEEPING AND WAKING

[1934]

WHEN SOME YEARS AGO I read a piece by Ernest Hemingway called *Now I Lay Me*, I thought there was nothing further to be said about insomnia. I see now that that was because I had never had much; it appears that every man's insomnia is as different from his neighbour's as are their daytime hopes and aspirations.

Now if insomnia is going to be one of your naturals, it begins to appear in the late 'thirties. Those seven precious hours of sleep suddenly break in two. There is, if one is lucky, the 'first sweet sleep of night' and the last deep sleep of morning, but between the two appears a sinister, ever widening interval. This is the time of which it is written in the Psalms: *Scuto circumdabit te veritas eius: non timebis a timore nocturno, a sagitta volante in die, a negotio perambulante in tenebris.*

With a man I knew the trouble commenced with a mouse; in my case I like to trace it to a single mosquito.

My friend was in course of opening up his country house unassisted, and after a fatiguing day discovered that the only practical bed was a child's affair—long enough but scarcely wider than a crib. Into this he flopped and was presently deeply engrossed in rest *but* with one arm irrepressibly extending over the side of the crib. Hours later he was awakened by what seemed to be a pin-prick in his finger. He shifted his arm sleepily and dozed off again—to be again awakened by the same feeling.

This time he flipped on the bed-light—and there attached to the bleeding end of his finger was a small and avid mouse. My friend, to use his own words, 'uttered an exclamation' but probably he gave a wild scream.

The mouse let go. It had been about the business of

devouring the man as thoroughly as if his sleep were permanent. From then on it threatened to be not even temporary.
The victim sat shivering, and very, very tired. He considered how he would have a cage made to fit over the bed
and sleep under it the rest of his life. But it was too late to
have the cage made that night and finally he dozed, to wake
in intermittent horrors from dreams of being a Pied Piper
whose rats turned and pursued him.

He has never since been able to sleep without a dog or cat
in the room.

My own experience with night pets was at a time of
utter exhaustion—too much work undertaken, interlocking
circumstances that made the work twice as arduous, illness
within and around—the old story of troubles never coming
singly. And ah, how I had planned that sleep that was to
crown the end of the struggle—how I had looked forward to
the relaxation into a bed soft as a cloud and permanent as a
grave. An invitation to dine à deux with Greta Garbo would
have left me indifferent.

But had there been such an invitation I would have done
well to accept it, for instead I dined alone, or rather was
dined upon by one solitary mosquito.

It is astonishing how much worse one mosquito can be
than a swarm. A swarm can be prepared against, but *one*
mosquito takes on a personality—a hatefulness, a sinister
quality of the struggle to the death. This personality appeared all by himself in September on the twentieth floor of
a New York hotel, as out of place as an armadillo. He was
the result of New Jersey's decreased appropriation for
swamp drainage, which had sent him and other younger
sons into neighbouring states for food.

The night was warm—but after the first encounter, the
vague slappings of the air, the futile searches, the punishment of my own ears a split second too late, I followed the
ancient formula and drew the sheet over my head.

And so continued the old story, the bitings through the
sheet, the sniping of exposed sections of hand holding the
sheet in place, the pulling up of the blanket with ensuing

suffocation—followed by the psychological change of attitude, increasing wakefulness, wild impotent anger—finally a second hunt.

This inaugurated the maniacal phase—the crawl under the bed with the standing lamp for torch, the tour of the room with final detection of the insect's retreat on the ceiling and attack with knotted towels, the wounding of oneself— my God!

—After that there was a short convalescence that my opponent seemed aware of, for he perched insolently beside my head—but I missed again.

At last, after another half hour that whipped the nerves into a frantic state of alertness came the Pyrrhic victory, and the small mangled spot of blood, *my* blood, on the headboard of the bed.

As I said, I think of that night, two years ago, as the beginning of my sleeplessness—because it gave me the sense of how sleep can be spoiled by one infinitesimal incalculable element. It made me, in the now archaic phraseology, 'sleep-conscious'. I worried whether or not it was going to be allowed me. I was drinking, intermittently but generously, and on the nights when I took no liquor the problem of whether or not sleep was specified began to haunt me long before bedtime.

A typical night (and I wish I could say such nights were all in the past) comes after a particularly sedentary work-and-cigarette day. It ends, say without any relaxing interval, at the time for going to bed. All is prepared, the books, the glass of water, the extra pyjamas lest I awake in rivulets of sweat, the luminol pills in the little round tube, the notebook and pencil in case of a night thought worth recording. (Few have been—they generally seem thin in the morning, which does not diminish their force and urgency at night.)

I turn in, perhaps with a night-cap—I am doing some comparatively scholarly reading for a coincident work so I choose a lighter volume on the subject and read till drowsy on a last cigarette. At the yawning point I snap the book on a marker, the cigarette at the hearth, the button on the lamp.

I turn first to the left side, for that, so I've heard, slows the heart, and then—coma.

So far so good. From midnight until two-thirty peace in the room. Then suddenly I am awake, harassed by one of the ills or functions of the body, a too vivid dream, a change in the weather for warm or cold.

The adjustment is made quickly, with the vain hope that the continuity of sleep can be preserved, but no—so with a sigh I slip on the light, take a minute pill of luminol and reopen my book. The *real* night, the darkest hour, has begun. I am too tired to read unless I get myself a drink and hence feel bad next day—so I get up and walk. I walk from my bedroom through the hall to my study, and then back again, and if it's summer out to my back porch. There is a mist over Baltimore; I cannot count a single steeple. Once more to the study, where my eye is caught by a pile of unfinished business: letters, proofs, notes, etc. I start toward it, but No! this would be fatal. Now the luminol is having some slight effect, so I try bed again, this time half circling the pillow on edge about my neck.

'Once upon a time' (I tell myself) 'they needed a quarterback at Princeton, and they had nobody and were in despair. The head coach noticed me kicking and passing on the side of the field, and cried: "Who is *that* man—why haven't we noticed *him* before ?" The under coach answered, "He hasn't been out," and the response was: "Bring him to me."

'. . . we go to the day of the Yale game. I weigh only one hundred and thirty-five, so they save me until the third quarter, with the score——'

—But it's no use—I have used that dream of a defeated dream to induce sleep for almost twenty years, but it has worn thin at last. I can no longer count on it—though even now on easier nights it has a certain lull. . . .

The war dream then: the Japanese are everywhere victorious—my division is cut to rags and stands on the defensive in a part of Minnesota where I know every bit of the ground. The headquarters staff and the regimental battalion commanders who were in conference with them at the time have been killed by one shell. The command devolved upon Captain Fitzgerald. With superb presence . . .

—But enough; this also is worn thin with years of usage. The character who bears my name has become blurred. In the dead of the night I am only one of the dark millions riding forward in black buses toward the unknown.

Back again to the rear porch, and conditioned by intense fatigue of mind and perverse alertness of the nervous system—like a broken-stringed bow upon a throbbing fiddle—I see the real horror develop over the roof-tops, and in the strident horns of night-owl taxis and the shrill monody of revellers' arrival over the way. Horror and waste——

—Waste and horror—what I might have been and done that is lost, spent, gone, dissipated, unrecapturable. I could have acted thus, refrained from this, been bold where I was timid, cautious where I was rash.

I need not have hurt her like that.

Nor said this to him.

Nor broken myself trying to break what was unbreakable.

The horror has come now like a storm—what if this night prefigured the night after death—what if all thereafter was an eternal quivering on the edge of an abyss, with everything base and vicious in oneself urging one forward and the baseness and viciousness of the world just ahead. No choice, no road, no hope—only the endless repetition of the sordid and the semi-tragic. Or to stand forever, perhaps, on the threshold of life unable to pass it and return to it. I am a ghost now as the clock strikes four.

On the side of the bed I put my head in my hands. Then silence, silence—and suddenly—or so it seems in retrospect —suddenly I am asleep.

Sleep—real sleep, the dear, the cherished one, the lullaby. So deep and warm the bed and the pillow enfolding me, letting me sink into peace, nothingness—my dreams now, after the catharsis of the dark hours, are of young and lovely people doing young, lovely things, the girls I knew once, with big brown eyes, real yellow hair.

In the fall of '16 in the cool of the afternoon
I met Caroline under a white moon
There was an orchestra—Bingo-Bango
Playing for us to dance the tango
And the people all clapped as we arose
For her sweet face and my new clothes——

Life *was* like that, after all; my spirit soars in the moment of its oblivion; then down, down deep into the pillow . . . .

'. . . Yes, Essie, yes.—Oh, My God, all right, I'll take the call myself.'

Irresistible, iridescent—here is Aurora—here is another day.

AFTERNOON OF AN
AUTHOR
[1936]

WHEN HE WOKE up he felt better than he had for many
weeks, a fact that became plain to him negatively—he did
not feel ill. He leaned for a moment against the door frame
between his bedroom and bath till he could be sure he was
not dizzy. Not a bit, not even when he stooped for a slipper
under the bed.

It was a bright April morning, he had no idea what time
because his clock was long unwound but as he went back
through the apartment to the kitchen he saw that his daughter had breakfasted and departed and that the mail was in, so
it was after nine.

'I think I'll go out today,' he said to the maid.

'Do you good—it's a lovely day.' She was from New
Orleans, with the features and colouring of an Arab.

'I want two eggs like yesterday and toast, orange juice,
and tea.'

He lingered for a moment in his daughter's end of the
apartment and read his mail. It was an annoying mail with
nothing cheerful in it—mostly bills and advertisements with
the diurnal Oklahoma school boy and his gaping autograph
album. Sam Goldwyn might do a ballet picture with Spes-
siwitza and might not—it would all have to wait till Mr
Goldwyn got back from Europe when he might have
half a dozen new ideas. Paramount wanted a release on
a poem that had appeared in one of the author's books, as
they didn't know whether it was an original or quoted.
Maybe they were going to get a title from it. Anyhow
he had no more equity in that property—he had sold the

374

silent rights many years ago and the sound rights last year.

'Never any luck with movies,' he said to himself. 'Stick to your last, boy.'

He looked out the window during breakfast at the students changing classes on the college campus across the way.

'Twenty years ago I was changing classes,' he said to the maid. She laughed her debutante's laugh.

'I'll need a cheque,' she said, 'if you're going out.'

'Oh, I'm not going out yet. I've got two or three hours' work. I meant late this afternoon.'

'Going for a drive?'

'I wouldn't drive that old junk—I'd sell it for fifty dollars. I'm going on the top of a bus.'

After breakfast he lay down for fifteen minutes. Then he went into the study and began to work.

The problem was a magazine story that had become so thin in the middle that it was about to blow away. The plot was like climbing endless stairs, he had no element of surprise in reserve, and the characters who started so bravely day-before-yesterday couldn't have qualified for a newspaper serial.

'Yes, I certainly need to get out,' he thought. 'I'd like to drive down the Shenandoah Valley, or go to Norfolk on the boat.'

But both of these ideas were impractical—they took time and energy and he had not much of either—what there was must be conserved for work. He went through the manuscript underlining good phrases in red crayon and after tucking these into a file slowly tore up the rest of the story and dropped it in the waste-basket. Then he walked the room and smoked, occasionally talking to himself.

'Wee-l, let's see——'

'Nau-ow, the next thing—would be——'

'Now let's see, now——'

After a while he sat down thinking:

'I'm just stale—I shouldn't have touched a pencil for two days.'

He looked through the heading 'Story Ideas' in his note-book until the maid came to tell him his secretary was on the phone—part-time secretary since he had been ill.

'Not a thing,' he said. 'I just tore up everything I'd written. It wasn't worth a damn. I'm going out this after-noon.'

'Good for you. It's a fine day.'

'Better come up tomorrow afternoon—there's a lot of mail and bills.'

He shaved, and then as a precaution rested five minutes before he dressed. It was exciting to be going out—he hoped the elevator boys wouldn't say they were glad to see him up and he decided to go down the back elevator where they did not know him. He put on his best suit with the coat and trousers that didn't match. He had bought only two suits in six years but they were the very best suits—the coat alone of this one had cost a hundred and ten dollars. As he must have a destination—it wasn't good to go places without a des-tination—he put a tube of shampoo ointment in his pocket for his barber to use, and also a small phial of luminol.

'The perfect neurotic,' he said, regarding himself in the mirror. 'By-product of an idea, slag of a dream.'

He went into the kitchen and said good-bye to the maid as if he were going to Little America. Once in the war he had commandeered an engine on sheer bluff and had it driven from New York to Washington to keep from being A.W.O.L. Now he stood carefully on the street corner waiting for the light to change, while young people hurried past him with a fine disregard for traffic. On the bus corner under the trees it was green and cool and he thought of Stonewall Jackson's last words: 'Let us cross over the river and rest under the shade of the trees.' Those Civil War leaders seemed to have realized very suddenly how tired they were—Lee shrivelling into another man, Grant with his desperate memoir-writing at the end.

The bus was all he expected—only the other man on the

roof and the green branches ticking against each window through whole blocks. They would probably have to trim those branches and it seemed a pity. There was so much to look at—he tried to define the colour of one line of houses and could only think of an old opera cloak of his mother's that was full of tints and yet was of no tint—a mere reflector of light. Somewhere church bells were playing '*Venite Adoremus*' and he wondered why, because Christmas was eight months off. He didn't like bells but it had been very moving when they played '*Maryland, My Maryland*' at the governor's funeral.

On the college football field men were working with rollers and a title occurred to him: 'Turf-keeper' or else 'The Grass Grows,' something about a man working on turf for years and bringing up his son to go to college and play football there. Then the son dying in youth and the man's going to work in the cemetery and putting turf over his son instead of under his feet. It would be the kind of piece that is often placed in anthologies, but not this sort of thing—it was sheer swollen antithesis, as formalized as a popular magazine and easier to write. Many people, however would consider it excellent because it was melancholy, had digging in it and was simple to understand.

The bus went past a pale Athenian railroad station brought to life by the blue-shirted redcaps out in front. The street narrowed as the business section began and there were suddenly brightly dressed girls, all very beautiful—he thought he had never seen such beautiful girls. There were men too but they all looked rather silly, like himself in the mirror, and there were old undecorative women, and presently, too, there were plain and unpleasant faces among the girls; but in general they were lovely, dressed in real colours all the way from six to thirty, no plans or struggles in their faces, only a state of sweet suspension, provocative and serene. He loved life terribly for a minute, not wanting to give it up at all. He thought perhaps he had made a mistake in coming out so soon.

He got off the bus, holding carefully to all the railings and walked a block to the hotel barbershop. He passed a sporting goods store and looked in the window unmoved except by a first baseman's glove which was already dark in the pocket. Next to that was a haberdasher's and here he stood for quite a while looking at the deep shade of shirts and the ones of checker and plaid. Ten years ago on the summer Riviera the author and some others had bought dark blue workmen's shirts, and probably that had started that style. The checkered shirts were nice looking, bright as uniforms and he wished he were twenty and going to a beach club all dolled up like a Turner sunset or Guido Reni's dawn.

The barbershop was large, shining and scented—it had been several months since the author had come downtown on such a mission and he found that his familiar barber was laid up with arthritis; however, he explained to another man how to use the ointment, refused a newspaper and sat, rather happy and sensually content at the strong fingers on his scalp, while a pleasant mingled memory of all the barbershops he had ever known flowed through his mind.

Once he had written a story about a barber. Back in 1929 the proprietor of his favourite shop in the city where he was then living had made a fortune of $300,000 on tips from a local industrialist and was about to retire. The author had no stake in the market, in fact, was about to sail for Europe for a few years with such accumulation as he had, and that autumn hearing how the barber had all lost his fortune he was prompted to write a story, thoroughly disguised in every way yet hinging on the fact of a barber rising in the world and then tumbling; he heard, nevertheless, that the story had been identified in the city and caused some hard feelings.

The shampoo ended. When he came out into the hall an orchestra had started to play in the cocktail room across the way and he stood for a moment in the door listening. So long since he had danced, perhaps two evenings in five years, yet a review of his last book had mentioned him as being fond of night clubs; the same review had also spoken of him as being indefatigable. Something in the sound of the word in his mind broke him momentarily and feeling tears of weakness behind his eyes he turned away. It was like in the beginning fifteen years ago when they said he had 'fatal facility', and he laboured like a slave over every sentence so as not to be like that.

'I'm getting bitter again,' he said to himself. 'That's no good, no good—I've got to go home.'

The bus was a long time coming but he didn't like taxis and he still hoped that something would occur to him on that upper-deck passing through the green leaves of the boulevard. When it came finally he had some trouble climbing the steps but it was worth it, for the first thing he saw was a pair of high school kids, a boy and a girl, sitting without any self-consciousness on the high pedestal of the Lafayette statue, their attention fast upon each other. Their isolation moved him and he knew he would get something out of it professionally, if only in contrast to the growing seclusion of his life and the increasing necessity of picking over an already well-picked past. He needed reforestation and he was well aware of it, and he hoped the soil would stand one more growth. It had never been the very best soil, for he had had an early weakness of showing off instead of listening and observing.

Here was the apartment house—he glanced up at his own windows on the top floor before he went in.

'The residence of the successful writer,' he said to himself. 'I wonder what marvellous books he's tearing off up there. It must be great to have a gift like that—just sit down with pencil and paper. Work when you want—go where you please.'

His child wasn't home yet but the maid came out of the kitchen and said:

'Did you have a nice time?'

'Perfect,' he said. 'I went roller skating and bowled and played around with Man Mountain Dean and finished up in a Turkish bath. Any telegrams?'

'Not a thing.'

'Bring me a glass of milk, will you?'

He went through the dining-room and turned into his study, struck blind for a moment with the glow of his two thousand books in the late sunshine. He was quite tired— he would lie down for ten minutes and then see if he could get started on an idea in the two hours before dinner.

AUTHOR'S HOUSE
[1936]

I HAVE SEEN NUMEROUS photographs and read many accounts of the houses of Joan Crawford, Virginia Bruce, and Claudette Colbert, usually with the hostess done up from behind with a bib explaining how on God's earth to make a Hollywood soufflé or open a can of soup without removing the appendix in the same motion. But it has been a long time since I have seen a picture of an author's house and it occurs to me to supply the deficiency.

Of course I must begin with an apology for writing about authors at all. In the days of the old *Smart Set* Mencken and Nathan had a rejection slip which notified the aspirant that they would not consider stories about painters, musicians, and authors—perhaps because these classes are supposed to express themselves fully in their own work and are not a subject for portraiture. And having made the timorous bow I proceed with the portrait.

Rather than leave a sombre effect at the end we begin at the bottom, in a dark, damp, unmodernized cellar. As your host's pale yellow flashlight moves slowly around through the spiderwebs, past old boxes and barrels and empty bottles and parts of old machines you feel a little uneasy.

'Not a bad cellar—as cellars go,' the author says. 'You can't see it very well and I can't either—it's mostly forgotten.'

'What do you mean?'

'It's everything I've forgotten—all the complicated dark mixture of my youth and infancy that made me a fiction writer instead of a fireman or a soldier.

'You see fiction is a trick of the mind and heart composed of as many separate emotions as a magician uses in executing a pass or a palm. When you've learned it you forget it and leave it down here.'

'When did you learn it?'

'Oh every time I begin I have to learn it all over again in a way. But the intangibles are down here. Why I chose this God-awful metier of sedentary days and sleepless nights and endless dissatisfaction. Why I would choose it again. All that's down here and I'm just as glad I can't look at it too closely. See that dark corner?'

'Yes.'

'Well, three months before I was born my mother lost her two other children and I think that came first of all though I don't know how it worked exactly. I think I started then to be a writer.'

Your eyes fall on another corner and you give a start of alarm.

'What's that?' you demand.

'That?' The author tries to change the subject, moving around so as to obscure your view of the too recent mound of dirt in the corner that has made you think of certain things in police reports.

But you insist.

'That is where it is buried,' he says.

'What's buried?'

'That's where I buried my love after—' he hesitates.

'After you *killed* her?'

'After I killed *it*.'

'I don't understand what you mean.'

The author does not look at the pile of earth.

'That is where I buried my first childish love of myself, my belief that I would never die like other people, and that I wasn't the son of my parents but a son of a king, a king who ruled the whole world.'

He breaks off.

'But let's get out of here. We'll go upstairs.'

In the living-room the author's eye is immediately caught by a scene outside the window. The visitor looks—he sees some children playing football on the lawn next door.

'There is another reason why I became an author.'

'How's that?'

'Well, I used to play football in a school and there was a coach who didn't like me for a damn. Well, our school was going to play a game up on the Hudson, and I had been substituting for our climax runner who had been hurt the week before. I had a good day substituting for him so now that he was well and had taken his old place I was moved into what might be called the position of blocking back. I wasn't adapted to it, perhaps because there was less glory and less stimulation. It was cold, too, and I don't stand cold, so instead of doing my job I got thinking how grey the skies were. When the coach took me out of the game he said briefly:

'"We simply can't depend on you."

'I could only answer, "Yes sir."

'That was as far as I could explain to him literally what happened—and it's taken me years to figure it out for my own benefit. I had been playing listlessly. We had the other team licked by a couple of touchdowns, and it suddenly occurred to me that I might as well let the opposing end—who hadn't so far made a single tackle—catch a forward pass, but at the last moment I came to life and realized that I couldn't let him catch the pass, but that at least I wouldn't intercept it, so I just knocked it down.

'That was the point where I was taken out of the game. I remember the desolate ride in the bus back to the train and the desolate ride back to school with everybody thinking I had been yellow on the occasion, when actually I was just distracted and sorry for that opposing end. That's the truth. I've been afraid plenty of times but that wasn't one of the times. The point is it inspired me to write a poem for the school paper which made me as big a hit with my father as if I had become a football hero. So when I went home that Christmas vacation it was in my mind that if you weren't able to function in action you might at least be able to tell about it, because you felt the same intensity—it was a back door way out of facing reality.'

They go into a dining-room now. The author walks through it in haste and a certain aversion.

'Don't you enjoy food?' the visitor asks.

'Food—yes! But not the miserable mixture of fruit juices and milk and whole-wheat bread I live on now.'

'Are you dyspeptic?'

'Dyspeptic! I'm simply ruined.'

'How so?'

'Well, in the middle west in those days children started life with fried food and waffles and that led into endless malted milks and bacon buns in college and then a little later I jumped to meals at Foyot's and the Castelli dei Caesari and the Escargot and every spice merchant in France and Italy. And under the name of alcohol—Clarets and Burgundys, Château Yquems and Champagnes, Pilsener and Dago Red, prohibition Scotch and Alabama white mule. It was very good while it lasted but I didn't see what pap lay at the end.' He shivered, 'Let's forget it—it isn't dinner time. Now this—' he says opening a door, 'is my study.'

A secretary is typing there or rather in a little alcove adjoining. As they come in she hands the author some letters. His eye falls on the envelope of the first one, his face takes on an expectant smile and he says to the visitor:

'This is the sequel to something that was rather funny. Let me tell you the first part before I open this. Well, about two weeks ago I got a letter under cover from *The Saturday Evening Post*, addressed not to me but to

Thomas Kracklin,
Saturday Evening post
Philadelphia
pennsylvania Pa

On the envelope were several notations evidently by the *Post*'s mail department:

Not known here
Try a story series in 1930 files
Think this is character in story by X in 1927 files

'This last person had guessed it, for Thomas Kracklin was indeed a character in some stories of mine. Here's what the letter said:

Mr Kracklin I wonder if you are any kin to mine because my name was Kracklin an I had a brother an he did not see us much any more we was worried about him an I thought when I read your story that you was that Kracklin an I thought if I wrote you I would find out yours truly Mrs Kracklin Lee.

'The address was a small town in Michigan. The letter amused me and was so different from any that I had received for a long time that I made up an answer to it. It went something like this:

My dear Mrs Kracklin Lee:
I am indeed your long lost brother. I am now in the Baltimore Penitentiary awaiting execution by hanging. If I get out I will be glad to come to visit you. I think you would find me all right except I cannot be irritated as I sometimes kill people if the coffee is cold. But I think I won't be much trouble except for that but I will be pretty poor when I get out of the penitentiary and will be glad if you can take care of me—unless they string me up next Thursday. Write me care of my lawyer.

'Here I gave my name and then signed the letter, "Sincerely, Thomas Kracklin". This is undoubtedly the answer.'
The author opened the envelope—there were two letters inside. The first was addressed to him by his real name.

Dear Sir I hope my brother has not been hung an I thank you for sending his letter I am a poor woman an have no potatoes this day an can just buy the stamp but I hope my brother has not been hung an if not I would

13

like to see him an will you give him this letter yours
truly Mrs Kracklin Lee.

This was the second letter:

Dear brother I have not got much but if you get off you
come back here an I could not promise to suply you
with much but maybe we could get along cannot really
promise anythin but I hope you get off an wish you
the very best always your sister Mrs Kracklin Lee.

When he had finished reading the author said:

'Now isn't it fun to be so damn smart! Miss Palmer,
please write a letter saying her brother's been reprieved and
gone to China and put five dollars in the envelope.'

'But it's too late,' he continued as he and his visitor went
upstairs. 'You can pay a little money but what can you do
for meddling with a human heart? A writer's temperament
is continually making him do things he can never repair.

'This is my bedroom. I write a good deal lying down and
when there are not too many children around, but in summer
it's hot up here in the daytime and my hand sticks to the
paper.'

The visitor moved a fold of cloth to perch himself on the
side of a chair but the author warned him quickly:

'Don't touch that! It's just the way somebody left it.'

'Oh I beg your pardon.'

'Oh it's all right—it was a long time ago. Sit here for a
moment and rest yourself and then we'll go on up.'

'Up?'

'Up to the attic. This is a big house you see—on the old-
fashioned side.'

The attic was the attic of Victorian fiction. It was pleasant,
with beams of light slanting in on piles and piles of magazines and pamphlets and children's school books and
college year books and 'little' magazines from Paris and
ballet programmes and the old *Dial* and *Mercury* and *L'Illus-
tration* unbound and the *St Nicholas* and the journal of the
Maryland Historical Society, and piles of maps and guide

books from the Golden Gate to Bou Saada. There were files
bulging with letters, one marked 'letters from my grandfather to my grandmother' and several dozen scrap books
and clipping books and photograph books and albums and
'baby books' and great envelopes full of unfiled items. . . .

'This is the loot,' the author said grimly. 'This is what
one has instead of a bank balance.'

'Are you satisfied?'

'No. But it's nice here sometimes in the late afternoon.
This is a sort of library in its way, you see—the library of a
life. And nothing is as depressing as a library if you stay long
in it. Unless of course you stay there all the time because
then you adjust yourself and become a little crazy. Part of
you gets dead. Come on let's go up.'

'Where?'

'Up to the cupola—the turret, the watch-tower, whatever
you want to call it. I'll lead the way.'

It is small up there and full of baked silent heat until the
author opens two of the glass sides that surround it and the
twilight wind blows through. As far as your eye can see there
is a river winding between green lawns and trees and purple
buildings and red slums blended in by a merciful dusk.
Even as they stand there the wind increases until it is a gale
whistling around the tower and blowing birds past them.

'I lived up here once,' the author said after a moment.

'Here? For a long time?'

'No. For just a little while when I was young.'

'It must have been rather cramped.'

'I didn't notice it.'

'Would you like to try it again?'

'No. And I couldn't if I wanted to.'

He shivered slightly and closed the windows. As they
went downstairs the visitor said, half apologetically:

'It's really just like all houses isn't it?'

The author nodded.

'I didn't think it was when I built it, but in the end I
suppose it's just like other houses after all.'

February, 1936

OF COURSE ALL LIFE is a process of breaking down, but
the blows that do the dramatic side of the work—the big
sudden blows that come, or seem to come, from outside—
the ones you remember and blame things on and, in
moments of weakness, tell your friends about, don't show
their effect all at once. There is another sort of blow that
comes from within—that you don't feel until it's too late to
do anything about it, until you realize with finality that in
some regard you will never be as good a man again. The
first sort of breakage seems to happen quick—the second
kind happens almost without your knowing it but is realized
suddenly indeed.

Before I go on with this short history, let me make a
general observation—the test of a first-rate intelligence is
the ability to hold two opposed ideas in the mind at the
same time, and still retain the ability to function. One
should, for example, be able to see that things are hopeless
and yet be determined to make them otherwise. This
philosophy fitted on to my early adult life, when I saw the
improbable, the implausible, often the 'impossible,' come
true. Life was something you dominated if you were any
good. Life yielded easily to intelligence and effort, or to what
proportion could be mustered of both. It seemed a romantic
business to be a successful literary man—you were not ever
going to be as famous as a movie star but what note you had
was probably longer-lived—you were never going to have
the power of a man of strong political or religious convictions but you were certainly more independent. Of course

within the practice of your trade you were forever un-satisfied—but I, for one, would not have chosen any other.

As the twenties passed, with my own twenties marching a little ahead of them, my two juvenile regrets—at not being big enough (or good enough) to play football in college, and at not getting overseas during the war—resolved themselves into childish waking dreams of imaginary heroism that were good enough to go to sleep on in restless nights. The big problems of life seemed to solve themselves, and if the business of fixing them was difficult, it made one too tired to think of more general problems.

Life, ten years ago, was largely a personal matter. I must hold in balance the sense of the futility of effort and the sense of the necessity to struggle; the conviction of the in-evitability of failure and still the determination to 'succeed' —and, more than these, the contradiction between the dead hand of the past and the high intentions of the future. If I could do this through the common ills—domestic, profes-sional and personal—then the ego would continue as an arrow shot from nothingness to nothingness with such force that only gravity would bring it to earth at last.

For seventeen years, with a year of deliberate loafing and resting out in the centre—things went on like that, with a new chore only a nice prospect for the next day. I was living hard, too, but: 'Up to forty-nine it'll be all right,' I said. 'I can count on that. For a man who's lived as I have, that's all you could ask.'

—And then, ten years this side of forty-nine, I suddenly realized that I had prematurely cracked.

II

Now a man can crack in many ways—can crack in the head —in which case the power of decision is taken from you by others! or in the body, when one can but submit to the white hospital world; or in the nerves. William Seabrook in an unsympathetic book tells, with some pride and a movie ending, of how he became a public charge. What led to his alcoholism or was bound up with it, was a collapse of his nervous system. Though the present writer was not so entangled—having at the time not tasted so much as a glass of beer for six months—it was his nervous reflexes that were giving way—too much anger and too many tears.

Moreover, to go back to my thesis that life has a varying offensive, the realization of having cracked was not simultaneous with a blow, but with a reprieve.

Not long before, I had sat in the office of a great doctor and listened to a grave sentence. With what, in retrospect, seems some equanimity, I had gone on about my affairs in the city where I was then living, not caring much, not thinking how much had been left undone, or what would become of this and that responsibility, like people do in books; I was well insured and anyhow I had been only a mediocre caretaker of most of the things left in my hands, even of my talent.

But I had a strong sudden instinct that I must be alone. I didn't want to see any people at all. I had seen so many people all my life—I was an average mixer, but more than average in a tendency to identify myself, my ideas, my destiny, with those of all classes that I came in contact with. I was always saving or being saved—in a single morning I would go through the emotions ascribable to Wellington at Waterloo. I lived in a world of inscrutable hostiles and inalienable friends and supporters.

But now I wanted to be absolutely alone and so arranged a certain insulation from ordinary cares.

It was not an unhappy time. I went away and there were fewer people. I found I was good-and-tired. I could lie around and was glad to, sleeping or dozing sometimes twenty hours a day and in the intervals trying resolutely not to think—instead I made lists—made lists and tore them up, hundreds of lists: of cavalry leaders and football players and cities, and popular tunes and pitchers, and happy times, and hobbies and houses lived in and how many suits since I left the army and how many pairs of shoes (I didn't count the suit I bought in Sorrento that shrunk, nor the pumps and dress shirt and collar that I carried around for years and never wore, because the pumps got damp and grainy and the shirt and collar got yellow and starch-rotted). And lists of women I'd liked, and of the times I had let myself be snubbed by people who had not been my betters in character or ability.

—And then suddenly, surprisingly, I got better.

—And cracked like an old plate as soon as I heard the news.

That is the real end of this story. What was to be done about it will have to rest in what used to be called the 'womb of time.' Suffice it to say that after about an hour of solitary pillow-hugging, I began to realize that for two years my life had been a drawing on resources that I did not possess, but I had been mortgaging myself physically and spiritually up to the hilt. What was the small gift of life given back in comparison to that?—when there had once been a pride of direction and a confidence in enduring independence.

I realized that in those two years, in order to preserve something—an inner hush maybe, maybe not—I had weaned myself from all the things I used to love—that every act of life from the morning tooth-brush to the friend at dinner had become an effort. I saw that for a long time I had not liked people and things, but only followed the rickety old pretence of liking. I saw that even my love for those closest to me was become only an attempt to love, that my casual relations—with an editor, a tobacco seller, the child of a friend, were only what I remembered I *should* do, from other days. All in the same month I became bitter about such things as the sound of the radio, the advertisements in the magazines, the screech of tracks, the dead silence of the country—contemptuous at human softness, immediately (if secretively) quarrelsome towards hardness—hating the night when I couldn't sleep and hating the day because it went towards night. I slept on the heart side now because I knew that the sooner I could tire that out, even a little, the sooner would come that blessed hour of nightmare which, like a catharsis, would enable me to better meet the new day.

There were certain spots, certain faces I could look at. Like most Middle Westerners, I have never had any but the vaguest race prejudices—I always had a secret yen for the lovely Scandinavian blondes who sat on porches in St. Paul but hadn't emerged enough economically to be part of what was then society. They were too nice to be 'chickens' and too quickly off the farmlands to seize a place in the sun, but I remembered going round blocks to catch a single glimpse of shining hair—the bright shock of a girl I'd never know. This is urban, unpopular talk. It strays afield from the fact that in these latter days I couldn't stand the sight of Celts, English, Politicians, Strangers, Virginians, Negroes (light or dark), Hunting People, or retail clerks, and middlemen in general, all writers (I avoided writers very carefully because they can perpetuate trouble as no one else can)—and all the classes as classes and most of them as members of their class. . . .

Trying to cling to something, I liked doctors and girl children up to the age of about thirteen and well-brought-up boy children from about eight years old on. I could have peace and happiness with these few categories of people. I forgot to add that I liked old men—men over seventy, sometimes over sixty if their faces looked seasoned. I liked Katharine Hepburn's face on the screen, no matter what was said about her pretentiousness, and Miriam Hopkins' face, and old friends if I only saw them once a year and could remember their ghosts.

All rather inhuman and undernourished, isn't it? Well, that, children, is the true sign of cracking up.

It is not a pretty picture. Inevitably it was carted here and there within its frame and exposed to various critics. One of them can only be described as a person whose life makes other people's lives seem like death—even this time when she was cast in the usually unappealing role of Job's comforter. In spite of the fact that this story is over, let me append our conversation as a sort of postscript:

'Instead of being so sorry for yourself, listen—' she said. (She always says 'Listen,' because she thinks while she talks—*really* thinks.) So she said: 'Listen. Suppose this wasn't a crack in you—suppose it was a crack in the Grand Canyon.'

'The crack's in me,' I said heroically.

'Listen! The world only exists in your eyes—your conception of it. You can make it as big or as small as you want to. And you're trying to be a little·puny individual. By God, if I ever cracked, I'd try to make the world crack with me. Listen! The world only exists through your apprehension of it, and so it's much better to say that it's not you that's cracked—it's the Grand Canyon.'

'Baby et up all her Spinoza?'

'I don't know anything about Spinoza. I know—' She spoke, then, of old woes of her own, that seemed, in the telling, to have been more dolorous than mine, and how she had met them, over-ridden them, beaten them.

I felt a certain reaction to what she said, but I am a slow-thinking man, and it occurred to me simultaneously that of all natural forces, vitality is the incommunicable one. In days when juice came into one as an article without duty, one tried to distribute it—but always without success; to further mix metaphors, vitality never 'takes.' You have it or you haven't it, like health or brown eyes or honour or a baritone voice. I might have asked some of it from her, neatly wrapped and ready for home cooking and digestion, but I could never have got it—not if I'd waited around for a thousand hours with the tin cup of self-pity. I could walk from her door, holding myself very carefully like cracked crockery, and go away into the world of bitterness, where I was making a home with such materials as are found there —and quote to myself after I left her door:

'*Ye are the salt of the earth. But if the salt hath lost its savour, wherewith shall it be salted?*'

Matthew 5-13.

HANDLE WITH CARE

March, 1936

In a previous article this writer told about his realization that what he had before him was not the dish that he had ordered for his forties. In fact—since he and the dish were one, he described himself as a cracked plate, the kind that one wonders whether it is worth preserving. Your editor thought that the article suggested too many aspects without regarding them closely, and probably many readers felt the same way—and there are always those to whom all self-revelation is contemptible, unless it ends with a noble thanks to the gods for the Unconquerable Soul.

But I had been thanking the gods too long, and thanking them for nothing. I wanted to put a lament into my record, without even the background of the Euganean Hills to give it colour. There weren't any Euganean hills that I could see.

Sometimes, though, the cracked plate has to be retained in the pantry, has to be kept in service as a household necessity. It can never again be warmed on the stove nor shuffled with the other plates in the dishpan; it will not be brought out for company, but it will do to hold crackers late at night or to go into the ice box under left-overs. . . .

Hence this sequel—a cracked plate's further history.

Now the standard cure for one who is sunk is to consider those in actual destitution or physical suffering—this is an all-weather beatitude for gloom in general and fairly salutary day-time advice for everyone. But at three o'clock in the morning, a forgotten package has the same tragic importance as a death sentence, and the cure doesn't work —and in a real dark night of the soul it is always three o'clock in the morning, day after day. At that hour the tendency is to refuse to face things as long as possible by retiring into an infantile dream—but one is continually startled out of this by various contacts with the world. One meets these occasions as quickly and carelessly as possible and retires once more back into the dream, hoping that things will adjust themselves by some great material or spiritual bonanza. But as the withdrawal persists there is less and less chance of the bonanza—one is not waiting for the fade-out of a single sorrow, but rather being an unwilling witness of an execution, the disintegration of one's own personality. . . .

Unless madness or drugs or drink come into it, this phase comes to a dead-end, eventually, and is succeeded by a vacuous quiet. In this you can try to estimate what has been sheared away and what is left. Only when this quiet came to me, did I realize that I had gone through two parallel experiences.

The first time was twenty years ago, when I left Princeton in junior year with a complaint diagnosed as malaria. It transpired, through an X-ray taken a dozen years later, that it had been tuberculosis—a mild case, and after a few months of rest I went back to college. But I had lost certain offices, the chief one was the presidency of the Triangle Club, a musical comedy idea, and also I dropped back a class. To me college would never be the same. There were to be no badges of pride, no medals, after all. It seemed on one March afternoon that I had lost every single thing I wanted—and that night was the first time that I hunted down the spectre of womanhood that, for a little while, makes everything else seem unimportant.

Years later I realized that my failure as a big shot in college was all right—instead of serving on committees, I took a beating on English poetry; when I got the idea of what it was all about, I set about learning how to write. On Shaw's principle that 'If you don't get what you like, you better like what you get.' it was a lucky break—at the moment it was a harsh and bitter business to know that my career as a leader of men was over.

Since that day I have not been able to fire a bad servant, and I am astonished and impressed by people who can. Some old desire for personal dominance was broken and gone. Life around me was a solemn dream, and I lived on the letters I wrote to a girl in another city. A man does not recover from such jolts—he becomes a different person and, eventually, the new person finds new things to care about.

The other episode parallel to my current situation took place after the war, when I had again over-extended my flank. It was one of those tragic loves doomed for lack of money, and one day the girl closed it out on the basis of common sense. During a long summer of despair I wrote a novel instead of letters, so it came out all right, but it came out all right for a different person. The man with the jingle of money in his pocket who married the girl a year later would always cherish an abiding distrust, an animosity, towards the leisure class—not the conviction of a revolutionist but the smouldering hatred of a peasant. In the years since then I have never been able to stop wondering where my friends' money came from, nor to stop thinking that at one time a sort of *droit de seigneur* might have been exercised to give one of them my girl.

For sixteen years I lived pretty much as this latter person, distrusting the rich, yet working for money with which to share their mobility and the grace that some of them brought into their lives. During this time I had plenty of the usual horses shot from under me—I remember some of their names—*Punctured Pride*, *Thwarted Expectation*, *Faithless*, *Show-off*, *Hard Hit*, *Never Again*. And after a while I wasn't twenty-five, then not even thirty-five, and nothing was quite as good. But in all these years I don't remember a moment of discouragement. I saw honest men through moods of suicidal gloom—some of them gave up and died; others adjusted themselves and went on to a larger success than mine; but my morale never sank below the level of self-disgust when I had put on some unsightly personal show. Trouble has no necessary connection with discouragement—discouragement has a germ of its own, as different from trouble as arthritis is different from a stiff joint.

When a new sky cut off the sun last spring, I didn't at first relate it to what had happened fifteen or twenty years ago.

Only gradually did a certain family resemblance come
through—an over-extension of the flank, a burning of the
candle at both ends; a call upon physical resources that I
did not command, like a man over-drawing at his bank. In
its impact this blow was more violent than the other two
but it was the same in kind—a feeling that I was standing
at twilight on a deserted range, with an empty rifle in my
hands and the targets down. No problem set—simply a
silence with only the sound of my own breathing.

In this silence there was a vast irresponsibility towards
every obligation, a deflation of all my values. A passionate
belief in order, a disregard of motives or consequences in
favour of guess work and prophecy, a feeling that craft and
industry would have a place in any world—one by one,
these and other convictions were swept away. I saw that the
novel, which at my maturity was the strongest and supplest
medium for conveying thought and emotion from one
human being to another, was becoming subordinated to a
mechanical and communal art that, whether in the hands of
Hollywood merchants or Russian idealists, was capable of
reflecting only the tritest thought, the most obvious
emotion. It was an art in which words were subordinate to
images, where personality was worn down to the inevitable
low gear of collaboration. As long past as 1930, I had a
hunch that the talkies would make even the best selling
novelist as archaic as silent pictures. People still read, if only
Professor Canby's book of the month—curious children
nosed at the slime of Mr. Tiffany Thayer in the drug-store
libraries—but there was a rankling indignity, that to me had
become almost an obsession, in seeing the power of the
written word subordinate to another power, a more glittering, a grosser power. . . .

I set that down as an example of what haunted me during
the long night—this was something I could neither accept
nor struggle against, something which tended to make my
efforts obsolescent, as the chain stores have crippled the
small merchant, an exterior force, unbeatable—

(I have the sense of lecturing now, looking at a watch

on the desk before me and seeing how many more minutes—)

Well, when I had reached this period of silence, I was forced into a measure that no one ever adopts voluntarily: I was impelled to think. God, was it difficult! The moving about of great secret trunks. In the first exhausted halt, I wondered whether I had ever thought. After a long time I came to these conclusions, just as I write them here:

(1) That I had done very little thinking, save within the problems of my craft. For twenty years a certain man had been my intellectual conscience. That was Edmund Wilson.

(2) That another man represented my sense of the 'good life,' though I saw him once in a decade, and since then he might have been hung. He is in the fur business in the Northwest and wouldn't like his name set down here. But in difficult situations I had tried to think what *he* would have thought, how *he* would have acted.

(3) That a third contemporary had been an artistic conscience to me—I had not imitated his infectious style, because my own style, such as it is, was formed before he published anything, but there was an awful pull towards him when I was on a spot.

(4) That a fourth man had come to dictate my relations with other people when these relations were successful: how to do, what to say. How to make people at least momentarily happy (in opposition to Mrs. Post's theories of how to make everyone thoroughly uncomfortable with a sort of systematized vulgarity). This always confused me and made me want to go out and get drunk, but this man had seen the game, analyzed it and beaten it, and his word was good enough for me.

(5) That my political conscience had scarcely existed for ten years save as an element of irony in my stuff. When I became again concerned with the system I should function under, it was a man much younger than myself who brought it to me, with a mixture of passion and fresh air.

So there was not an 'I' any more—not a basis on which I could organize my self-respect—save my limitless capacity for toil that it seemed I possessed no more. It was strange to have no self—to be like a little boy left alone in a big house, who knew that now he could do anything he wanted to do, but found that there was nothing that he wanted to do—

(The watch is past the hour and I have barely reached my thesis. I have some doubts as to whether this is of general interest, but if anyone wants more, there is plenty left, and your editor will tell me. If you've had enough, say so—but not too loud, because I have the feeling that someone, I'm not sure who, is sound asleep—someone who could have helped me to keep my shop open. It wasn't Lenin, and it wasn't God.)

PASTING IT TOGETHER

April, 1936

I have spoken in these pages of how an exceptionally optimistic young man experienced a crack-up of all values, a crack-up that he scarcely knew of until long after it occurred. I told of the succeeding period of desolation and of the necessity of going on, but without benefit of Henley's familiar heroics, 'my head is bloody but unbowed.' For a check-up of my spiritual liabilities indicated that I had no particular head to be bowed or unbowed. Once I had a heart but that was about all I was sure of.

This was at least a starting place out of the morass in which I floundered: 'I felt—therefore I was.' At one time or another there had been many people who had leaned on me, come to me in difficulties or written me from afar, believed implicitly in my advice and my attitude towards life. The dullest platitude monger or the most unscrupulous Rasputin who can influence the destinies of many people must have some individuality, so the question became one of finding why and where I had changed, where was the leak through which, unknown to myself, my enthusiasm and my vitality had been steadily and prematurely trickling away.

One harassed and despairing night I packed a brief-case and went off a thousand miles to think it over. I took a dollar room in a drab little town where I knew no one and sunk all the money I had with me in a stock of potted meat, crackers and apples. But don't let me suggest that the change from a rather overstuffed world to a comparative asceticism was any Research Magnificent—I only wanted absolute quiet to think out why I had developed a sad attitude to-wards sadness, a melancholy attitude towards melancholy and a tragic attitude towards tragedy—*why I had become identified with the objects of my horror or compassion.*

Does this seem a fine distinction? It isn't: identification such as this spells the death of accomplishment. It is some-thing like this that keeps insane people from working. Lenin did not willingly endure the sufferings of his proletariat, nor Washington of his troops, nor Dickens of his London poor. And when Tolstoy tried some such merging of himself with the objects of his attention, it was a fake and a failure. I mention these because they are the men best known to us all.

It was dangerous mist. When Wordsworth decided that 'there had passed away a glory from the earth,' he felt no compulsion to pass away with it, and the Fiery Particle Keats never ceased his struggle against t.b. nor in his last moments relinquished his hope of being among the English poets.

My self-immolation was something sodden-dark. It was very distinctly not modern—yet I saw it in others, saw it in a dozen men of honour and industry since the war. (I heard you, but that's too easy—there were Marxians among these men.) I had stood by while one famous contemporary of mine played with the idea of the Big Out for half a year; I had watched when another, equally eminent, spent months in an asylum unable to endure any contact with his fellow men. And of those who had given up and passed on I could list a score.

This led me to the idea that the ones who had survived

had made some sort of clean break. This is a big word and is no parallel to a jail-break when one is probably headed for a new jail or will be forced back to the old one. The famous 'Escape' or 'run away from it all' is an excursion in a trap even if the trap includes the south seas, which are only for those who want to paint them or sail them. A clean break is something you cannot come back from; that is irretrievable because it makes the past cease to exist. So, since I could no longer fulfil the obligations that life had set for me or that I had set for myself, why not slay the empty shell who had been posturing at it for four years? I must continue to be a writer because that was my only way of life, but I would cease any attempts to be a person—to be kind, just or generous. There were plenty of counterfeit coins around that would pass instead of these and I knew where I could get them at a nickel on the dollar. In thirty-nine years an observant eye has learned to detect where the milk is watered and the sugar is sanded, the rhinestone passed for diamond and the stucco for stone. There was to be no more giving of myself—all giving was to be outlawed henceforth under a new name, and that name was Waste.

The decision made me rather exuberant, like anything that is both real and new. As a sort of beginning there was a whole shaft of letters to be tipped into the waste basket when I went home, letters that wanted something for nothing—to read this man's manuscript, market this man's poem, speak free on the radio, indite notes of introduction, give this interview, help with the plot of this play, with this domestic situation, perform this act of thoughtfulness or charity.

The conjuror's hat was empty. To draw things out of it had long been a sort of sleight of hand, and now, to change the metaphor, I was off the dispensing end of the relief roll forever.

The heady villainous feeling continued.

I felt like the beady-eyed men I used to see on the commuting train from Great Neck fifteen years back—men who didn't care whether the world tumbled into chaos to-morrow if it spared their houses. I was one with them now, one with the smooth articles who said:

'I'm sorry but business is business.' Or:

'You ought to have thought of that before you got into this trouble.' Or:

'I'm not the person to see about that.'

And a smile—ah, I would get me a smile. I'm still working on that smile. It is to combine the best qualities of an hotel manager, an experienced old social weasel, a headmaster on visitors' day, a coloured elevator man, a pansy pulling a profile, a producer getting stuff at half its market value, a trained nurse coming on a new job, a body-vender in her first rotogravure, a hopeful extra swept near the camera, a ballet dancer with an infected toe, and of course the great beam of loving kindness common to all those from Washington to Beverly Hills who must exist by virtue of the contorted pan.

The voice too—I am working with a teacher on the voice. When I have perfected it the larynx will show no ring of conviction except the conviction of the person I am talking to. Since it will be largely called upon for the elicitation of the word 'Yes,' my teacher (a lawyer) and I are concentrating on that, but in extra hours. I am learning to bring into it that polite acerbity that makes people feel that far from being welcome they are not even tolerated and are under continual and scathing analysis at every moment. These times will of course not coincide with the smile. This will be reserved exclusively for those from whom I have nothing to gain, old worn-out people or young struggling people. They won't mind—what the hell, they get it most of the time anyhow.

But enough. It is not a matter of levity. If you are young and you should write asking to see me and learn how to be a sombre literary man writing pieces upon the state of emotional exhaustion that often overtakes writers in their prime—if you should be so young and so fatuous as to do this, I would not do so much as acknowledge your letter, unless you were related to someone very rich and important

indeed. And if you were dying of starvation outside my
window, I would go out quickly and give you the smile and
the voice (if no longer the hand) and stick around till somebody raised a nickel to phone for the ambulance, that is if
I thought there would be any copy in it for me.

I have now at last become a writer only. The man I had
persistently tried to be became such a burden that I have
'cut him loose' with as little compunction as a Negro lady
cuts loose a rival on Saturday night. Let the good people
function as such—let the overworked doctors die in harness,
with one week's 'vacation' a year that they can devote to
straightening out their family affairs, and let the under-
worked doctors scramble for cases at one dollar a throw;
let the soldiers be killed and enter immediately into the
Valhalla of their profession. That is their contract with the
gods. A writer need have no such ideals unless he makes
them for himself, and this one has quit. The old dream of
being an entire man in the Goethe-Byron-Shaw tradition,
with an opulent American touch, a sort of combination of
J. P. Morgan, Topham Beauclerk and St. Francis of Assisi,
has been relegated to the junk heap of the shoulder pads
worn for one day on the Princeton freshman football field
and the overseas cap never worn overseas.

So what? This is what I think now: that the natural state
of the sentient adult is a qualified unhappiness. I think also
that in an adult the desire to be finer in grain than you are,
'a constant striving' (as those people say who gain their
bread by saying it) only adds to this unhappiness in the end
—that end that comes to our youth and hope. My own
happiness in the past often approached such an ecstasy that
I could not share it even with the person dearest to me but
had to walk it away in quiet streets and lanes with only
fragments of it to distil into little lines in books—and I think
that my happiness, or talent for self-delusion or what you
will, was an exception. It was not the natural thing but the
unnatural—unnatural as the Boom; and my recent experience parallels the wave of despair that swept the nation
when the Boom was over.

I shall manage to live with the new dispensation, though it has taken some months to be certain of the fact. And just as the laughing stoicism which has enabled the American Negro to endure the intolerable conditions of his existence has cost him his sense of the truth—so in my case there is a price to pay. I do not any longer like the postman, nor the grocer, nor the editor, nor the cousin's husband, and he in turn will come to dislike me, so that life will never be very pleasant again, and the sign *Cave Canem* is hung permanently just above my door. I will try to be a correct animal though, and if you throw me a bone with enough meat on it I may even lick your hand.

EARLY SUCCESS

[1937]

SEVENTEEN YEARS AGO this month I quit work or, if you prefer, I retired from business. I was through—let the Street Railway Advertising Company carry along under its own power. I retired, not on my profit, but on my liabilities, which included debts, despair, and a broken engagement, and crept home to St. Paul to 'finish a novel.'

That novel, begun in a training camp late in the war, was my ace in the hole. I had put it aside when I got a job in New York, but I was as constantly aware of it as of the shoe with cardboard in the sole, during all one desolate spring. It was like the fox and goose and the bag of beans. If I stopped working to finish the novel, I lost the girl.

So I struggled on in a business I detested and all the confidence I had garnered at Princeton and in a haughty career as an army's worst aide-de-camp melted gradually away. Lost and forgotten, I walked quickly from certain places—from the pawnshop where one left the field-glasses, from prosperous friends whom one met when wearing the suit from before the war—from restaurants after tipping with the last nickel, from busy cheerful offices that were saving the jobs for their own boys from the war.

Even having a first story accepted had not proved very exciting. Dutch Mount and I sat across from each other in a car-card slogan advertising office, and the same mail brought each of us an acceptance from the same magazine —the old *Smart Set*.

'My cheque was thirty—how much was yours?'

'Thirty-five.'

The real blight, however, was that my story had been

405

written in college two years before, and a dozen new ones hadn't even drawn a personal letter. The implication was that I was on the down-grade at twenty-two. I spent the thirty dollars on a magenta feather fan for a girl in Alabama.

My friends who were not in love, or who had waiting arrangements with 'sensible' girls, braced themselves patiently for a long pull. Not I—I was in love with a whirl-wind and I must spin a net big enough to catch it out of my head, a head full of trickling nickels and sliding dimes, the incessant music box of the poor. It couldn't be done like that, so when the girl threw me over I went home and finished my novel. And then, suddenly, everything changed, and this article is about that first wild wind of success and the delicious mist it brings with it. It is a short and precious time—for when the mist rises in a few weeks, or a few months, one finds that the very best is over.

It began to happen in the autumn of 1919 when I was an empty bucket, so mentally blunted with the summer's writing that I'd taken a job repairing car roofs at the North-ern Pacific shops. Then the postman rang, and that day I quit work and ran along the street, stopping automobiles to tell friends and acquaintances about it—my novel *This Side of Paradise* was accepted for publication. That week the postman rang and rang, and I paid off my terrible small debts, bought a suit, and woke up every morning with a world of ineffable toploftiness and promise.

While I waited for the novel to appear, the metamor-phosis of amateur into professional began to take place—a sort of stitching together of your whole life into a pattern of work, so that the end of one job is automatically the begin-ning of another. I had been an amateur before; in October, when I strolled with a girl among the stones of a southern graveyard, I was a professional and my enchantment with certain things that she felt and said was already paced by an anxiety to set them down in a story—it was called *The Ice Palace* and it was published later. Similarly, during Christmas week in St. Paul, there was a night when I had stayed home from two dances to work on a story. Three friends called up during the evening to tell me I had missed some rare doings: a well-known man-about-town had disguised himself as a camel and, with a taxi-driver as the rear half, managed to attend the wrong party. Aghast with myself for not being there, I spent the next day trying to collect the fragments of the story.

'Well, all I can say is it was funny when it happened.' 'No, I don't know where he got the taxi-man.' 'You'd have to know him well to understand how funny it was.'

In despair I said:

'Well, I can't seem to find out exactly what happened but I'm going to write about it as if it was ten times funnier than anything you've said.' So I wrote it, in twenty-two consecutive hours, and wrote it 'funny,' simply because I was so emphatically told it was funny. *The Camel's Back* was published and still crops up in the humorous anthologies.

With the end of the winter set in another pleasant pumped-dry period, and, while I took a little time off, a fresh picture of life in America began to form before my eyes. The uncertainties of 1919 were over—there seemed little doubt about what was going to happen—America was going on the greatest, gaudiest spree in history and there was going to be plenty to tell about it. The whole golden boom was in the air—its splendid generosities, its outrageous corruptions and the tortuous death struggle of the old America in prohibition. All the stories that came into my head had a touch of disaster in them—the lovely young creatures in my novels went to ruin, the diamond mountains of my short stories blew up, my millionaires were as beautiful and damned as Thomas Hardy's peasants. In life these things hadn't happened yet, but I was pretty sure living wasn't the reckless, careless business these people thought—this generation just younger than me.

For my point of vantage was the dividing line between the two generations, and there I sat—somewhat self-consciously. When my first big mail came in—hundreds and hundreds of letters on a story about a girl who bobbed her hair—it seemed rather absurd that they should come to me about it. On the other hand, for a shy man it was nice to be somebody except oneself again: 'to be the Author' as one had been 'the Lieutenant'. Of course one wasn't really an author any more than one had been an army officer, but nobody seemed to guess behind the false face.

All in three days I got married and the presses were pounding out *This Side of Paradise* like they pound out extras in the movies.

With its publication I had reached a stage of manic-depressive insanity. Rage and bliss alternated hour by hour. A lot of people thought it was a fake, and perhaps it was, and a lot of others thought it was a lie, which it was not. In a daze I gave out an interview—I told what a great writer I was and how I'd achieved the heights. Heywood Broun, who was on my trail, simply quoted it with the comment that I seemed to be a very self-satisfied young man, and for some days I was notably poor company. I invited him to lunch and in a kindly way told him that it was too bad he had let his life slide away without accomplishing anything. He had just turned thirty and it was about then that I wrote a line which certain people will not let me forget: 'She was a faded but still lovely woman of twenty-seven.'

In a daze I told the Scribner Company that I didn't expect my novel to sell more than twenty thousand copies and when the laughter died away I was told that a sale of five thousand was excellent for a first novel. I think it was a week after publication that it passed the twenty thousand mark, but I took myself so seriously that I didn't even think it was funny.

These weeks in the clouds ended abruptly a week later when Princeton turned on the book—not undergraduate Princeton but the black mass of faculty and alumni. There was a kind but reproachful letter from President Hibben, and a room full of classmates who suddenly turned on me with condemnation. We had been part of a rather gay party staged conspicuously in Harvey Firestone's car of robin's-egg blue, and in the course of it I got an accidental black eye trying to stop a fight. This was magnified into an orgy, and in spite of a delegation of undergraduates who went to the board of Governors, I was suspended from my club for a couple of months. The *Alumni Weekly* got after my book and only Dean Gauss had a good word to say for me. The unctuousness and hypocrisy of the proceedings was exasperating and for seven years I didn't go to Princeton. Then a magazine asked me for an article about it, and when I started to write it, I found I really loved the place and that the experience of one week was a small item in the total budget. But on that day in 1920 most of the joy went out of my success.

But one was now a professional—and the new world couldn't possibly be presented without bumping the old out of the way. One gradually developed a protective hardness against both praise and blame. Too often people liked your things for the wrong reasons or people liked them whose dislike would be a compliment. No decent career was ever founded on a public and one learned to go ahead without precedents and without fear. Counting the bag, I found that in 1919 I had made $800 by writing, that in 1920 I had made $18,000, stories, picture rights, and book. My story price had gone from $30 to $1,000. That's a small price to what was paid later in the Boom, but what it sounded like to me couldn't be exaggerated.

The dream had been early realized and the realization carried with it a certain bonus and a certain burden. Premature success gives one an almost mystical conception of destiny as opposed to will-power—at its worst the Napoleonic delusion. The man who arrives young believes that he exercises his will because his star is shining. The man who only asserts himself at thirty has a balanced idea of what will-power and fate have each contributed, the one who gets there at forty is liable to put the emphasis on will alone. This comes out when the storms strike your craft.

The compensation of a very early success is a conviction that life is a romantic matter. In the best sense one stays young. When the primary objects of love and money could be taken for granted and a shaky eminence had lost its fascination, I had fair years to waste, years that I can't honestly regret, in seeking the eternal Carnival by the Sea. Once in the middle twenties I was driving along the High Corniche Road through the twilight with the whole French Riviera twinkling on the sea below. As far ahead as I could see was Monte Carlo, and though it was out of season and there were no Grand Dukes left to gamble and E. Phillips Oppenheim was a fat industrious man in my hotel, who lived in a bath-robe—the very name was so incorrigibly enchanting that I could only stop the car and like the Chinese whisper: 'Ah me! Ah me!' It was not Monte Carlo I was looking at. It was back into the mind of the young man with cardboard soles who had walked the streets of New York. I was him again—for an instant I had the good fortune to share his dreams, I who had no more dreams of my own. And there are still times when I creep up on him, surprise him on an autumn morning in New York or a spring night in Carolina when it is so quiet that you can hear a dog barking in the next county. But never again as during that all too short period when he and I were one person, when the fulfilled future and the wistful past were mingled in a single gorgeous moment—when life was literally a dream.